TRADE $ 4.95

HANDBOOK OF ADVERTISING ART PRODUCTION

HANDBOOK

OF ADVERTISING ART PRODUCTION

Richard M. Schlemmer

Assistant Professor
Department of Advertising Art and Design
State University of New York
Agricultural and Technical College
at Farmingdale

WITH ILLUSTRATIONS BY THE AUTHOR

PRENTICE-HALL, INC., *Englewood Cliffs, New Jersey*

FOR SCOTT AND ROSS

© 1966 *by* Richard M. Schlemmer.
All rights reserved.
No part of this book may be reproduced in any form, by mimeograph or any other means, without permission in writing from the publisher.
Library of Congress Catalog Card Number: 66-13644
Printed in the United States of America C-37395

current printing (last digit)
10 9 8 7 6 5 4 3 2 1

Prentice-Hall International, Inc., *London*
Prentice-Hall of Australia, Pty. Ltd., *Sydney*
Prentice-Hall of Canada, Ltd., *Toronto*
Prentice-Hall of India (Private) Ltd., *New Delhi*
Prentice-Hall of Japan, Inc., *Tokyo*

PREFACE

Much has been written about advertising production; little has been written of the manner of preparation of that which is to be produced. The objective of this book is to provide the advertising artist with a working knowledge of the processes of printed reproduction, and of the techniques with which artwork is best prepared in order to be adaptable to these processes. It offers a description of the areas in which an advertising artist may be employed, the skills he may be called upon to perform, and the varieties of printed matter with which he may become concerned.

The ability to understand the processes of reproduction depends upon the assimilation of an appropriate vocabulary. This text is designed to aid in the orderly acquisition of such a vocabulary. In its sequential development, none but the most elementary terminology is used prior to its having been adequately defined. In order to facilitate this, pertinent definitions are included at the beginnings of chapters and are further amplified in the ensuing text.

The chapters on the processes of reproduction have value for anyone who might require multiple duplication of word or picture. Beginning with the invention of movable type, they trace the development of printing —examining the techniques of letterpress, lithography, gravure, silk screen, and the newest innovation: wrap-around printing. Typography, from hand composition to the latest photographic methods, is described in detail. This material, together with a chapter on the manufacture, classification and selection of paper, has been compiled to provide essential knowledge for the planning and production of the printed piece.

The chapters on the preparation of art are presented in the logical order of its production, beginning with illustrative matter and proceeding through the ordering of typography, photostats, and the ultimate preparation of the mechanical art. A separate chapter deals with art production requirements for each of the major printing processes.

There is little presented here, however, that can be accomplished without practice. The artist is a doer of deeds, not a retainer of facts. It is not by his ability to disseminate factual knowledge that he makes his mark; it is the manner in which he puts his knowledge to work.

ACKNOWLEDGMENTS

I am indebted to those who have assisted me in the preparation of this text. Professor Arthur R. Young of Pratt Institute and my colleagues, Professors Thomas D. Greenley, Richard M. Halls, and Robert J. Lovell of the State University at Farmingdale have called upon their personal knowledge in my behalf, as has Professor Charles R. Anderson of Castleton (Vermont) State College. The Library Staff at my college has provided, without threat of sudden recall, the reference material I have required.

My wife, Virginia, has edited and typed my manuscript with considerable patience, skill, and understanding.

Mr. J. R. Greig of the American Type Founders Co., Mr. Arthur L. Koop of the Mergenthaler Linotype Co., Mr. Richard C. Malmin of the Ludlow Typograph Co., and Mr. Walter Hutt of Walter Hutt Studios have each rendered special assistance. I owe a particular debt to those who have been both patient and impatient with me in the studios in which I have been employed and in the agencies and corporations which I have serviced.

R. M. S.

CONTENTS

4 THE LITHOGRAPHIC PROCESS 64

5 THE GRAVURE PROCESS 80

6 THE REPRODUCTION OF COLOR 92

7 SCREENLESS PRINTING: THE PHOTOGELATIN PROCESS 116

HANDBOOK OF ADVERTISING ART PRODUCTION

1 THE FUNCTIONS OF THE ADVERTISING ARTIST

Advertising art is a broad, loosely-defined profession which encompasses most of the artistic effort that is put forth in order to enhance and ultimately sell almost any product or service. More artists find steady employment in areas directly related to advertising than in all other art fields combined.

Unlike the painter who gambles for fame and fortune, the advertising artist expects to be remunerated for services rendered. Although work is sometimes produced on a speculative basis, the risk is usually underwritten by the employer; seldom by the individual artist. In return for this remuneration, the artist is expected to evidence a high degree of dependability and consistency of quality.

Salaried employment generally occurs in one of three categories:

1. In organizations whose principal business is to supply art for profit.
2. In departments whose function is to supply art as a service to their parent firm, where no direct profit results from the sale of the art which has been produced.
3. In publishing firms which utilize art as a means of enhancing their product and which may provide art facilities as a service to their advertisers.

The first category includes art studios, the art departments of advertising agencies, public-relations firms, display houses, firms which produce technical literature, package designers, producers of sales-promotional aids, direct-mail houses, and catalog houses. Many creative printers employ art departments. They may or may not provide art as a service, but the resulting product is sold for a profit.

The second category includes the art, advertising and/or sales-promotion departments of any commercial enterprise, the technical publication department, and the public-relations department—which often includes the educational department and the governmental art department. The industrial design department, whose responsibility is to enhance the product, may or may not fall within this category.

The third category includes the advertising art departments of newspapers and magazines. The editorial artist, who is responsible for the format of the publication, is not properly classified as an advertising artist, but the functions he performs are almost the same. Book publishers also employ editorial art departments.

The free-lance artist, while operating as an independent business, solicits work from one or more of these sources. The artist's agent also solicits these sources as his representative.

It is impossible to generalize on the structure of art departments, since each may have been formed for a specific purpose. This purpose may range from the production of advertising material to the design of wallpaper; from technical illustration to fashion drawing. However, the artist himself can be classified by the area of his particular skill: design, lettering, illustration, retouching, etc. Since the art studio is but a free-lance art department, an examination of the duties of its personnel will provide a basis for determining the organization of any art department, because the basic skills involved will be similar.

The advertising agency is a more complex organization. In addition to art, it must also provide written copy, as well as a multitude of informational services for the guidance of the advertiser. Although the organizational plan may differ from agency to agency, the duties of agency personnel remain basically similar.

Advertising departments vary greatly in structure depending upon the specific advertising needs of the firm and its degree of reliance upon its agency. Advertising departments of large retail firms employ no agencies, but utilize an art staff similar to that of the studio. A study of the employee functions of a typical advertising department will provide a basis for comparison.

The advertising art department of a newspaper or magazine furnishes art service for its clients and is organized along the general lines of the art studio.

Generally, the duties of any person directly involved with the production of advertising art will fall into one or more of the following categories:

Sales. Provides liaison with the client.

Research. Provides information for planning advertising.

Copy. Writes advertising copy.

Art. Designs art. Executes art. Purchases art.

Production. Supervises work of staff. Orders work from outside sources.

Although the organizational structure may vary, and there may be considerable overlap of duties and responsibilities, certain job categories are applicable to almost any art-producing firm or department. The following breakdown of studio, agency, and advertising department personnel will describe these job categories in detail.

THE ART STUDIO

The principal function of the art studio is the production of art. It may produce one or more elements of the composition; it may produce and deliver finished art to the client; or it may sometimes assume the responsibility for the production and delivery of printed matter reproduced from the finished art. The studio solicits business from any firm that is a potential purchaser of art. It may serve as an art department for the client who has none, or it may handle the overflow with which the client's art department cannot cope. The studio can ill afford to refuse any type of assignment, since the studio business is highly competitive. As a result, the successful studio will become involved with almost every facet of advertising art.

The artist's working arrangement

Artists have various working arrangements with their employers. The following examples are typical.

Salaried Artists. Salaried artists are staff members who are paid a stipulated weekly salary. Even when there is a temporary lack of work in the studio they are expected to remain on the premises. There is no interruption of pay during slack periods. Paid vacations, plus fringe benefits, are generally provided by management.

The salaried artist is selected for his versatility; therefore, he can usually be kept busy. Sound management requires that job assignments be given to staff artists in preference to free-lance artists whenever practicable.

Free-Lance Artists. "Free-lancers" are self-employed artists who work at a location of their own choosing—often at home. These are the specialists who are called upon to perform a specific function, or to assist when the work load is too heavy for the salaried staff. The free-lance artist has no obligation other than to himself and to the completion of any assignment he accepts. He is free to come and go as he pleases, and may do work for competing studios and agencies. If he has an "exclusive" arrangement with a studio, he is not expected to work for competitors.

The free-lance artist is paid well, but only for the work he performs. If his is a top creative talent he may receive a retainer, but there is seldom any guarantee as to when or how often he will be called upon. He must be his own salesman, keep his own books, and provide his own fringe benefits. His principal problem is to obtain sufficient work, and the more specialized his talent, the more difficult this may be. He func-

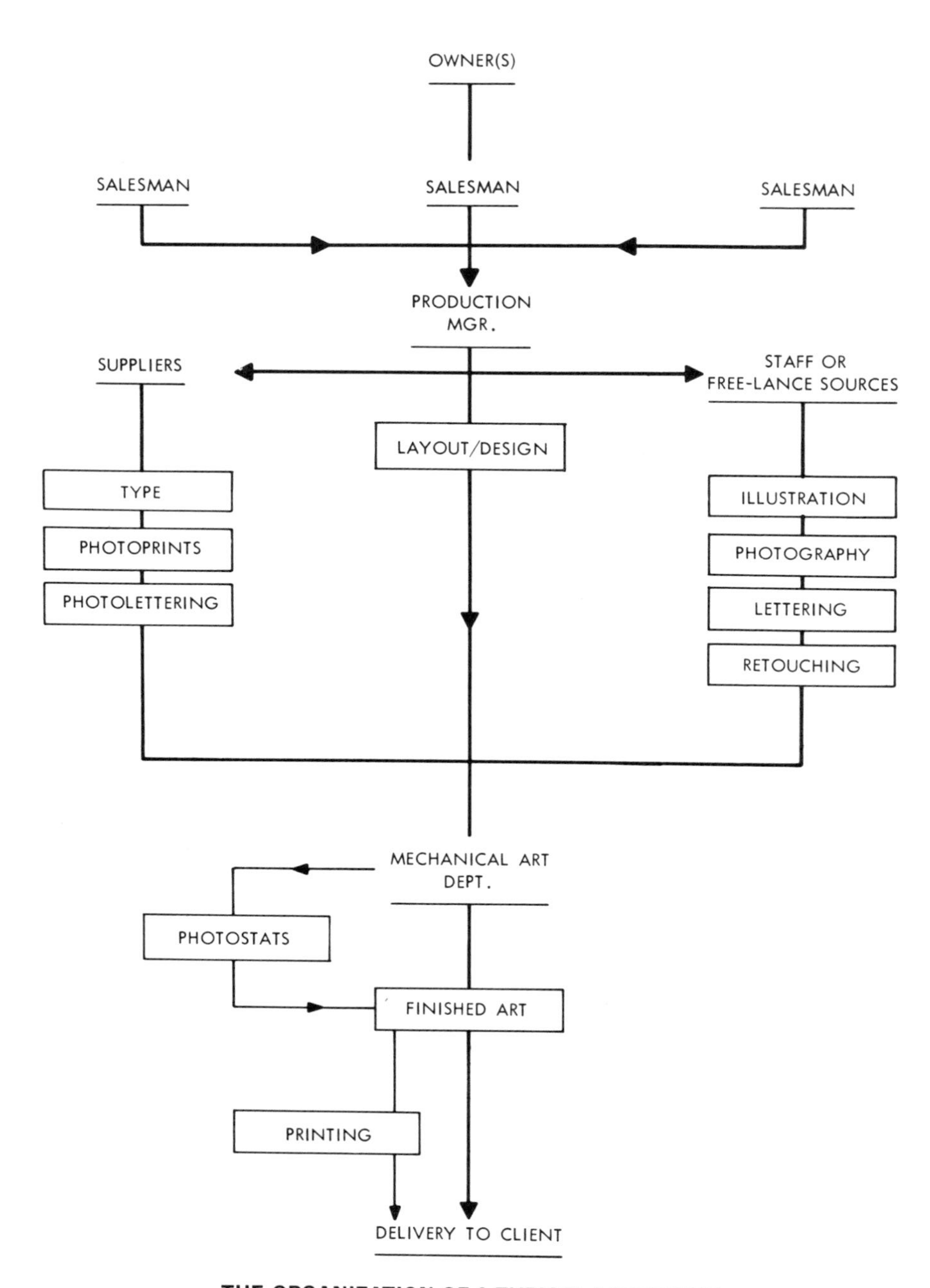

THE ORGANIZATION OF A TYPICAL ART STUDIO

tions as an extra asset or an emergency factor to a sometime employer who owes him no contractual allegiance.

THE WORK-SPACE ARRANGEMENT. "Work-space" is an arrangement whereby an artist is retained for a flat hourly fee or on a per-job basis. He is paid only for the work he performs, and there is no extra compensation for overtime; however, his hourly rate is higher than the salaried artist of comparable ability.

This variety of artist is provided with working space, telephone service, and often clerical help. He is expected to show a certain allegiance to the studio, but is permitted more freedom of action than the staff artist. Free to leave the premises when he is not busy, he is allowed to solicit work from the studio's competitors and perform it at his drawing board.

In return for these concessions, the artist is expected to give priority to his employer's assignments and to perform his work for less money than an outside free-lance artist would.

The organization of the studio

There is considerable overlap of talent and responsibility in any establishment where art is produced. Job titles are ambiguous and confusing—especially the title of "Art Director," a term often used to indicate a degree of importance rather than a specific function.

Following is a description of a typical studio organization, using job titles which most closely describe the skills and duties of each type of artist.

THE OWNER(S). The studio may be a sole proprietorship, a partnership, or a closed corporation. If the owner is a single individual, he must have a rapport with his clients which will cause them to retain his services; thus, he usually functions primarily as a salesman. If partners are involved, they often complement each other's talent. One may specialize in selling; the other in design or production. The partner who maintains contact with the clients is usually designated as the head of the studio.

THE SALESMAN. Considered part of management, the salesman solicits new business, and services it once it has been obtained. Though the work is performed by the studio staff, such accounts are considered to be his. He is generally hired because it is anticipated that he can bring new business with him. He may also service "house accounts"—accounts which have been established by the owners but which have grown too large for them to handle without help.

The salesman's remuneration is flexible. It can be either a salary, a salary plus commission, or a straight commission—depending upon the volume of his own accounts and the amount of servicing he performs for the house.

A good salesman should be well versed in production, able to provide technical advice to the client, and able to supervise the execution of the art.

The salesman is responsible for:

1. Obtaining the work from the client, together with the appropriate instructions.
2. Entering the job in the studio's records.
3. Explaining the job to the production manager and, if required, to the layout artist, illustrator, or photographer.
4. Maintaining the work schedule.
5. Delivery of the finished job, on time, to the client.
6. Preparation of the billing.

THE PRODUCTION MANAGER. Sometimes known as the studio manager, the production manager is the key man in the studio operation. In charge of the scheduling, traffic, and production of all work passing through the studio, he is directly accountable to management or to the salesman. It is his responsibility to see that all job deadlines are met. In the absence of a salesman, he may be expected to furnish technical advice to clients who visit the studio. In an emergency, he may be sent to the client's office to receive job instructions. The production manager is a highly-paid, salaried employee whose wide area of responsibility may include:

1. Receiving the job and pertinent instructions from the salesman.
2. Assigning the job to the appropriate artist(s); ordering and supervising layout, illustration, photography, and retouching from staff or free-lance sources; issuing purchase orders to free-lance artists.
3. Ordering necessary elements of the job from outside suppliers—typography, photolettering, photoprints, and photostats; issuing purchase orders.
4. Maintaining a schedule of the work in progress; scheduling the arrival of elements in time for mechanical assembly.
5. Supervising and assigning jobs to mechanical artists; checking the job while in progress and upon completion; marking up instructions for platemaking or printing and ordering such when required.
6. Submitting job to the salesman for rechecking before final delivery to client.

7. Checking the accuracy of the artists' bills and time sheets.

8. Keeping costs within reason.

9. Assisting the salesmen in the preparation of their billing.

THE LAYOUT ARTIST. Often called the "art director" or the "designer," the layout artist is responsible for the creative effort of the studio. He designs all material for which no layout has been provided by the client.

The competent layout artist should be well acquainted with all aspects of production. He is responsible for the aesthetic evaluation of all illustration produced by or for the studio. He selects hand or photolettering styles and specifies typography, and he may supervise photography and retouching.

The layout artist executes rough layouts, comprehensive (semifinished) layouts, or both. He may be provided with one or more assistants, or free-lance layout artists may be called upon to assist him when the work load is heavy. He is probably the most highly-paid artist in the studio.

Two types of artist are employed by the studio for the execution of finished art: the specialist and the "board man," or mechanical artist. The specialist may be salaried—if there is a full-time work load for him—or he may be employed on a work-space or a free-lance basis. Specialists who work at the studio usually have private or semiprivate working areas since they are considered the "elite" of the organization. They are generally more highly paid than board men.

THE ILLUSTRATOR. The illustrator is a specialist who produces drawings and illustrations, from simple black-and-white "spots" to full-color renderings. There are few artists who excel in every type of illustration. As a result, they generally concentrate their efforts within certain areas, such as fashion, still-life, or product illustration. Some artists will specialize in areas of masculine interest: boats, automobiles, aircraft, sport, hunting, and fishing. Each artist generally develops a technique that becomes his hallmark and which will cause him to be sought after for specific assignments.

The illustrator usually works on a work-space or a free-lance basis. He is seldom on salary unless the studio has considerable work that requires his particular talent. Many illustrators find steady employment producing story boards (visualized television scripts) for the agencies. Competent illustrators are well paid for their work.

THE PHOTOGRAPHER. A source of original photography, both in black-and-white and in color, the photographer will process as well as shoot his pictures, and will provide his client with processed results. Photographic facilities require considerable space and equipment for "staging" backgrounds and processing film. Few art studios have their own facilities unless their photographic needs are substantial. Most photographers prefer to establish their own studios and work for their clients on a free-lance basis. A good professional photographer should be completely familiar with the production requirements of the printing processes.

THE LETTERING ARTIST. The "lettering man" is an artist who designs and produces hand lettering. There are two varieties of hand lettering: finished and comprehensive ("comp"). Finished lettering is rendered exactly as it will appear on the printed work. Comprehensive lettering is carefully rendered and is used on semi-finished layouts, providing a close approximation of its appearance in the finished work.

The expert letterer may operate on a free-lance basis, but studios usually retain at least one staff member who can letter well. The lettering artist is a well-paid craftsman.

THE RETOUCHER. The retoucher is an artist who specializes in the retouching and clarification of photographs in order to render them more suitable for reproduction. He works with an airbrush and chemicals, clarifying, restoring, or eliminating areas of the photograph which might prove unclear or confusing in the printed result. He is generally the busiest of the specialists, since few photographs are taken which do not require some degree of retouching. He should be well versed in all aspects of production, as his major concern is with photographs that will appear in printed form. He may also become involved with the correction of continuous-tone art.

The retouch artist may be salaried or free-lance, depending upon the nature of the studio's needs and the degree of his skill. Regardless of the financial arrangement, most studios attempt to keep a retoucher readily available.

THE MECHANICAL ARTIST. Mechanical artists, or "board men," are the backbone of the studio staff. These are artists who will produce for management a greater profit-ratio than the better-paid free-lance specialists. Board men are seldom provided with private working areas, but work side by side in a large room known as the "bullpen." This arrangement facilitates communication and cooperative effort during the assembly of the finished art. It also enables the production manager to keep a closer check on the progress of the job. The cooperative atmosphere of the bullpen affords a better learning situation for the beginner.

The basic function of the board man is the execution of mechanical art. Mechanical art is the assembly of the specialist-produced elements into a unified composition—or "mechanical"—conforming to the layout and properly prepared for a particular process of reproduction. Since the elements must be pasted in position on the mechanical, the operation is called paste-up, and the mechanical artist is often known as a "paste-up man."

Such an artist should be a meticulous craftsman and should be familiar with production. He should be capable of assisting the production manager in the ordering of photostats and photoprints.

The board man is salaried in proportion to his experience and his capabilities beyond the immediate area of mechanical art. The beginner is usually hired as a mechanical artist; hired with an eye to his potential for developing one or more specialties, as well as his abılity to perform his basic task. As his capability increases, so will his value to the organization. He should aspire to become familiar with typographic production; to learn to letter, render comprehensives or simple layouts, handle an air-brush, or do simple illustration. If his capacity for specialization matures, he will be given the opportunity to specialize on a full-time basis. He will probably be replaced by another mechanical artist, who, in turn, will also be given the opportunity to move up.

Some artists become so adept at mechanical art that their services are highly regarded. Such artists are capable of utilizing taste and judgment in the mechanical interpretation of a layout. They can execute an entire mechanical, from start to finish, with little immediate supervision—ordering photostats, photoprints, typograhy, and executing simple line illustrations when required. Such artists are paid a substantial salary, perhaps receiving the title of assistant production manager, in order to retain their services. Often, so-qualified mechanical artists will operate on a free-lance basis, circulating from studio to studio to assist with heavy work loads or rush jobs.

Suppliers of the studio

Suppliers are outside firms which furnish materials or perform services which relate to the production of art and printed matter. They operate as independent businesses because of the specialized nature of their plant equipment. They supply the studio, agency, and advertising department.

The ordering of work that will be performed by these suppliers requires a high degree of production knowledge. Since each job represents an individual and often unique assignment, its requirements must be carefully specified by the purchaser in order to insure the desired result. Production can be defined as the preparation for, and/or the ordering of, the work performed by these suppliers.

THE TYPOGRAPHER. The typographer sets and makes up type by hand or with an automatic machine. He may furnish the client's printer with the actual metal type, or the client with proofs which have been printed from the type. These proofs are used in the paste-up assembly of the mechanical art.

THE FILM-LETTERING SERVICE. The film-lettering service provides lettering for headline and display copy. This lettering is produced from master photographic alphabets and is supplied to the client on either transparent film or on photographic paper. Film lettering is superior to cast type; it compares favorably with some styles of hand lettering, but is considered inferior to the best. Film lettering is necessarily a stock item. Although it may be distorted to meet certain requirements of the layout, it cannot be designed to fulfill a specific purpose.

THE PHOTOPRINTER. The photoprinter is not to be confused with the photographer. He does not take original photographs; he provides copy photographs of existing material. The photoprinter copies, enlarges, or reduces photographs or artwork and produces screened photographic prints or other related material.

THE PHOTOSTAT HOUSE. The "stat house" copies existing line art, lettering, or typography—utilizing a process which employs paper photographic negatives. This process has its limitations, but it is fast and inexpensive. Photostats may be furnished in any desired size, on any of several varieties of paper.

THE ENGRAVER. The engraver produces plates for the letterpress printing process.

THE ELECTROTYPER-STEREOTYPER. The electrotyper produces duplicate plates for the letterpress printing process. The stereotyper produces papier-mâché molds, or mats, from which duplicate letterpress plates can be made.

THE LITHOGRAPHIC PLATEMAKER. The "litho platemaker" produces plates for the lithographic printing process.

THE GRAVURE SERVICE. The gravure service, also known as the "intaglio service," produces plates for the gravure printing process.

THE PRINTER. The printer produces multiple reproductions of the subject matter, employing one of the several printing processes.

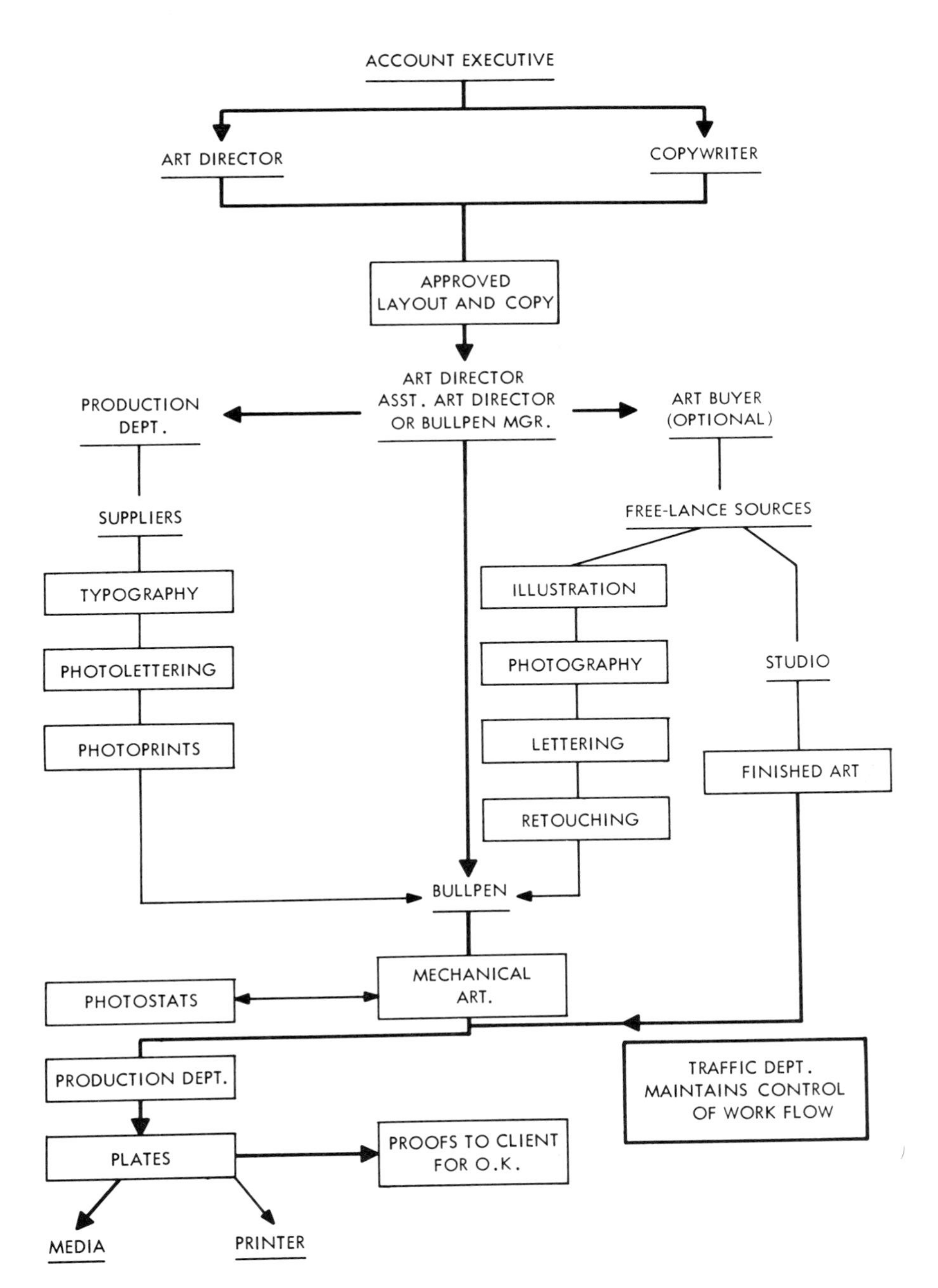

PRODUCTION IN A TYPICAL AGENCY

The printer may be retained by the studio, the agency, or the advertiser, but his product will ultimately be delivered to the organization which will put it to actual use. Printing plants range from small shops with limited facilities to huge plants with multimillion-dollar equipment.

THE ADVERTISING AGENCY

The advertising agency is also in business to produce advertising for a profit. This profit comes in the form of a commission, paid by advertising media, for all time or space that is purchased by the agency on behalf of its clients. In order for the agency to earn this commission, it must be recognized by media as a bona fide advertising agent. Once recognized, the agency becomes responsible for the payment of the media charges, even if the client defaults.

Agency commission is generally 15 per cent of the media cost, which, in view of some firms' multimillion-dollar advertising budgets, is often considerable. Production charges for materials and special services provided by the agency—finished art, typography, plates and duplicate plates, specific research, and publicity—are usually billed on a cost-plus-commission basis. This commission, or "service charge," is generally 15 per cent. Copy and creative art (layout) are provided as a service, as are the normal counseling facilities of the agency. This arrangement provides a norm for agency compensation, but it is by no means a fixed rule. Existing variations, ranging from the billing for service at actual cost to performing it for a flat fee, are too numerous to mention.

The advertiser considers that the services of his agency cost him little. Research, media selection, copywriting, and creative art facilities are his—paid for by a commission which he would not save if he were to purchase the time and space directly from media. Production costs must still be borne, even if the advertiser purchases this material himself. It is often well worth the service charge to have a staff of experts to perform this function. Thus, the agency serves as an extension of his own advertising department.

The purpose of the advertising agency is to plan, prepare, and place (with media) advertising for its clients. In order to do so efficiently, it may be organized in either of two ways.

The two types of agency organization are the *departmentalized type* and the *group type*. In the departmentalized organization, the executive responsible for the account calls upon the services of each department when needed. Each department serves all accounts. In the group organization, a group of persons consisting of a specialist from each department, is assigned to work on a particular account. Each group operates independently of groups assigned to other accounts. The group's activity is supervised by a "plans board"—an advisory board consisting of the agency's senior specialists. Each department of the agency is organized to perform a specific function.

Account Management. Each account is managed by an account executive, who acts as the liaison between the agency and the client's advertising manager. He draws upon the talents of the agency's staff and supervises the agency's part in the advertising program. He must be familiar with all facets of his client's business and capable of advising him knowledgeably on any aspect of his advertising program. He may service one or more small accounts. On large accounts, he is often provided with one or more assistants.

Research. The research department provides the statistical information necessary for the planning of a successful campaign. It provides data on such subjects as population and income distribution, buying habits, regional preferences, and motivational factors. The department is prepared to conduct any historical or market research that may be required.

Media Selection. The media department analyzes the reading, viewing, listening habits of the potential consumer. It compiles statistics on the coverage, effectiveness, and cost of all the available media. Equipped with this information, the department can make recommendations to the client, suggesting effective placement of his advertising, and advising him of its appropriateness, scope, and cost.

Creativity. The creative department is divided into two branches, copy and art. The copywriter and the creative artist work in close coordination. Depending upon the assignment, the copy may determine the nature of the art that will be used, the art may determine the copy that will be written, or both art and copy may be developed simultaneously. Some agencies place more importance on copy than on art, and vice versa.

The copy department is responsible for the writing of all material that will be used in the client's advertising. Copywriters are generally assigned to a specific account so that they may become fully familiar with the client's business.

The art department is responsible for the creation of all the visual material to be produced for the advertiser. This material is submitted for the client's approval in either layout or comprehensive form. Such work is designed by the art director, a highly-paid creative artist. Assigned to one or more accounts, he may or may not be responsible for the production of the finished art. Finished art is either executed by the mechanical art department, or purchased from studios or free-lance artists. The art director is responsible for the aesthetic evaluation of the elements of the finished art.

PRODUCTION. The production department specifies and orders the necessary material or service for producing or reproducing the finished art. From outside suppliers it orders plates or duplicate plates for submission to media, or plates and printing for delivery to the client. The production department also purchases typography and photoprinted material for the use of the agency's mechanical art department or free-lance sources.

TRAFFIC. The traffic department assumes control over the scheduling and flow of work through the various departments of the agency. It makes certain that the printing plates, made from the mechanical art, reach the publication before the closing date or "deadline." The closing date is the latest date that a publication will accept advertising for insertion in a particular issue.

BILLING. The billing department keeps an accounting of the costs incurred in the preparation of the advertising material, and bills the client accordingly.

Once the research and the media departments have provided the planning for the advertisement, and the copywriter and the art director have created a layout that meets with the client's approval, the advertisement is processed through the art and production departments in the following manner.

The approved art and copy is returned to the agency for the execution of the finished art. As previously noted, the art director may or may not supervise its production, but he is responsible for evaluating the aesthetic qualities and the suitability for reproduction of all the elements of the particular job. The art director seldom personally executes finished art.

The actual production may be supervised by the art director assigned to the account, by one of his assistants, or by the agency's mechanical art department ("bullpen") manager. Illustration, photography, lettering, and retouching may be purchased from free-lance sources and assembled into mechanical art by the agency's staff artists. Often the agency will employ an art buyer, whose principal duty is to purchase art from free-lance sources. Agencies seldom employ art specialists.

Most agencies employ art directors, but many, because of their modest size, do not have mechanical art departments. If this is the case, the art is usually purchased as a "package" from a studio, with the studio providing the individual elements, as well as the finished art. In this manner, the studio serves as the agency's art department. Larger agencies generally have their own mechanical art departments, but will call upon the studios when the work load gets too heavy.

The copy is sent to the agency's production department, where the necessary typography is specified and ordered for use by the mechanical art department. If the agency is heavily involved with typography, a type director—an expert whose sole concern is the specification and ordering of typography—may be employed by the production department. Either the production or the mechanical art department may order the photoprints and photostats required for the mechanical assembly.

The completed mechanical art is approved by the art director and/or the client and is returned to the production department. If the advertisement is to appear in a publication, the production department orders the necessary original and duplicate printing plates. Printed impressions (proofs) of these plates are submitted to the client for final approval. The traffic department then forwards the plate(s) to the appropriate publication(s).

If the job is to be furnished to the client in printed form, the production department forwards the plates to the printer, together with the necessary specifications. In some printing processes, the printer will produce the plates, returning proofs to the agency for approval. The planning and ordering of printing is an important part of the production department's function.

THE ADVERTISING DEPARTMENT

The advertising department is formed by the advertiser to handle, and sometimes perform, certain aspects of his advertising program within his own organization. The size and scope of this department varies greatly from firm to firm.

The advertising department is faced with the choice of providing itself with a salaried staff capable of producing its own requirements, or purchasing from external sources, or combining both systems. The latter approach is the one most generally taken.

When the agency purchases in behalf of the client, it acts as a middleman, attaching appropriate service charges. Knowledgeable purchasing eliminates the middleman in many items of the advertising budget—

its advertising program. This person may be a one-man department, or he may be a Vice-President in Charge of Advertising. Additionally, sales promotion and public relations may come within his jurisdiction. In order to consider the maximum distribution of duties, the large department which is headed by a Vice-President in Charge of Advertising, Sales Promotion, and Public Relations will be examined. This executive, obviously, is responsible for the over-all advertising policy of the firm. The department heads reporting to him are responsible for the production of the various elements of the advertising program.

The Advertising Manager. The advertising manager is responsible for all consumer and/or retail advertising. Consumer advertising is a sales message addressed to the ultimate consumer—the general public. Retail advertising is advertising disseminated by merchants selling consumer goods not produced by themselves. The advertising manager may also be responsible for the advertising of producer goods—goods that will be utilized in the production of other goods.

The media of the advertising manager are print, radio, and television. He supervises the work of the agency, communicating his firm's needs through close cooperation with the agency's account executive.

The Sales Promotion Manager. The sales promotion manager is responsible for the purchase, either directly or through a middleman, of all sales-promotional advertising. Sales-promotional advertising is advertising which is presented directly to the consumer in order to directly influence buying. The medium employed is usually the printed image, although fabricated dimensional items are sometimes utilized. Promotional material may be displayed at the point of purchase, mailed to the consumer, or presented directly to him—either at his door or by the advertiser's salesman.

Such material takes the form of point-of-purchase displays, premiums and free offers, printed folders and catalogs, direct-mail, and miscellaneous nonprinted items. Sales promotion is a continuing effort, not necessarily conducted as a campaign. It may be tied in with current consumer media advertising or developed around a timely or seasonal theme. Often several manufacturers of related products will engage in a cooperative sales-promotional endeavor.

The Public Relations Manager. The public relations manager is responsible for all matters pertaining to the public image of the firm. His tool is publicity, and his media are almost any facets of communication that can be called upon to serve his purpose. Among the specific items produced by the public-relations department may be the house organ (the firm's internal magazine or newspaper) and the annual report.

Each of these managers may be provided with one or more assistants. In addition, any department may employ the services of an art director or a production manager. Their duties would be similar to those of their studio counterparts.

ADVERTISING MATERIAL PRODUCED BY THE ARTIST

Advertising material may be generally classified in five categories:

1. Material that is presented to the consumer by means of an advertising medium.
2. Material that is presented to the consumer at the point of purchase.
3. Material that is presented to the consumer by mail or by door-to-door distribution.
4. Material that is produced either to instruct the salesman or aid him directly in selling the product.
5. Material that is produced to promote the corporate image.

Media advertising is handled almost exclusively by the agency, because the resulting commission represents the agency's principal source of revenue. The artwork for this advertising is produced by the agency's staff, or by studios or free-lance artists employed by the agency.

Point-of-purchase material, direct-mail material, premiums, and salesman's aids come under the general classification of sales-promotional materials. The advertiser often purchases these items directly from studios or free-lance sources. Some agencies encourage this because their own participation in sales promotion often becomes unprofitable, since no media commission results. However, in recent years many agencies have established special departments or subsidiary firms devoted solely to the preparation of sales-promotional material. Promotional material destined for mailing is produced for the advertiser by the agency or studio, but a mailing service is usually employed for the physical operation of mailing. Premiums are provided by specialty firms. The art for printed sales aids is usually purchased from studios, free-lance sources, or houses which specialize in such material.

Material used to promote the corporate image comes under the jurisdiction of the public-relations department. The art for public-relations material may be produced by either the agency or free-lance sources.

The studio artist is generally concerned with the entire spectrum of advertising material, since the studio must solicit business from both the agency and the advertiser. The agency artist's concern is governed by the degree of the agency's involvement in sales promotion and public relations. Some of the varieties of advertising material which fall within the province of the advertising artist are described in the following sections.

CONSUMER ADVERTISING

Consumer advertising is a sales message addressed to the ultimate consumer—the general public—informing it of the qualities of the merchandise or services offered by the advertiser. Advertising disseminated by merchants selling consumer goods not produced by themselves is known specifically as *retail advertising*.

Consumer advertising is developed around a particular theme or "campaign." The campaign is presented to the potential consumer through various media: print (magazines and newspapers), television, radio, transportation advertising, and billboards. It usually follows a predetermined theme. The trial offer, the improved formula, the results of laboratory tests, or the results of performance tests are typical campaign themes. The campaign may be based upon the product's attributes: utility, economy, safety, durability, or status appeal. It may feature a contest, a give-away, or a free-sample offer. It may be built around the theme of the advertiser's television or radio show, using the image of the star(s) or a cartoon character to draw attention to the advertiser's message. The testimonials of celebrities are often utilized in the advertising campaign.

The basic purpose of the campaign is to inform the consumer of the inherent advantages of the product, enhance its reputation, and persuade the consumer to purchase the product. Each campaign represents an attempt to "reach" the consumer by attracting his attention and motivating him to buy. When the possibilities of one approach have been exhausted, another will be developed to replace it. The theme of the new campaign may or may not have a direct relationship to its predecessor.

Often the activities of the advertiser are considerably more complex or abstract than the marketing of one or more related consumer products. If the firm produces a group of entirely unrelated items, it may be desirable to enhance the reputation of the company rather than its individual products. The firm's product may be a service or it may represent an intangible commodity such as security, prestige, or reliability. The ethical nature of the product or service may render the more competitive advertising themes inappropriate.

In any of these cases, the advertising campaign will attempt to present a favorable corporate image, build good will, and stress the attributes of the firm as a whole. Such advertising is known as *institutional advertising*. Institutional advertising may utilize a wide variety of informative or image-producing themes which demand no direct response from the consumer.

A wide variety of media is employed for consumer advertising.

DISTRIBUTION OF ADVERTISING EXPENDITURES

The Magazine Advertisement. The magazine advertisement is one which is placed in a magazine circulated to the reading public, whether the magazine is of general or specific interest. The size of such an advertisement is of prime importance to the artist, since it must be adaptable to the mechanical requirements of the particular publication and will determine the cost of the insertion. Magazine advertisements may be prepared in black-and-white or in two or more colors.

The Newspaper Advertisement. Most retail advertising is placed in newspapers, as are consumer advertisements of universal interest. The preparation of the newspaper advertisement follows the same lines as a magazine advertisement, but its size is determined by a different system of measurement. Although many newspapers are now equipped to accept color advertising, the bulk of newspaper advertising is still in black-and-white.

The Television Commercial. The television show—sponsored by an advertiser or by a group of advertisers—is produced by the agency, by the network, or is bought in a series of prefilmed programs, usually produced by the motion picture industry. The show itself ordinarily carries no sales message. The message is provided by the insertion of filmed "commercials." If the advertiser has no show of his own sponsorship the message may be inserted during station breaks. The production of television commercials is a highly complex procedure involving motion picture and animation techniques. It is done by firms specializing in such work.

Creative artists (usually illustrators) and copywriters employed by the agency will produce the *story board*. This is a visualized television commercial script, submitted for the client's approval before the actual filming is undertaken. The agency or the studio will sometimes produce the television *flip card*. This is a piece of nonanimated art employed during station breaks, or as a background to an audio commercial.

The Radio Commercial. Since the radio commercial is purely a verbal affair, no artwork whatever is required.

The Trade Advertisement. The trade advertisement is a sales message directed to the manufacturer, distributor, or retailer who is not the ultimate consumer of the product, but who incorporates it into a manufactured product of his own, distributes it to retail sources, or offers it for resale to the general public. Other than the more specific nature of its sales message, there is little difference in format from the consumer advertisement, except that unusual artistic embellishments are seldom employed. The trade advertisement is placed in a *trade publication*—a magazine or newspaper directed to a specific industry, profession, or group of merchants. These magazines seldom reach the general public. The size of such an advertisement is governed by the mechanical requirements of the publication.

The Directory Advertisement. The directory advertisement is prepared for insertion in some form of directory, apart from the listing the firm is normally accorded. Such advertisements are placed in telephone directories, business directories, organizational and club directories, etc. Their size is also governed by the mechanical requirements of the publication.

The Transportation Advertisement. A sales message in the form of a printed card or poster which is directed to the consumer and placed in busses, streetcars, subways, and commuter trains, as well as on the exteriors of busses and streetcars, is known as a transportation advertisement or "car card." Standard-sized cards are placed in frames above the windows and at the ends of the cars. Station and platform advertisements take the form of various standard-sized posters. Car cards are produced by lithography, letterpress, or silk-screen and are specifically designed for the transportation medium. Advertising space in commuter timetables falls in the category of transportation advertising.

The Outdoor Advertisement. Outdoor consumer advertising takes the form of large-sized printed paper posters, painted signs, or electric displays placed at strategic, well-trafficked locations. These are often designed by the agency or the studio, but are seldom executed by them. Billboard posters require lithographic presses of considerable size capacity. The lithographers produce their own art, executing the drawing directly on the lithographic plates. Painted or electric displays are usually produced by a contractor.

SALES PROMOTION

Sales-promotional advertising is any advertising that is presented directly to the consumer in order to influence retail buying. *Dealer-promotional advertising* is directed to the dealer, persuading him to stock specific merchandise. Both come under the heading of sales promotion. The medium employed for sales promotion is usually the printed image, although fabricated dimensional items are sometimes utilized. Promotional material may be displayed at the point of purchase, mailed to the consumer, or distributed to his door. It may be mailed to the dealer or presented to him by the advertiser's salesman.

Such material takes the form of point-of-purchase signs and displays, premiums and free offers, printed folders, brochures, catalogs for mailing purposes, and miscellaneous nonprinted items. The salesman may be equipped with easeled presentations, charts, and slides to help him "sell" the dealer.

Sales promotion is a continuing effort, not necessarily conducted as a campaign, although it may be tied in with current consumer media advertising, or developed around a timely or seasonal theme. Often several manufacturers of related products will engage in a cooperative sales promotional endeavor.

Point-of-purchase advertising

Point-of-purchase advertising is a sales message that appears at the retail level, designed to influence customers who are either passing or are inside the store. Furnished by the advertiser for the retailer's use, its purpose is to act as a reminder, or as an instigator of impulse buying. If the store is solely the advertiser's outlet, it can be assumed that most of the available promotional material will be displayed. If the store stocks competitive items, the material should be designed to be more utilitarian and decorative than that provided by the competition, thereby encouraging the merchant to devote more than average space to its display.

Point-of-purchase psychology attempts to induce the retail merchant to display the product in more locations than its normally allocated shelf area by utilizing specially constructed bins and displays. This purpose in mind, point-of-purchase material is often developed around a timely theme—holidays, civic events, bargain days, and dietary consciousness—in the hope that the merchant will allow the theme to dominate the store. For this purpose, both "selfish" and "nonselfish" material is designed. Selfish material prominently displays the name of the advertiser's product, while nonselfish material allows the merchant to insert the name of any related item he wishes to feature. Inexpensive displays and posters are provided free, while more complex units are sold to the merchant or given free upon receipt of a specified order.

The most competitive retail area is the supermarket, where promotional material of one nature or another is generally used to decorate the store.

Three-dimensional displays

The three-dimensional display is the principal device used to draw attention to the product. These displays are produced in a wide variety of forms.

THE COUNTER DISPLAY. Few retail outlets decorate their stores with promotional material to the extent that supermarkets do, since the modern store often has interior decor that would be spoiled by an abundance of promotional material. Thus, if a product is displayed elsewhere than on the shelves, it is generally in a self-contained unit. The most common of these is the counter display—a display designed to take advantage of any excess counter space. These may range from simple folding cardboard units to complex constructions of wire, plastic, or metal designed by the advertiser to display the product to its best advantage. Such displays are generally printed or fabricated by lithographers or specialty firms. The artwork for any printed components is often provided by the studio or the agency.

THE BIN OR "DUMP." The bin is a simple, corrugated cardboard stand of a nonpermanent nature in which products may be placed in order to take advantage of aisle space for display purposes. The advertising message, for which the studio or the agency may supply the art, is either printed directly on the corrugated board or on a paper wrap-around. Bins sometimes come with metal inserts, so that dry ice may be utilized for the display of perishable products.

THE FLOOR DISPLAY. The floor display is larger and more complex than the bin, and is designed to move the product off the shelves and into the aisles where it will be more readily noticed. It is created around a timely or seasonal theme, and is designed to hold a large quantity of the product. The display may also hold related items which have been "tied in" by cooperating advertisers, or items which the merchant wishes to feature. The size of such displays generally relegates them to supermarket use, and their design and construction utilize the full range of the artist's imagination and ingenuity. Usually made of printed corrugated board, they are provided free, or at a minimal cost. Such displays are discarded after a short period of use.

Floor displays in the form of permanent, replenishable racks are provided for a fee or on a loan basis. No promotional theme is employed, as their prime function is to secure a permanent display site for the advertiser. There is little art other than an identifying metal or plastic sign.

THE WINDOW DISPLAY. A dimensional display, often employing some variety of motion or animation, the window display is lavishly designed to draw the attention of the passer-by to a particular product sold within the store. A window display usually features the actual product in some manner so that the customer can readily identify it when he sees it on the shelves. Based on timely or seasonal themes, such displays are often ingenious and complex in nature. Their design requires unique skills, particularly in the application of motors, lights, and other constructional devices. Although there are firms that specialize in this type of design and fabrication, artists at the studio and agency level are also often involved in both the design and execution of illustrative and mechanical art for displays.

DISPLAY CARTONS. Display cartons are packing cartons constructed so that when opened, and folded in various manners, they become self-contained display units. As a result, the products can be displayed in one of these units on the counter or on the floor; they need not be removed for placement on the shelves. These display cartons, more decorative than shipping cartons, are often constructed of quality cardboard and are printed in a variety of attractive colors.

THE MOBILE. Inspired by the artistic creations of Alexander Calder, the mobile is a hanging display. It consists of geometric shapes suspended from wires, and so balanced that it will be kept in motion by air currents, thus attracting attention to its advertising message. Die-cut, printed cardboard shapes are utilized; the product itself often forms one of the shapes. The design of the mobile display requires a good degree of artistic ability.

MISCELLANEOUS ITEMS. Display material may be produced in many other forms, each designed for a specific sales area—from giant department store to neighborhood bar. They range from a simple sign to a complex mechanical display utilizing motion and sound. Some typical examples are: glass signs, wall plaques or shadow boxes, dioramas, advertising clocks, back-bar menu signs, mirror displays, large dummy products, and decalcomanias. Such items are produced by varied sources, but it is not unusual for the advertising artist to find himself involved in some aspect of their creation or production.

Two-dimensional promotional material

Two-dimensional promotional material consists of printed pieces, unmounted or mounted on heavy cardboard. These are used to draw attention to the product in an area where there may not be sufficient room for a display. They are created by the studio or the agency and are printed by various processes.

The Counter Card. The counter card is a printed card, sometimes die-cut and usually easeled for on-the-counter display. The counter card is designed to serve as a means of brand identification or as an initiator of impulse buying. It may often remind the prospective purchaser that the product is nationally advertised and may carry a reprint of a particular national advertisement.

The "Shelf-Talker." The shelf-talker is a small folded sign that is inserted beneath the merchandise and hangs down over the price-marker rail below, giving emphasis to the location of the product and containing a large area for the insertion of the price. The shelf-talker is utilized particularly when the item is on sale.

The Window Streamer. Window streamers are paper posters of varying sizes, usually taped to the store window, calling attention to particular products that are on sale within the store.

The Banner. A large paper sign or banner may be used to call attention to featured products, and is generally displayed on the wall inside the store. Banners are sometimes furnished in cloth for exterior display.

The Wire Hanger. Wire hangers are large paper signs of varying shape, hung from wires across the aisles over the heads of the customers. These may feature the particular brand, product, or the theme of the sale in which the product is being featured.

The Ad Reprint Holder. The ad reprint holder is a counter card or a small poster that may be used to feature a reprint of the current national consumer advertisement. This capitalizes upon a supposed consumer preference for nationally advertised brands, reminding the prospective purchaser that this is such a brand. It also ties in products with the type of guarantee furnished by such organizations as the Good Housekeeping Institute.

The Pole Sign. A double-sided cardboard sign may be displayed on a pole over the shelves, bins, or floor displays, calling attention to the location of the particular product.

Packaging

Since it is intended to enhance and draw attention to the product at the point of purchase, package design is generally, though not always, supervised by the sales-promotion department. The agency, the studio, or the company's own art department may become involved in package design. Package design is a profitable business because such work can be billed with consideration of the long-range use to which the design will be put, rather than merely the man-hours spent in the execution of the design. As a result, there are firms which specialize exclusively in package designing.

Package design encompasses not only the design of the individual package or container, but the design of the carton and the shipping carton as well.

The design enhancement of the actual product is known as *industrial design*. This is a distinct field of endeavor, completely separate from advertising design. Although both advertising designers and industrial designers may become involved in package design, advertising artists are seldom called upon to perform industrial design and vice versa.

Exhibits and booths

The sales promotion department is usually responsible for supervising the design and construction of stationary and traveling exhibits, as well as sales booths for shows, conventions, fairs, etc. Such projects require mechanical construction; therefore, they are built by firms which specialize in this type of work. The design of the exhibit or booth, and the production of the necessary graphic elements, may be executed by the agency, the studio, or the firm's own art department.

Specialties, premiums, and free offers

Specialties are items given to regular or frequent customers, not necessarily in return for a specific purchase.

Premiums are items offered to the public in order to induce purchase of a product. They are given in return for proof of purchase.

Free Offers are items or samples given indiscriminately to the general public. No proof of purchase is required.

METHODS OF DISTRIBUTION. The above items are distributed in the following manner:

Specialties are mailed, personally presented by salesmen, or given to regular customers by the merchant. Holidays often present an occasion for the presentation of such items. Cigarette lighters, pens, desk pads, calendars, key chains, and card cases are typical specialty items.

Premiums are given automatically at the point of sale, mailed upon receipt of a coupon attached to the package, or obtained at a central redemption center upon presentation of coupons which have been attached to the merchandise. Expensive premiums often require the consumer to pay a charge in addition to the presentation of the coupon.

The free offer is given upon receipt of a mailed request—often a coupon from a consumer advertisement; given on the occasion of a visit to the dealer—even though no purchase is made; or given if the consumer agrees to a demonstration of the particular product.

Obviously the premium can take almost any form—from the imprinted balloon to the household appliance. The artist's involvement depends upon the nature of the item. In most cases, the artist becomes concerned with the production of imprint art for mass-produced, give-away items which bear the advertiser's name or sales message. The production of premium catalogs is a major art area; so is the production of the coupons, stamps, or other devices with which the premiums are to be obtained.

DIRECT ADVERTISING

Direct advertising is advertising matter presented directly to the potential consumer, describing the features of a product. Its purpose may be to attract customers to a retail outlet; to invite customers to witness a demonstration; to develop a list of prospects for a salesman; to build good will; to establish a corporate image; to solicit inquiries for specific services; to persuade professional people to recommend products; or to persuade dealers to stock specific merchandise.

Direct-mail advertising is advertising matter sent to the consumer through the mail.

Nonmail direct advertising is advertising matter presented directly to the consumer in some other manner, such as door-to-door distribution. It may be distributed at the retail source, distributed to organized groups, or handed out at public gatherings.

Mail-order selling is advertising designed specifically to elicit orders through the mail, using an attached order blank.

A *mail-order house* is a firm that receives its orders and delivers its goods through the mail. The principal sales tool of the mail-order house is the catalog. The mail-order house employs both direct and consumer advertising techniques.

Next to the personal salesman, direct-mail is one of the most effective sales media. Utilizing the postal system, direct-mail has the capacity to deliver a sales message personally and confidentially to a *selected* prospect.

Direct-mail eliminates the wasted circulation of mass media, since it may be sent only to qualified customers. It may be directed to specific geographical areas. Direct-mail is fast; its timing can be controlled; and it serves to extend the influence of other advertising media. Follow-up material can be sent to the same prospects. Sales information can be solicited.

Direct advertising is unique because of its flexibility of production. Since there are no fixed media charges, the cost of the direct advertising piece can be tailored to the budget of the advertiser. The piece may be modest or ambitious, simple or elaborate, depending on its particular purpose. If a twelve-page folder should prove too expensive, the advertising message may be condensed to eight pages, thereby reducing the cost. Material from previous sources can be reprinted. A slight reduction in size, making possible the use of a smaller printing press, may result in a considerable saving. Careful use of color, the preseparation of art, the proper selection of paper, and the selection of the appropriate printing process all play an important part in the economics of the medium.

If an advertising artist is involved with the full range of his client's advertising program, a good portion of his efforts will be devoted to the production of direct advertising. Direct advertising is used to convey a great variety of sales messages—descriptive, promotional, educational, or institutional. Some of the more commonly used forms of direct advertising are:

The Letter. Direct advertising often takes the form of the standard business letter. This may be printed on one, two, or four pages and may or may not be illustrated. Although mass-produced, considerable effort is expended to make it appear to have been individually typed and signed.

The Leaflet. A printed sheet, folded once or twice.

The Folder. A printed sheet, folded several times. A large folder is known as a broadside.

The Booklet. A book form consisting of several pages and bound with a paper cover. The words "booklet" and "pamphlet" are used interchangeably. The word "brochure" implies a similar, but more ambitious effort.

The Self-mailer. A folder or a broadside designed so that it will not require an envelope for mailing. Space is left for stamping and addressing; it will then be fastened shut with a seal.

The Postcard. A standard-sized postcard sent through the mail, it is used to announce a merchandising event, or a product or service.

The Reply Card. A standard-sized, often postpaid postcard, enclosed in a mailing for the convenience of those who wish to reply to an offer.

The Envelope Stuffer. A single-sheet form featuring a specific product or service, often included with a monthly bill or other periodic mailing.

The Handbill. A single sheet, printed on one side, generally distributed door-to-door. Handbills are also known as *throwaways* because there is little likelihood of their retention by the recipient.

SALES AIDS

Sales aids are materials furnished to the firm's salesmen, designed to instruct them or to assist them in the presentation of their sales message. Instructional material may take the form of material to be shown to a group of retailers or consumers, or to individual retailers or consumers.

THE SALES PRESENTATION. The sales presentation is usually designed to be shown to a group. The size and importance of the group will determine the effort and expense expended in the production of the presentation. A typical presentational device is the "flip-flop"—a series of easeled pages which are turned as the salesman delivers his message. Large charts and photographic slides are often employed to complement the sales message. The motion picture may also be utilized as a medium of sales presentation.

THE SALES MANUAL. Firms frequently provide their salesmen with manuals or handbooks which instruct them as to the best methods for selling the product or service. These manuals may also contain technical information about the product.

THE TECHNICAL MANUAL. Also known as a *service manual,* technical manuals contain technical information concerning the specifications, installation, maintenance, and repair of the product. These may be retained by the salesman for his own use, or presented to the customer after purchase.

THE CATALOG. The catalog is a listing and description of the products produced by the manufacturer. There are two types of catalog: consumer and industrial. Of the two, the industrial catalog is generally more permanent in nature. Some catalogs are designed to be self-selling, while others require the services of a salesman for interpretation and ordering. Large, comprehensive catalogs are seldom distributed to the public but are retained for the salesman's use, or presented to the established customer for his convenience.

THE SALES KIT. A kit containing informative material is often used when making a sales presentation to an individual customer. The kit may contain one or more items which may be left with the customer as a reminder of the salesman's visit.

PUBLIC-RELATIONS MATERIAL

Printed public-relations material is used for the promotion of the firm's corporate image, both externally and internally. The principal tool of the public relations department is the press release; however, there are other forms utilized to achieve this purpose.

Stationery

Letterheads, business cards, billheads, shipping lists, and other stationery are designed with a unified theme intended to reflect the function and the reputation of the company. Almost any art source might be called upon to design such material.

The annual report

The annual report is the yearly statement of the financial status of a corporation which is submitted to stockholders and employees. Its publication is required by law. This report often takes the form of an elaborate brochure, delineating the progress and changes which have occurred during the particular fiscal period. The format of such a report is considered extremely important; therefore, it requires the services of competent copywriters and designers. The report is usually written and designed by the staff of the advertising agency; however, the studio sometimes executes the artwork.

The house organ

The house organ is a periodical publication used to build good will and promote the interests of the company. It may take the form of a magazine or a newspaper. There are two types of house organs: external and internal. The external house organ is published for customers, while the internal house organ is published principally to disseminate news and information to employees.

The educational publication

The production and publication of any literature designed as educational material may be undertaken by the public relations department. Distributed as a public service, it is felt that such literature, usually without a sales message, serves to enhance the reputation of the firm.

3 THE LETTERPRESS PROCESS

The history of printing is the history of production. While the duplication of the printed message remained in the hands of the scribe or the monastic, there was no need for technical knowledge; the process of graphic communication was governed by individual artistry.

However, with the invention of movable type by Johann Gutenberg around 1450, printing came into the realm of mechanical technology, creating a situation in which the artistic and technical aspects of graphic communication became dependent upon each other and have remained so ever since.

The early process employed a metal of low melting temperature which allowed any quantity of an individual letter to be cast from a mold, or matrix. Each letter was cast as a *raised, backward* surface which, when inked, would transfer the image to paper. The paper was fed to the press by hand and the inked type brought into contact with it by the pressure of a hand-operated platen.

This method of printing from a raised surface is known as *letterpress* (or relief) printing.

Modern letterpress printing employs exactly the same principle. Technological advances have not altered the concept of relief printing, but have been developed in order to make the following improvements possible:

1. Increase the fidelity and speed with which the printing surface can be produced—fidelity with which illustrative matter can be translated into a raised printing surface; speed with which the individual letter characters can be assembled into words and sentences.
2. Increase the durability of the printing surface.
3. Increase the speed of printing equipment.
4. Increase the size capacity of printing equipment.
5. Print on both sides of the paper in one operation.
6. Print multiple color with the same press.

The great innovation was not the invention of *printing*, but the invention of movable type. Relief printing, in which illustrative pages were carved from wooden blocks, had been known in fifth-century China. Western relief prints were produced in the early fifteenth century. Thus, while the invention of movable type brought incredible flexibility in the printing of text, the process for reproducing illustrative matter was already at hand.

Use of the wood engraving remained the principal method for the relief printing of illustration for four centuries. Hand carved on the surface of close-grained wood blocks, it was the result of a slow, laborious process. In order to fully understand the development of relief-printed illustrative matter, one must examine the techniques involved. Until the advent of photoengraving, there was no method for converting an *existing* illustration to a letterpress plate. The illustration had to be drawn directly, backwards, on the printing surface. Then the printing area had to be raised above the nonprinting area; or, more logically, the nonprinting area had to be lowered.

A graver is a tool used for making incisions in a printing plate. Consider, now, a single line. If the line is cut into the plate with the graver, the surrounding area, which is higher, will receive the ink and the line will print white against a black background—a negative image. In order to print a positive image—a black line against a white background—the line itself must be left standing and the *surrounding area* must be cut away with the graver. The first technique is called *white-line engraving;* the second, *black-line engraving.* Each requires a different artistic approach to the subject matter.

Black-line engraving, for the purpose of printing, was employed in the fifteenth century and prevailed until the introduction of the easier white-line technique in the early nineteenth century. American wood engravers achieved remarkable results in the 1860's working in both black- and white-line techniques.

The engraver had to be able to draw well backwards, in addition to being able to carve. Any examination of Civil War periodicals will disclose that there were those who could, and those who could not. A mechanical means for transferring the artist's work to the plate was needed; so was a more durable plate. Photography provided the answer.

Photography was invented in the early nineteenth century, and the photographic industry as such began in the 1870's. The advent of practical photography provided two vital factors in the field of graphic art: (1) the ability to produce a factual image of the subject matter, and (2) the ability to photographically produce a printing plate—thereby eliminating the necessity for the artist to work directly on the plate.

To appreciate photography's contribution to printing, one must understand the difference between line and tone. *Line* is any solid stroke or area applied to a surface without tonal variation, such as a pen-stroke or a brush-stroke of undiluted color. *Tone* is diluted color applied to a surface—the dilution being caused by addition of a solvent, as in oil or water-color painting; or by lessening pressure—as in a pencil or chalk (pastel) rendering. Continuous tone is the gradual flow of one tone into another, artistically known as "blending."

All three techniques existed in art before the advent of printing. So far, only the line technique was suitable for reproduction. The raised surface printed only solid lines and areas; one could hardly carve middle-tone areas into a block of wood. The raised surface had to print solid color, or none at all. Any tonal variation had to be simulated by closely spaced lines or cross-hatching.

Photography is the result of the sensitivity of silver compounds to light. When silver bromide, deposited on a gelatin (film) surface, is exposed to light, it undergoes a chemical change which causes it to become *developable*. The developing process (immersion in a chemical solution) causes the exposed bromide to reduce to metallic silver, forming an image relative to the intensity of the light to which it was exposed. The resultant image—in which the lightest portions of the subject become the blackest areas of the film and the blackest portions of the subject become the lightest, more transparent areas of the film—is called a *negative*.

In order to obtain a *positive* image, with light and dark areas corresponding to those of the original subject, the negative must be printed. This is done by placing it in contact with a piece of sensitized paper and exposing it to light. The sensitized paper reacts to light in the same manner as the sensitized film, but the light values, having become reversed on the negative *become reversed again* on the sensitized paper, thus resulting in a *positive* image—one in which the tonal values correspond to the original. Since the middle tones (grays) of the positive image constitute a chemical tinting of the emulsion (layer of sensitized coating) and represent a tonal gradation between the solid blacks and the whites, the resultant image is known as a *continuous tone positive*.

The production of a photograph involves the following steps:

1. Camera exposure of the sensitized negative (film).
2. Development of the negative.
3. Fixation (to prevent further chemical activation).
4. Washing and drying.
5. Printing—exposure of the sensitized positive (paper). The resultant print need not be the same size as the negative, but may be enlarged or reduced (by *projecting* onto the printing paper) to any convenient size.

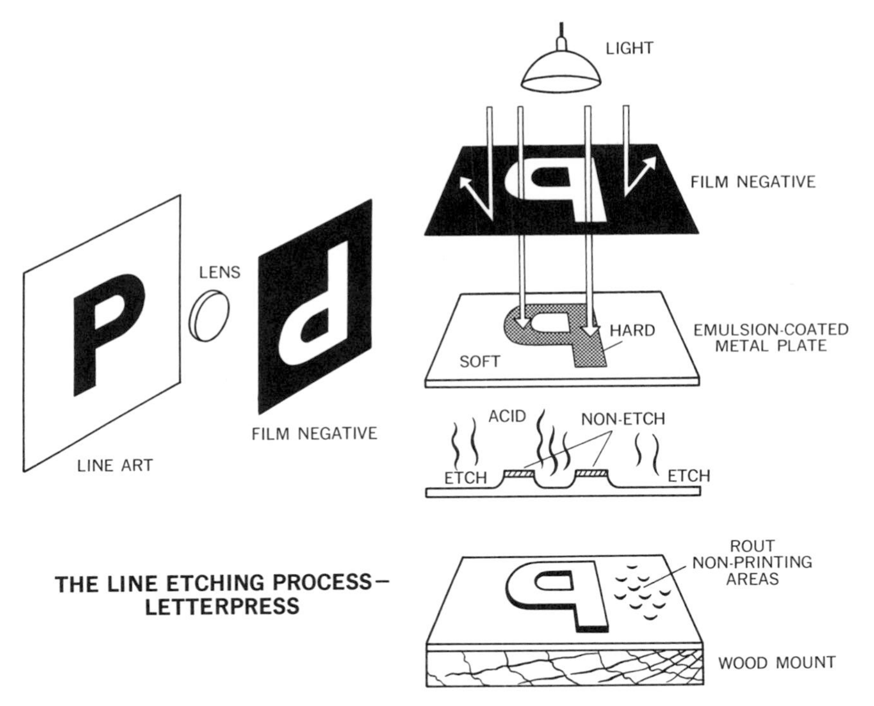

THE LINE ETCHING PROCESS—LETTERPRESS

6. Development of the positive.

7. Fixation, washing, and drying.

The invention of photography produced another continuous tone medium. At the time, no means for the printing of continuous tone had been developed. However, when art originally executed in line is photographed, the resultant image on the film negative remains in line. Its light values are the reverse of the original, but are either opaque or transparent; there is no tone. Thus, it became practical to utilize the *line* photographic negative in the production of the black-line engraving.

PHOTOENGRAVING

The line etching process

In photoengraving, a film negative is made photographically, but a sensitized metal plate is substituted for the sensitized paper and the image is exposed *backwards*. Since the light values of the negative are in reverse, the lines which will ultimately become the printing area are transparent. Light passing through the transparent area strikes the sensitized emulsion, causing it to *harden*. This hardened emulsion forms a protective, acid-resistant covering over the printing area of the plate. When the plate is submitted to an etching process, the acid eats away the nonprinting areas leaving a relief printing image on the surface of the metal. When inked, the image can be transferred to paper.

Definitions

Engraving. A general term for any relief printing plate produced by a hand, photomechanical, or electronic process.

Engraver. An artisan who executes hand tool work on an engraving.

Etching. Biting an image into a metal plate by either chemical or electrolytic action.

Photoengraving. An etched relief printing plate produced for the letterpress process by means of photography. The process of exposing film negatives to sensitized metal, causing the image to become acid-resistant. The nonprinting areas are then etched with acid to the required relief.

Line Etching. The photomechanical process by which any linear design is etched into relief.

Line Engraving. The relief printing plate produced by the line etching process. Also known as a line plate.

Line Cut. A line engraving.

Positive. Any image, transparent or printed, where the light and dark areas correspond to those of the original subject.

Negative. Any image, transparent or printed, where the light and dark areas are the reverse of those of the original subject.

Contact Printing. The process in which transparent film (negative or positive) is placed on top of a light-sensitive surface—film, paper, or plate—in order to expose one to the other. Light passing through the original film effects an image in the reverse. Contact printing is usually accomplished in a vacuum frame which exhausts the air and brings the two surfaces into absolute contact with each other.

Art. Art consists of any illustration, drawing, photograph, lettering, type proof, or photostat that has been prepared for the platemaking process. Finished art is often known as "copy."

Mechanical Art. When the elements of a composition have been assembled by the artist and mounted in proper position on illustration board preparatory to the platemaking process, the resulting assembly is known as mechanical art. The mechanical may be also known as "finished art" and, in cases where it has been completely assembled, "camera-ready art."

Stripping. The assembly, in negative form, of all the elements which are to appear on the plate. Often, illustrations, photographs, etc. are supplied separately from the mechanical—possibly larger than they are to appear in the finished product. These must be photographically reduced to the proper size and "stripped" into position on the master negative or "flat."

Opaquing. Applying red or black pigment to photographic negatives in order to block the passage of light and eliminate undesirable material (paste-up marks, blemishes, etc.). This operation is usually performed by hand, using a brush.

The production of a line engraving involves the following steps:

1. The mechanical is photographed with camera to exact size and sharpness.
2. Parts of the resultant film negatives are joined ("stripped") together to form the complete assembly.
3. Extraneous material is "opaqued" out.
4. The negative is "contact printed" onto a sensitized metal plate by placing it over the metal plate and exposing it to light. The light passes through the transparent areas of the negative, striking the sensitized surface of the plate and causing it to harden.
5. The metal plate is then "developed," causing the portions of the sensitized surface which have *not* been acted upon by the light to wash away. Those left on the plate are now acid-resistant. Etching begins at this point.
6. The metal plate is placed in an etching (acid) solution which eats away the portions of the plate that have not become acid-resistant. The first etching is mild in order to prevent loss of fine lines and to establish a slight relief.
7. The metal plate is rinsed, dried, and dusted with Dragon's Blood. This is a powdery substance which, when heated, forms an acid-resistant coating on the tops and sides (shoulders) of the relief formations. In recent years, a powderless etching process has come into use, in which the acid bath includes special chemicals that protect the shoulders of the line during etching.
8. Successive etchings (customarily four) follow in order to reach the required depth. Powdering accompanies every operation, each application brushed on in a different direction.
9. After completion of etching, the metal plate is placed upon a routing

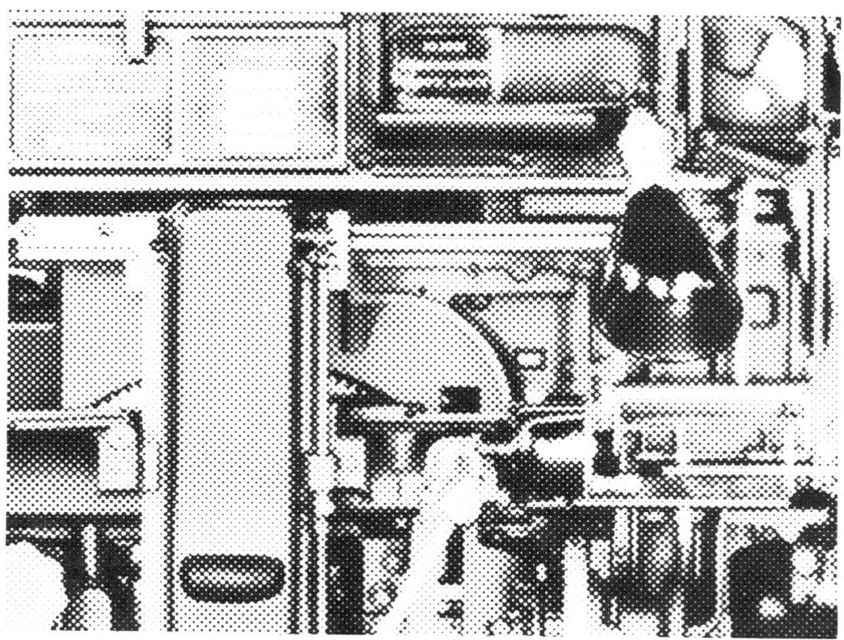

AN ENLARGEMENT OF THE HALFTONE DOT PATTERN

machine which cuts away large non-printing areas and grinds smaller areas to a greater depth.

10. The routed plate is then attached to a base—made of wood or metal, and planed to type height—.918 in. high.
11. An impression of the finished etching is printed on a proof press (hand operated) and submitted to the client for his approval.
12. Line engravings are usually etched on zinc. Reproductions of fine detail, halftones, or those destined for long press runs, are etched on copper, as well as those which will be employed for duplicate plates. Magnesium, light and durable, is coming into popular use.

The halftone process

The photoengraving process posed no problem as a means of producing a metal plate by which a design composed solely of lines could be printed. However, duplication of the middle gray tones (neither white nor black) found in a *continuous-tone* original required the development of other techniques.

The eye, observing minute juxtaposed areas (dots) of black and white, will mix them and perceive them as a gray tone—the darkness or lightness depending upon the ratio of black area to white area. Television, in which the image is caused by an electron beam scanning a phosphorescent screen in a pattern of thousands of fluorescent dots, is based upon this same principle.

A method was needed which would break up the halftone areas into such a pattern of minute dots—varying in size according to the value of the tone—and which would optically reproduce the tonal effect when inked and printed with a single color.

The halftone screen, which provided the solution to this problem, was developed in the 1880's. It consists of two sheets of clear glass, each having parallel lines etched on one surface and filled in with black composition. The glass sheets are locked together in a frame with their lines at right angles to each other.

The screen is placed in front of the photographic film in the camera and each square becomes a miniature lens. The light reflected from the subject passes through the squares onto the film, producing a dot formation over the entire image. Each dot represents a minute portion of the image and their size, shape, and proximity duplicate the tones of the original.

The fidelity of the image is dependent upon the fineness of the halftone screen, which is determined by the number of ruled lines per inch. Screen rulings range from 50 to over 200 lines per inch, with screens of 55 to 120 lines being utilized for normal printing purposes, depending upon the surface of the paper involved. Newspaper illustrations, printed on coarse, absorbent paper, employ 55 to 65 line screens—averaging 3600 dots per square inch. Magazine illustrations, printed on finer stock, are generally produced with 110 to 120 line halftones—containing some 14,440 dots per square inch.

Many feel that photoengraving is an automatic, mechanical process where the human element functions to a minimal degree. This is hardly so. The individual skill and judgment of the engraver is a vital factor in the production of the well-reproduced image—especially in the halftone process.

There is a distinct difference between line and halftone etching. In line etching it is necessary to faithfully reproduce every line on metal; in halftone etching it is desirable to reproduce the *tonal effect* of the original copy. In order to faithfully duplicate the contrast and brilliance of good copy, considerable handwork is involved.

50-LINE SCREEN 65-LINE SCREEN

100-LINE SCREEN

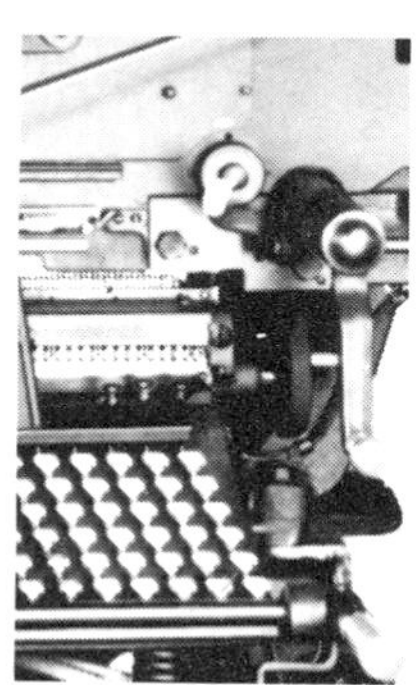

120-LINE SCREEN

FOUR COMMONLY USED HALFTONE SCREENS

(EXAMPLES OF SQUARE HALFTONES)

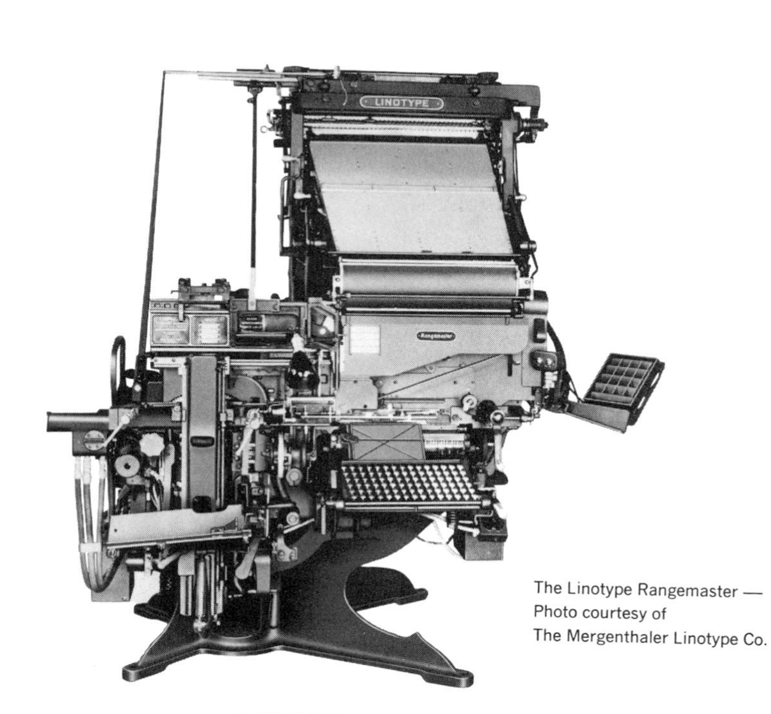

The Linotype Rangemaster —
Photo courtesy of
The Mergenthaler Linotype Co.

A SILHOUETTE HALFTONE

When the exposed plate is first submitted to the acid bath and *flat etched* (etched for a sufficient time to acquire the necessary printing depth), the resultant impression or *proof* shows a minimal contrast. Gray tones in the dark and in the highlight areas result in a dull and lifeless appearance. It becomes the responsibility of the engraver to rework these areas by hand in order to achieve maximum tonal range. The principle of this reworking is simple and should be thoroughly understood.

The highlight areas have a tendency to appear gray because the dots in these areas have not been sufficiently etched and are *too large*. These areas are *lightened* by chemically *reducing the size of the dot*. This process is known as *re-etching*.

The dark areas appear grayer because the dots have been overetched and are *too small*. These areas are darkened by mechanically *enlarging the size of the dot* by rubbing them with a polishing tool. This process is known as *burnishing*.

Thus, the halftone can be reworked to correspond to the full tonal range of the original art. The artistic discretion of the engraver in the application of these two processes becomes the deciding quality factor in the production of the halftone plate.

Definitions

Halftone Process. The photomechanical process by which continuous tones are photographed through a ruled halftone screen. This converts the tones into minute dot formations, which, when printed, will optically duplicate the tonal gradations of the original. The original utilized in this process is known as continuous tone. The printing plate is known as a halftone, as is the resultant impression made from the plate.

Depth of Etch. The depth and uniformity of the etched areas *between* the dots. Because shallow depth is one of the most serious and common problems of photoengraving, industry standards for etching depth have been established. There is no comparison between depth of etch in line etchings and halftones. The depth of line plates is readily noticeable, while the depth of halftones is but a few thousandths of an inch.

Flat Etching. The first acid application where the entire surface of the halftone plate is etched to the required printing depth.

Re-etching. The reworking of a flat-etched plate with acid in order to lighten desired areas by reducing the size of the dots.

Staging. The application of an acid-resistant solution to areas of the halftone which have attained the proper tonal value in order to prevent further etching.

Burnishing. The reworking of an etched plate with a burnisher (metal tool) in order to darken areas by enlarging the size of the dots.

Shoulder. The projecting edge left at the *sides* of lines and dots after etching. The presence of shoulders is the most common problem with engraving.

Undercutting. A condition where the acid has penetrated beneath the printing surface—thinning or weakening the lines and dots. Undercutting prevents the release of the electrotype (a duplicate plate) mold and the plate should be remade.

The production of a halftone etching involves the following steps:

1. The halftone screen is placed in the camera, immediately in front of the film. The distance between the screen and the film relates mathematically to the fineness of the screen.
2. The negative is contact-printed onto a sensitized copper plate.
3. The metal plate is "developed" and the surface is dyed to permit inspection.
4. The metal plate then goes to the etcher, who inspects and touches up imperfections preparatory to etching.
5. The first etching is known as the "depth bite." During the successive steps of the etching process, the dots will become smaller. The depth bite is etched to the point where the reduction in dot size becomes noticeable. This step largely determines the average depth of the plate.
6. The areas that have been etched sufficiently are "staged" to prevent further etching. The staged plate is heated, cooled, and re-etched for greater definition and contrast. This is repeated until a faithful reproduction with sufficient depth of etch is obtained.
7. The plate then goes to the engraver (finisher) who removes all spots and blemishes with fine-pointed tools and darkens necessary tones by burnishing.
8. The metal plate is then routed, mounted, and proofed.

The combination plate

A combination plate is any photoengraved plate which utilizes *both* line and halftone engraving. Obviously, any letterpress plate which combines halftone illustration and text is a combination plate. If no line work touches or intrudes upon the halftone area, no special techniques are required for its production.

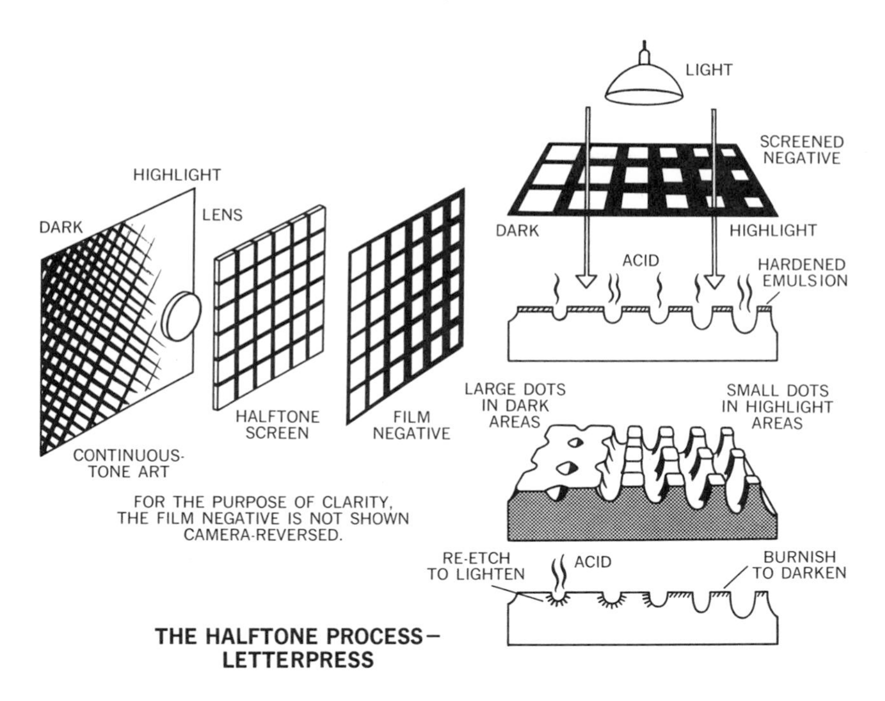

THE HALFTONE PROCESS–LETTERPRESS

Line which appears *within* the halftone area poses a special problem and may take one or more of the following forms:

The Surprint. Line work of the same color, *superimposed* or surprinted on the halftone area, thus appearing as a solid color on top of the halftone background.

The Drop-out. Line work which has been removed or "dropped out" of the halftone, thus appearing as white (or the paper color) against the halftone background. The tonal value of the background must be light enough to support a surprint, or dark enough to support a drop-out. If a *different color* is to be surprinted on a halftone, the halftone area directly underneath must first be dropped out. This prevents the dots of the halftone from showing through and altering the surprinted color.

The Mortise. A hole, regular or irregular in shape, which is cut out of the halftone in order to accommodate line work within it.

Suppose the letter "R" is to appear against a halftone background. If the letter is *painted* on the original continuous-tone art, and the art is photographed through the halftone screen, the letter—as well as the background art—will receive the dot pattern and the edges of the letter will appear ragged. Therefore, in order to retain the sharp edges of the letter, each must be photoengraved separately—the background through a screen as *halftone;* the letter, without the screen, as *line*. It is the manner in which these two film images are combined that determines the nature of the plate and the printed result.

A drop-out is made using a halftone *film negative* and a line *film positive,* which are sandwiched together in order to expose the plate. Since the line positive duplicates the values of the original, it will appear black against a transparent background, and will *block out* the dots on the halftone negative. When exposed to the plate, the values will reverse and the letter will appear on the plate as a *nonprinting* area, thus producing a white letter against the halftone background. If the line copy is prepared in *reverse*—for example a negative photostat positioned on an overlay—the resulting film negative will appear to be a positive and will block out the desired dots on the halftone negative. (See combination plate chart on page 48.)

A surprint is made using a halftone *film positive* and a line *film positive,* which are sandwiched and reshot as a single film negative. The line positive blocks out the dots on the halftone positive. When both are sandwiched and converted to negative form, the line letter, which was *opaque* on the positive, becomes a *transparent area* on the combined negative. When exposed to the plate, the letter will become a *solid printing*

area, and when printed, will appear to be a solid letter superimposed on the halftone background.

A mortise is made by dropping the desired shape out of the background and inserting the line copy within it. This may be accomplished in two ways: the mortise shape can be cut out of white paper and pasted in position on the original continuous tone art. A film negative, shot from this art, will show the shape as a black, *opaque* area. A film *positive* is now made, showing the shape as a *transparent* area. A film *positive* of the line copy is positioned in the transparent area, and a combination *negative* is made. On the plate, the halftone background and the inserted line work will be a printing area; the mortised shape will not. When the plate is printed, a positive letter will appear inside a white shape which has been dropped out of the halftone background.

The second method is to produce the halftone engraving in a normal manner and saw the mortise area out of the unmounted plate. The halftone is mounted and a line engraving of the letter is positioned within the mortised area.

Newsday, a prominent Long Island newspaper, has patented a type-stripping process for use in such mortised areas. The mortised engraving of the background is mounted, type-high, on base metal. The type is placed in a special saw which cuts it down to the same thickness as the engraving. It is then attached to the base metal, within the mortise, with double-sided tape. This eliminates the costly sawing operation required to insert type of normal height.

It is also possible to produce a *reverse mortise;* any black shape pasted on the art will appear as a transparent area on the film *negative.* A film *positive* of the letter is positioned in the transparent area. Sandwiched together, they are exposed to the plate. The resulting proof will show a black panel bearing a white (drop-out) letter, superimposed on the halftone background.

If the mortise shape is not provided on the art, it can be opaqued ("painted") on the halftone positive, which must then be converted to film negative form.

Combination plates need not necessarily utilize type as the line element. Drawings that employ line, surprinted or dropped out of a halftone background, are made as combination plates. These will be discussed in detail in Chapter 10.

The combination plate is first etched for the halftone bite. Halftone areas must then be staged to prevent further etching action. Deep-etch powder bites then produce the proper depth for the line work.

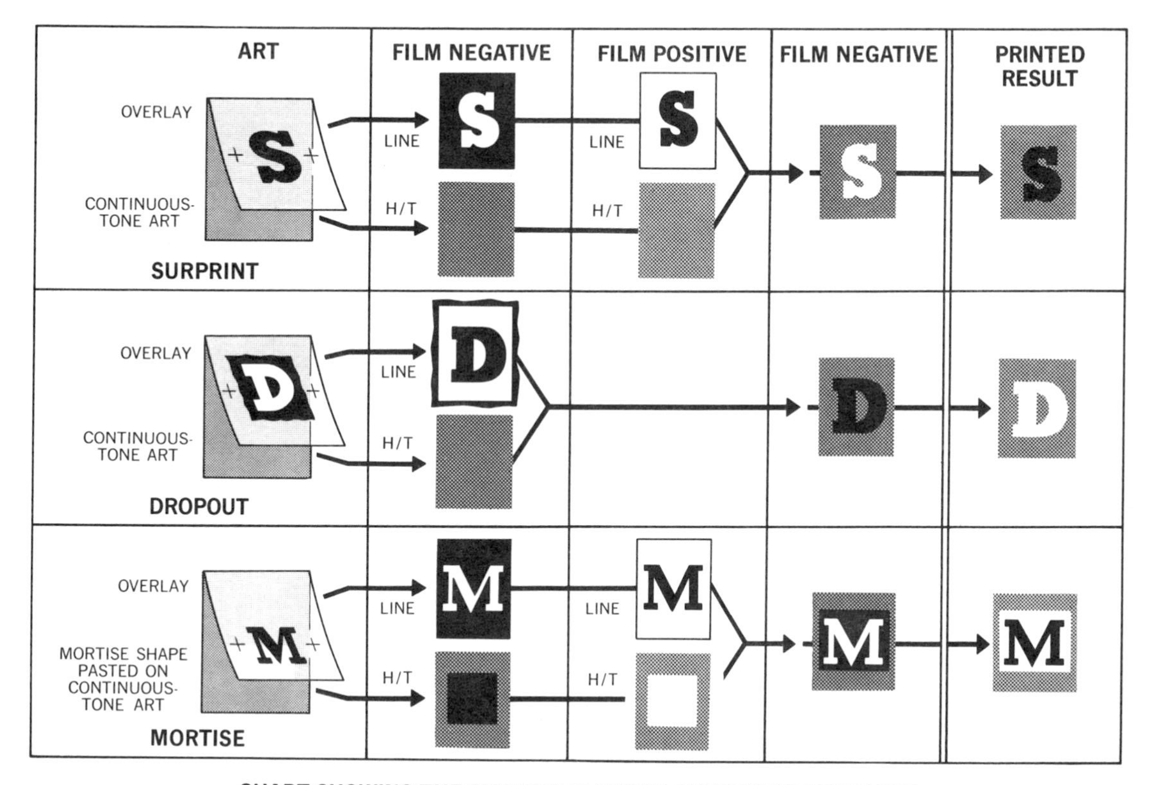

CHART SHOWING THE MANNER IN WHICH ARTWORK IS PREPARED AND FILM IS COMBINED TO PRODUCE A COMBINATION PLATE.

Electronic engraving

Scanning is the process of methodically scrutinizing the subject with minutely-spaced, moving pinpoints of light. Each impulse of light is capable of evaluating the tonal value it perceives, breaking the subject into a pattern similar to the halftone screen.

The perception of each impulse is transformed to electrical energy and transmitted to the receiver.

In the receiver of the radiophoto, each impulse results in a variation of the intensity of the recording light. Projected onto a film negative, each pinpoint exposes a minute area. The sum total of these impulses produces a duplicate of the continuous-tone or original. In the television receiver, the impulses activate an electron gun which projects them onto a phosphorescent screen, forming a pattern of thousands of fluorescent dots which are perceived by the eye as a photographic image.

THE FAIRCHILD SCAN-A-GRAVER. The Scan-A-Graver is an electronic engraving machine—a new innovation in letterpress engraving. This machine scans and perceives photographic copy, and the resulting electrical impulses operate a heated stylus which burns dot formations on the surface of a plastic plate.

Composed of four parts—the copy cylinder, the scanning head, the engraving head, and the engraving cylinder—it resembles a small lathe. An electric eye in the head scans the original photo as it rotates on the copy cylinder. The light impulses control a heated pyramid-shaped stylus which burns into the surface of the plastic plate mounted on the engraving cylinder. Where the original values are light, the stylus burns deeply; where they are dark, the impressions are shallow. Neither etching nor handwork is required. Plastic plates are proofed in the same manner as conventional photoengravings. Excess plastic is easily trimmed, and the plate is mounted on wood or base metal with double-sided tape.

The resulting plate is always the size of the original; there is no provision for enlargement or reduction. The maximum accommodation is 8″ x 10″. This size plate can be produced in 30 minutes.

The Scan-A-Graver can produce 65, 85, 100, and 120 screen halftones. The machine cannot make line cuts, nor is it suitable for color work.

THE FAIRCHILD SCAN-A-SIZER. This machine is an improved version of the Scan-A-Graver in that it will enlarge or reduce and engrave in a single operation. The original copy is placed flat in the machine and scanned with an oscillating mirror. The machine will make enlargements up to four and one-half times the original size.

LETTERPRESS PRINTING EQUIPMENT

Preparation for the press run

Letterpress printing requires considerable preparation for the press run. The printing surface must be mounted on the press and the press must be made ready to give a perfect impression.

LOCK-UP. Lock-up is the positioning and securing of the elements of the composition (type and/or mounted engravings), prior to the printing operation. It is accomplished on a level, steel-topped table, known as the *stone*.

The *chase* is a rectangular iron or steel frame in which the elements will be locked up. The elements are set within the chase and blocked into the desired position with wooden or steel blocks (less than type-high) known as *furniture*. *Bearers* are strips of type-high metal placed around the edges of the composition in order to prevent crushing, and to insure even inking. The bearers will leave an impression on the printed piece which must be trimmed off after the printing operation. *Quoins* (metal wedges that can be tightened with a key) are positioned around the furniture and wedged tight, thus locking the elements securely inside the chase.

The *planer,* a block of hardwood with a smooth surface, is laid over the elements and tapped with a mallet in order to make the printing surface uniformly level.

The locked-up chase, now known as the *form,* is ready to be positioned on the press.

MAKEREADY. Makeready is the process of adjusting the form to give a perfect impression.

Ideally, all the elements of the form should be precisely .918 in. high; however, an over-all height of .918 in. is an ideal that is seldom accomplished. Type may be produced by different processes which will cause minute variations in height—engravings may be insecurely mounted—wooden mounts may swell or shrink. Leveling the form with the planer seldom corrects this height variation.

When inked, the areas of the form that are high will print heavy, while the areas that are low will print light. Increasing the printing pressure will only cause the heavy areas to punch into the paper. Any type of duplicate plate will reproduce the surface irregularities of the original form. Thus, since neither the form nor the duplicate can be made *perfectly* level, the *paper* must be raised or lowered to conform to these irregularities.

The paper is delivered (brought into contact with the form) by either a flat plate (platen) or a cylinder. The platen or the cylinder is covered with several layers of paper and topped with a tough, oiled manila sheet called the *tympan*. In order to compensate for the unequal form pressure, the packing underlying the low areas of the form must be built up with layers of tissue. This will cause even pressure of the paper against the form and produce a uniformly-printed impression. Make-ready is a painstaking, time-consuming process, but it provides a great degree of control over the quality of the finished product.

PRE-MAKEREADY. Pre-makeready is based on the theory that, in the ideal printing situation, not all areas of the halftone plate should have the same printing height. The solid areas should be the highest and the light areas the lowest, while the middle-tone areas should fall between (an over-all variation of .004 in.). The high solid areas, which are capable of withstanding more wear, will bear the brunt of the impression and the plate will last longer.

Pre-makeready is a means of applying pressure to a plate in order to obtain this variation in the level of the printing surface. Original or duplicate plates produced in this manner reduce make-ready time on the press, especially when several "ganged-up" plates are to be used to print multiple images. There are several methods of pre-makeready:

The McKee Process. In this process the printing pressure of the plate is varied by manually bumping up the dark areas and lowering the highlight areas.

The Bac-Etch Process. A method which converts the dark and the connected-dot middle tones to line, and drops out the highlights and disconnected-dot middle tones. The resulting *conversion* of the original image is etched in reverse on the back of the plate; this is done in precise register with the original image, which has been normally etched on the front. The front of the plate is staged and the back is etched. When the plate is bumped, the highlights and the disconnected-dot middle-tone areas are recessed to the depth that has been etched out of the back.

The Bishop Process. This process keeps the middle tones of the plate at the printing height of the press while it raises the solids and lowers the highlights—each about .002 in. Matrices of three laminated .002-in. layers are used. Two are prepared; one for the front of the plate, one for the back. The matrix is placed over the plate and a knife cut is made around each area of tone so that the layers can be peeled off where desired. The cut lines in each matrix must match perfectly.

The top matrix is prepared by peeling off all three layers from over the solid areas; one layer from the middle tones; nothing from the highlights. On the bottom matrix the dark areas are not peeled; one layer is peeled from the middle tones; all three are peeled from the highlights.

When the plate and the attached matrices are passed between heavy rollers, the printing surface is raised or lowered in accordance with the thickness of the matrices.

Printing presses

A printing press is a machine designed to hold a printing form or a plate in such a manner that it can be inked and brought into contact with paper, thus enabling it to deposit the image of the plate onto the paper. This is a method for duplication in quantity.

However complex in outward appearances, all technical developments since Gutenberg's time have been to facilitate the speed with which printing can be accomplished.

Johann Gutenberg is credited with the invention of the practical printing press, as well as movable type. His device, which was probably a converted wine press, employed a wooden screw to lower a plate (platen) in order to press the paper against the type.

The evolution of printing technology was a slow process. It took 500 years to develop Gutenberg's press into its modern, complex counterpart.

1550. The wooden screw was replaced by a more efficient metal one. The tympan came into use at this time.

1601. William Blaew of Amsterdam introduced a spring to the platen so that it would return to the "open" position more rapidly. This cut the work of the pressman in half.

1781. M. Pierres, a Parisian, manufactured an iron printing press.

1790. William Nicholson of London patented a press which would print on a flat surface, utilizing the pressure of a cylinder.

1827. The Washington hand press replaced the platen screw with a toggle joint, considerably increasing the speed of the press action.

1839. Electroplated copies of wood engravings were produced for book publication.

1846. Richard M. Hoe of New York developed the "Hoe Cylinder," a rotary press. During the remainder of the century his son, Robert, improved the original design and invented the rotary-perfecting and the multicolor press.

1850. A vibrating platen press, capable of considerable speed and accuracy, was patented by George P. Gordon of New York.

Modern letterpress printing machines range in speed from 1,000 to 25,000 impressions per hour. They vary in capacity from postcard-size to 50″ x 70″, or larger. There is an ideal type of printing press for almost every job.

Some presses are fed paper in individual sheets, while others are supplied by a *web* (a large, continuous roll of paper). The web is cut into sheets *after* the printing has been accomplished. Many presses have folding attachments, enabling folding, pasting, and stapling to become part of the printing operation.

Perfecting presses print both sides of the paper almost simultaneously. *Multicolor* presses will print two, three, four, or more colors in a single operation.

The modern printer is a businessman, and his equipment must fall within the limitations of his capital. No printer has equipment of every speed and capacity. It is to his advantage to have fast presses; they enable him to produce a greater volume without increasing the size of his plant. As his business increases, he adds presses to increase his capability and versatility. No printer buys new equipment until he is certain that he can obtain work for it. It is better to work overtime, or to run two shifts, than to purchase new, expensive equipment which often may lie idle.

A printer should be selected on the basis of the quality of his work, the size-capacity of his presses, and his ability to deliver work when promised.

It is well to become familiar with the equipment of each printer with whom one does business. For greatest economy, either the press should be matched to the job, or the job designed for a particular press.

There are three types of modern letterpress equipment: *platen*, *cylinder*, and *rotary* presses.

THE PLATEN PRESS. This printing press utilizes a clamshell motion to bring the paper into contact with the form. The form, locked in a chase, is positioned on the flat bed of the press. As the press opens, inked rollers pass over the form, depositing viscous ink on the raised surface of the printing image. The tympan is placed on the flat platen (the paper-bearing surface), providing a cushion between it and the form. The thickness of the tympan compensates for the thickness of the paper to be printed, thus assuring correct printing pressure. The paper is positioned properly on the tympan by means of gauge pins.

The platen and the form come together. Iron fingers, or *grippers,* close over the paper, holding it in position as it is pressed against the printing surface. The press reopens to permit removal of the paper, and the ink rollers again pass over the form, assuring re-inking between each impression.

The platen press can be operated by foot treadle or electric motor, and the paper can be fed and removed either by hand or automatically. The automatic platen press utilizes small suction devices to convey the paper.

Platen presses will accommodate sheets ranging in size from 5″ x 8″ to 23″ x 33″. Hand feeding will produce from 1,000 to 1,800 impressions per hour, while automatic feeding will print up to 3,000 per hour.

The job printer who produces letterheads, business cards, and announcements usually employs a small platen press. The thickness of the platen regulates the squeeze, enabling the press to handle anything from thin paper to heavy cardboard. This makes the press especially adaptable for stamping, embossing, die-cutting, and creasing.

THE CYLINDER (OR FLAT-BED) PRESS. The cylinder press prints by means of a cylinder which rolls against the form. The paper, which is held to the *impression cylinder* by grippers, is passed between this cylinder and the flat form that is positioned in the flat bed of the press. The bed moves back and forth on its track, and as the cylinder turns, the form advances with it. Only a small segment of the paper touches the form at one time, since the form is flat and the paper is curved around the cylinder. After the impression, the form returns to its original position, where it is re-inked.

There are four types of cylinder presses:

The Drum Cylinder makes one revolution per impression. The paper covers half the circumference of the cylinder. The other half is recessed, allowing the form to pass clear as it returns.

The Two-revolution Cylinder prints during the first revolution and is lifted clear of the form during the second revolution to allow removal of the printed paper and the return of the form. The cylinder is only half as large as the drum cylinder, but the printing speed is considerably faster.

The Stop-cylinder is arranged so that the cylinder stops after the impression and remains stationary during the return of the form.

The Perfecting Flat-bed Press is a double cylinder press which prints both sides of the paper in a single operation.

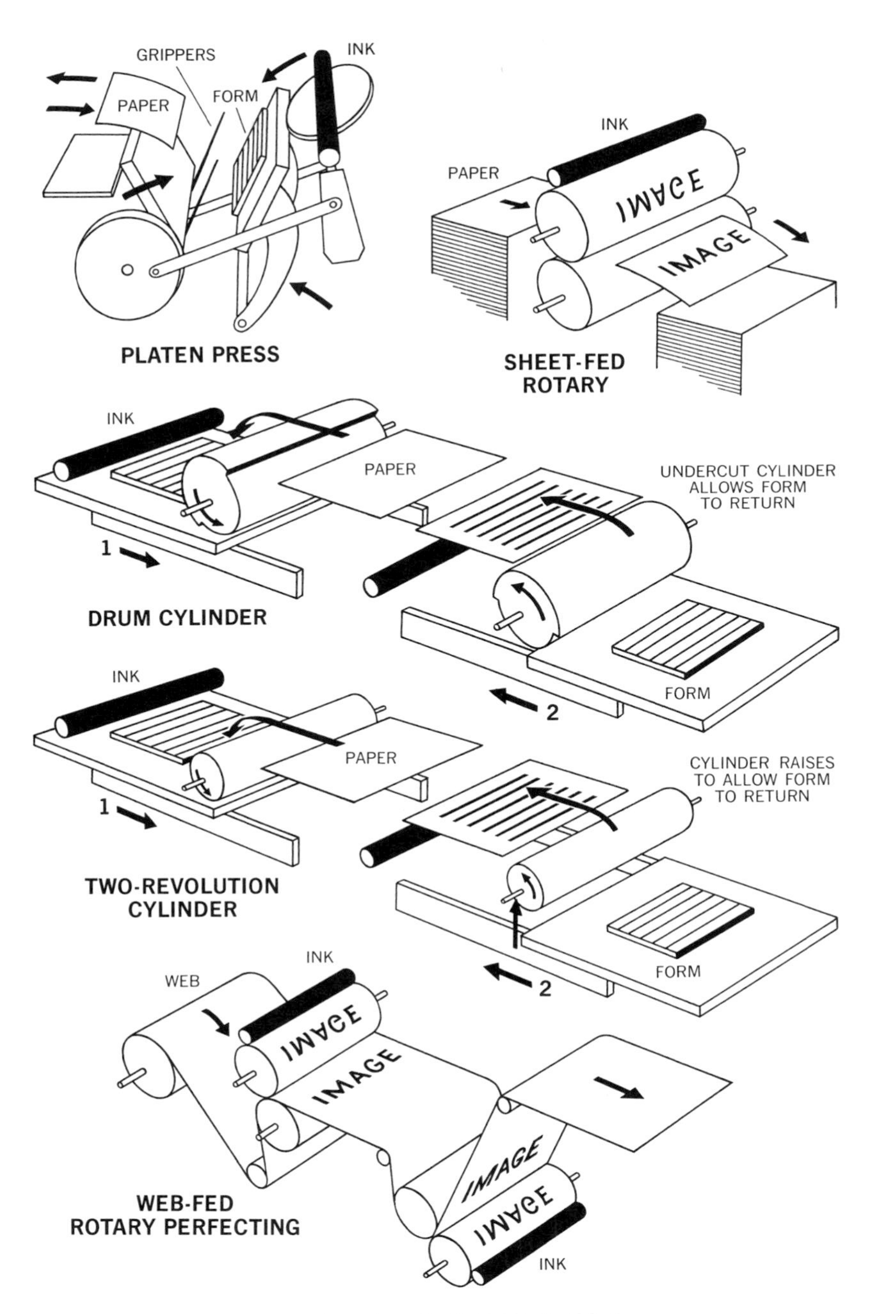

TYPES OF LETTERPRESS PRESSES

Cylinder presses range in size from 9″ x 12″ to 50″ x 73½″, with speeds up to 4,000 impressions per hour.

THE ROTARY PRESS. Rotary presses are built for high-speed work. The press passes the paper between two cylinders, one of which holds a *curved* printing plate. In the cylinder press, the form must return to its original position and the printing operation must be interrupted in order for it to do so. The action of the curved rotary plate is continuous, since by the time the plate cylinder has revolved to the printing position, the impression cylinder has fed new paper into place. Thus, the rotary is considerably faster, enabling speeds of up to 25,000 impressions per hour. Rotary presses may be either sheet- or web-fed. Inking is accomplished by a roller which is in continuous contact with the plate cylinder.

Rotary web-fed newspaper presses attain fantastic speeds. Presses are arranged in units, sometimes over a hundred feet long and two stories high, which print separate sections of the paper. Multiple plates are mounted on the cylinders. Some rotary presses utilize the *flying-paster*—a device which joins a new roll to the web of paper, assuring a continuous printing operation. These presses print, fold, count, and deliver the papers to the shipping department.

Rotary magazine presses, equally as fast and as large, can print four colors on both sides of the paper. Sheet-fed rotary presses accommodate sheet sizes from 20″ x 30″ to 52″ x 76″, and will print 6,000 to 7,000 impressions per hour. Web-fed presses will handle webs as wide as 82 in., with printing speeds as high as 1,000 ft. per minute.

DUPLICATE LETTERPRESS PLATES

There are many reasons for producing duplicate letterpress plates.

Letterpress printing can be accomplished from a combination of cast-type and photoengraved illustrative material, locked together in a flat press form. Cast type, especially a face which has delicate characteristics, is not durable enough for long press runs. Thus, it is often desirable to make a duplicate plate from the original form in order not to subject the type to undue wear, and retain it for further use.

It is impossible to curve the flat printing form to fit the rotary press. Rotary press plates must be produced as a single unit so that they may be curved to fit the press cylinder. Duplicate plates, produced as a single piece, may be curved as desired.

Most letterpress printing—except newspaper work—is accomplished with plates photoengraved from mechanical art. This type of copper engraving is sufficiently durable for a long press run; however, if the ad is running simultaneously, it may be necessary to send duplicates to several different publications. With all the necessary finishing procedures, it would prove too costly to re-engrave each from the original art. It is therefore more practical to produce one finished engraving and make copies from it.

It may be desirable to have several impressions printing simultaneously (*ganged-up*) in order to produce more copies, or to shorten the press run.

It may be necessary to preserve original plates to facilitate replacement in case of loss or damage.

The electrotype

An electrotype (electro) is a metal duplicate of a form of type and/or photoengraving—or of an original photoengraving made from mechanical art. Electrotypes are the highest quality of duplicate plate.

The production of an electrotype is based upon the principle of electrolytic action: a bar of pure metal, immersed in an acid solution and subjected to an electric current, will decompose and deposit (plate) a metallic coating upon another object suspended in the solution.

In the case of the electrotype, the object to be plated is a molded impression of the original form or photoengraving. A thin copper shell is

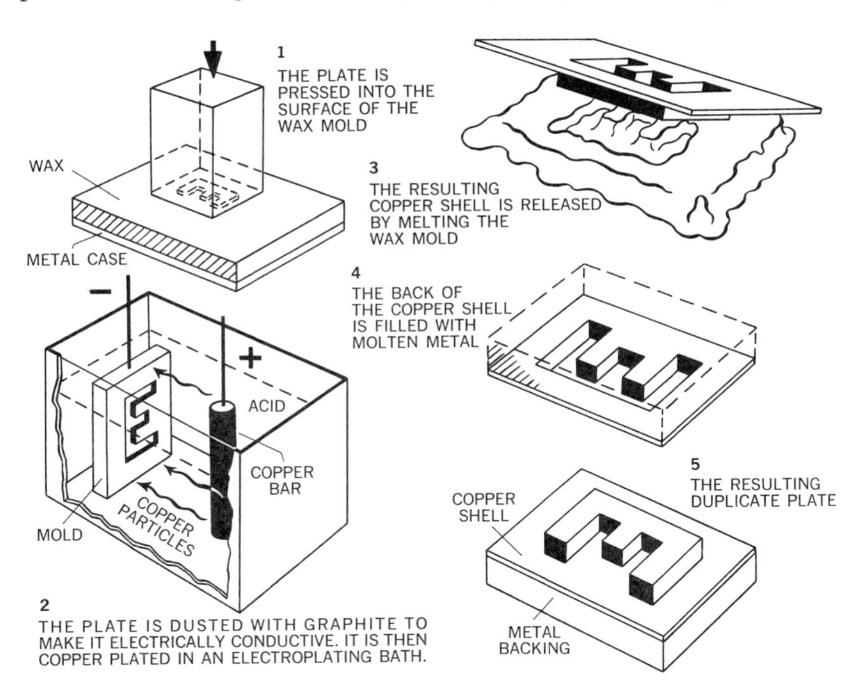

THE WAX MOLD ELECTROTYPE

deposited on the mold; when removed and strengthened by the addition of base metal it almost duplicates the quality of the original.

The variety of the substances used to produce the mold classifies the several types of electros.

WAX-MOLD ELECTROS. Wax is a standard molding material—less costly, but inadvisable for fine halftone work and color plates.

A wax electro is produced in the following manner:

1. The form or photoengraving is locked up in a steel frame or chase, surrounded by guard rules (bearers) to protect it.
2. The original is dusted with graphite, inverted, and pressed—under great pressure (200–400 tons)—into a wax case. Wax is so ductile that this results in an almost perfect mold.
3. The wax impression is further sensitized with graphite—making it conductive to electricity.
4. The wax impression is then suspended in an electrolytic bath (copper sulfate) in which bars of pure copper are hung. Electrolytic action removes particles of copper from the bars and deposits them on the wax. This results in a copper shell which is an exact duplicate of the original. The process takes from 4 to 8 hours, depending upon the thickness desired.
5. The copper plated wax is removed and the wax is melted away with boiling water.
6. The underside of the resultant copper shell is reinforced with tinfoil, allowing better adhesion to the base metal with which it is backed for additional strength.

TENAPLATE-MOLD ELECTROS. Tenaplate is a patented molding material which replaces the wax in the electrotyping process, producing a better quality mold than the wax.

VINYLITE-MOLD ELECTROS. Vinylite is a plastic molding material which achieves excellent halftone results.

LEAD-MOLD ELECTRO. The most faithful and expensive variety of mold utilizes a thin sheet of lead. Since it does not have to be dusted with graphite in order to conduct electricity, a slightly deeper impression can be obtained. Molded with a pressure of as much as 2,000 tons, lead molds produce the finest halftone plates, as well as master plates for making other electros. Lead cannot be used to mold directly from type. If the original engraving is undercut, the release of the mold will be impeded.

In the event of a long press run, the shell of an electro is faced with nickel in order to increase its wearing quality. Chromium plating can be employed for even greater durability.

An electrotype must be mounted on a base if it is to be used in the flat-bed form. *Metal base* is a flat block of type metal which, when placed in a chase, is used to mount the thin electros to type height. Wood mounts are sometimes used, but wood is affected by temperature and humidity and may cause discrepancies in printing height. *Patent base* is a honeycombed steel base on which electros are mounted and held snugly with patented hooks.

Electros can be patched or corrected by welding new pieces into position. They must be large enough to permit the incorrect copy to be sawed out without damaging any of the surrounding material.

Duplicate original plates

An advertisement may be scheduled to run simultaneously in several magazines, making it impossible to forward the original plates. Many of these publications, conscious of the quality of their product, will refuse to accept electros, especially of color ads. Since it is economically impractical to make several engravings from the original art, electrotypers have developed a process for making "duplicate originals." These are high-quality electros of nickel-faced copper. They duplicate the quality of the original engraving more closely than an ordinary electro, but are less expensive than individual engravings.

There are two kinds of duplicate electros—nickel and solid copper. Nickel is generally used; solid copper is utilized when reworking will be necessary. Both types require several days to produce.

The wax engraving

Wax engraving is a process for preparing a letterpress printing plate which lends itself to the printing of ruled forms, maps, logarithmic paper, and grids. Since cross-ruled lines cannot be set by the printer, the wax engraving method provides a means of ruling them directly on the plate.

Preparatory to engraving, a copper plate is coated with black wax, and the engraver rules his lines in the wax with tools that cut through to the base metal. The lines can also be precision-cut with an engraving machine. Lettering can be added by pressing the type, face down, into the wax. For complex, detailed work, the design can be printed photographically on the surface and then hand- or machine-cut. Corrections can easily be made by melting and resmoothing the wax.

When the wax plate is completed, it is treated as an electrotype mold.

Electrolytically copper-plated, it is backed up with base metal and made ready for printing.

The stereotype

A stereotype (stereo) is a duplicate letterpress plate cast in type metal (an alloy of lead, tin, and antimony). The stereo is cast from a *mat* (matrix), a papier-mâché mold impressed from the original form or engraving. The process is used almost exclusively in newspaper work. There are two types of mat—the wet mat and the dry mat. The finished mat is *right-reading*.

THE WET MAT. The wet mat consists of layers of French tissue paper—held together with layers of paste—forming a thick, blotter-like sheet (flong). Laid wet over the form and subjected to great pressure by a matrix press, the mat is formed into a right-reading mold of the original. The mat is dried by heat rising from underneath the form.

THE DRY MAT. Favored for modern use because of less shrinkage, the dry mat is a prepared piece of papier-mâché which is forced down on the form with great pressure. No drying is required, and better results are obtained than with the wet mat. Mat material comes in sheets, somewhat like smooth blotter paper, large enough to mold a full-sized newspaper page. Wood-mounted engravings should never be used to produce mats, since the moisture and/or pressure breaks down the wood.

The stereo is the *backwards reading* casting made from the mat, usually curved for use on the rotary press. Stereos cannot be curved after they have been cast. The mat must be curved first in a casting machine which has the same curvature as the press on which the plate is to be used. Molten metal is poured into the mold, which does not burn or melt. After casting, the stereo is planed to the proper thickness.

If a mat is supplied to a newspaper for a less-than-full-page size, the stereotype of the mat must be cast flat and locked up in the page form. The final stereo is made from the mat of the entire page form. This results in a stereo being cast from a stereo, and some quality loss can be expected.

Stereos are less expensive than electros and can be made more rapidly. Too crude for fine halftone printing, they are seldom employed for more than 65-line screen work. Mats and plates have a tendency to shrink during production. The metal will not stand up under long press runs, although it can be nickel-faced for greater longevity.

Pattern plates

Pattern plates are electros which are especially prepared to withstand repeated molding of additional electros and mats. They are made when a rerun is anticipated and it is not certain that the original plates will be available.

Plastic plates

Duplicate plates of thin plastic have proven a revolutionary development in the platemaking process.

Two types of plastic material are utilized—*thermoplastics,* such as Vinylite; *thermosetting* phenolic resins, such as Bakelite. Thermoplastics, once set, can be remelted. Thermosetting plastics, set with a combination of heat and pressure, will not soften or change in any manner.

A plastic matrix must first be produced, using thermosetting material. This matrix is produced from a *pattern plate* rather than from the form or the original engraving. A sheet of the plastic is positioned atop the pattern in a hydraulic press which applies heat and pressure. The plastic hardens and forms a right-reading matrix similar to a newspaper mat.

In order to form the printing plate, the mold is sprinkled with a thermoplastic vinyl powder. Heat, pressure, and subsequent chilling form the powder into a backward-reading printing plate. The matrix can be produced in twenty minutes; the plate in five. Any number of plates can be produced from the matrix.

Plastic plates are less expensive than electros. They do not stretch or shrink and are easily mounted. Speedily manufactured, they are exact duplicates of each other, as well as of the original. Virtually indestructible, they have a low mailing weight, resulting in considerable savings in shipping costs.

Acid-etched plastic originals are also available.

Rubber plates

The rubber plate is an inexpensive duplicate plate molded from type, engravings, electrotypes, or stereotypes.

A matrix of thermosetting resin is formed from the original. A sheet of the plastic material is positioned over the form, preheated, and subjected to pressure. The resulting right-reading matrix is removed, dried, and baked.

The matrix is then covered with a sheet of unvulcanized rubber.

Heat and pressure cure (vulcanize) the rubber for about ten minutes. The rubber is then removed, trimmed, and mounted. The resulting backward-reading relief plate is virtually indestructible.

Rubber plates can be made of soft rubber for printing on rough or uneven surfaces, or of hard rubber for finer work. They are often preferred over metal plates for printing on nonabsorbent surfaces. A versatile medium, rubber plates are used for printing on cloth bags, wood, cellophane, cardboard, foil, metal, fiberboard, and glass. Because of their durability, they are coming into more use in book printing.

The medium is not suitable for fine-screen reproduction, especially when the surface to be printed is coarse. Rubber plates can be readily curved. Lightweight rotary presses have been specifically designed for rubber-plate printing.

A SUMMARY OF THE LETTERPRESS PROCESS

Letterpress printing is printing from a raised, or relief, surface. The printing surface is backward-reading.

Letterpress printing can be accomplished from combinations of type and photoengravings (line or halftone), photoengravings of mechanical art, or duplicates produced from either.

Duplicate plates can be produced by a variety of methods. There is a plate suitable for almost any printing operation on a flat surface.

Letterpress is the standard of quality to which all other printing methods aspire. It is an excellent medium for halftone and color printing, provided suitable paper is utilized. It will produce a sharper, cleaner reproduction of type than any other process.

Both original and duplicate plates are expensive, but they can be surfaced with special metals to withstand extremely long runs. Their reuse is unlimited.

Letterpress plates can be converted for use in the lithographic process.

Since plates can be fabricated from a variety of substances, from heavy metal to light plastic, mailing and storage are variable factors.

Ease of correction is traditionally mentioned as an advantage of the process. Individual letters, lines of type, or individual engravings can be removed and replaced *if the printing is being done* directly from the form. However, in practice most letterpress plates (newspaper and book plates excepted) are engraved from mechanical art. A plate or an electro can be patched under certain limited conditions, but it is not universally practical. The correction must generally be made on the mechanical art and stripped into position on the negative, from which a new plate will be made. If the mechanical art is properly checked and proofread, this problem should not occur.

Letterpress is an ideal medium for printing items which are revised continually: directories, listings, catalogs, etc. The forms can be left standing and the old entries can be easily removed and replaced with new ones.

Proofs can be pulled directly from forms or plates. Proper proofing will indicate the quality of the finished product. Proofs can be submitted for approval before the plate is mounted in the press.

Makeready is an expensive, time-consuming process, but it gives the printer tighter control over his presswork.

4 THE LITHOGRAPHIC PROCESS

Until the advent of photoengraving, the letterpress process was incapable of faithfully reproducing the work of the artist. Unless the artist was personally involved with the execution of the engraving, an additional hand—that of the engraver—had to be interposed between the artist's drawing and the printed image. As can be readily noted from any examination of nineteenth-century letterpress printing, there was much latitude of interpretation on the part of the engraver. The artist needed a closer relationship, one in which he could maintain control over the end result. The invention of the lithographic printing process provided the means for direct reproduction of the work of the artist; it was a method that enabled him to draw directly on the printing plate without the intervention of the commercial engraver.

Lithography, the planographic method, is a process in which the printing area is flush with the surface of the plate. This process, based on the incompatibility of grease and water, was invented by Alois Senefelder, a Bavarian, in 1798. *Litho* means *stone,* and *graphos* means *write*. Lithography is, literally, "drawing on stone."

These steps are employed in making a stone lithograph:

1. The design is drawn, backwards, with *greasy* ink or crayon on a polished slab of fine-grained absorbent limestone. It may also be drawn frontwards on transfer paper, turned over, and transferred onto the stone.

2. The stone is sponged with dilute nitric acid and gum arabic. The acid decomposes the soap in the crayon or ink, releasing the grease. The gum prevents the grease from spreading.

3. The stone is dampened with water and inked. The ink, when applied with a roller, sticks to the greasy printing image but is repelled by the water on the nonprinting areas. This produces a printing surface which is in no higher relief than the thickness of the grease deposited by the crayon.

4. The paper is then laid atop the stone and the inked image is transferred onto it. After redampening and re-inking, the stone is ready for another impression.

The use of this process spread throughout Europe. Work was printed in black ink; additional colors were then applied by hand. In 1825, Goya executed his famous "bullfight" lithographs, using blunt crayons and scraping with a knife to achieve the light areas. This and ensuing techniques established lithography as an artist's medium.

By 1838, lithographs were being produced in many colors, and commercial work began to appear. This brought the medium somewhat into artistic disrepute, but it soon regained new heights as an art form in the hands of such masters as Manet, Daumier, Toulouse-Lautrec, and Whistler.

The first American lithographic plant was established in 1832 at Hartford, Connecticut. Lithographs of the American scene found a ready market; the lithographic efforts of Currier and Ives have become a part of our national folklore. Early prints were colored by hand. Demand necessitating faster production, the hand-operated flat-bed stone press gave way to the steam-powered press (1869) and output reached 600 sheets per hour.

As stones were scarce and expensive, easily damaged, and difficult to store, they began to be replaced by thin zinc sheets. The first rotary litho press (1889) featured such a plate on a cylinder, increasing production to 1500 sheets per hour.

The development of the offset lithographic press (1904-05), which transfers or offsets the image onto an intermediate surface before depositing it on the paper, opened up new areas of quality and quantity production for the lithographer.

In modern usage, there are two methods of depositing the design on the printing surface—by hand, or photographically. There are two methods of printing—directly from plate to paper, and by the offset method. Offset lithography is the most prevalent of all modern methods of printing.

Commercially, stone is no longer practical. Stone plates must be used on a flat-bed press, and are seldom employed except by individual artists who produce their own prints. Thin sheets of zinc or aluminum are currently utilized. These metal plates are far less expensive, can be curved to fit rotary presses, and pose no difficulties for the artist who draws on them. In addition, the design can be readily deposited on the surface of a photosensitized metal plate.

Posters and billboards have traditionally employed direct lithography, using hand drawn plates. However, with the current popularity of photography as an illustrative medium, and the universality of the rotary press, such methods have fallen into a general decline and are only employed when the specific nature of the design requires their use.

Definitions

Lithography. The process of printing from a design deposited with greasy crayon or ink on a flat, polished surface. The process is based upon the incompatibility of oil and water.

Stone Lithography. Lithographic printing in which a flat, polished slab of limestone is used as the printing surface.

Direct Lithography. Lithographic printing in which the impression is transferred directly onto the paper.

Offset Lithography. Lithographic printing in which the image is transferred to an intermediate or "offset" cylinder before being impressed on the paper.

Litho Stone. The flat slab of polished limestone used in stone lithography.

Litho Transfer. A design drawn or proofed from letterpress type on special paper used to transfer the image onto the stone of the press plate.

Litho Crayon. A greasy crayon made from soap, tallow, wax, and lampblack; used for direct drawing on the stone or plate. The commercially available black pencil which is sharpened by unwinding a string is a litho or "grease pencil."

Gum Arabic. A gum obtained from acacia trees, used to prevent any affinity for ink in the nonprinting areas of lithographic plates.

Stripping. The assembly, in film negative form, of all the elements which are to appear on the lithographic plate; the act of producing a "flat."

Flat. The completed negative assembly, ready for the plate-making process. The equivalent of the letterpress "form."

Imposition. The assembly of the negatives of individual pages on the flat in proper sequence, in the event that several pages are to be printed simultaneously.

Key Line. A thin line, or outline, placed by the artist on the mechanical art to indicate the location of various elements that are to be stripped into position.

Dot-etching. The tonal correction of halftone areas through chemically-controlled dot alteration on the film negatives or the film positives.

Asphaltum. A natural bituminous mixture used to protect areas of the film during the dot-etching process.

Farmer's Reducer. A solution of potassium ferricyanide and sodium thiosulfate which attacks the exposed areas of photographic film. It is used in the dot-etching process to reduce the dot sizes.

Graining. The treatment of a lithographic plate with an abrasive in order to render the metal surface capable of water retention. This operation is performed by machine.

Surface Plate. A metal lithographic plate, with a light-sensitized surface coating, on which an image is formed by the action of light rays passing through the film negative.

Albumin Plate. A plate using the most common form of surface coating, made from a water-soluble protein found in egg whites. It is light-sensitized by the addition of ammonium bichromate.

Deep-etch Plate. A metal lithographic plate in which the area beneath the printing surface has been *slightly* etched in order to prolong its ink-receptive quality for long press runs.

Developing Ink. A greasy liquid applied to the printing surface of the plate in order to make the image ink-receptive.

Photo-typesetting Machine. A machine that produces typographic composition in the form of positive and negative photographic film, rather than in relief metal. This film composition is finding widespread use in the lithographic industry.

Cold Type. Typography produced by the photo-typesetting machine, rather than by the standard typesetting machine which casts characters from "hot" metal. The term cold type also refers to Varitype and typewriter composition used for lithographic printing.

OFFSET LITHOGRAPHY

The word "offset" refers to an additional press cylinder known as the *blanket* cylinder, which receives the image from the plate before transferring it to the paper. Of necessity, the offset press is a rotary press. A thin metal (zinc or aluminum) "frontwards reading" plate is wrapped around the plate cylinder. The greasy image, which has been deposited on the plate photomechanically, is inked and watered. The inked image is then brought in contact with, and is transferred "backwards reading" onto, the rubber-blanketed offset cylinder. Paper, fed to the press by the impression cylinder, comes in contact with the blanket and receives a "frontwards reading" impression. The softness of the rubber blanket enables the offset cylinder to "lay" an impression on coarse-textured paper without the resultant distortion that would be caused by squashed fibers, should similar paper be used in letterpress. Offset lithography enables fine-screened halftones to be printed on rough or uncoated paper stock, a feature which produces one of the economies inherent in the process.

Offset lithographic presses

The principal parts of the offset lithographic press are:

The Plate Cylinder. The cylinder around which the flat metal plate is wrapped.

The Blanket Cylinder. A fabric-based, rubber-surfaced cylinder which receives the image from the plate.

The Impression Cylinder. The cylinder which brings the paper into contact with the blanket cylinder, thus receiving the image.

The Feeder. The mechanism which feeds the paper into the press.

The Receiver or Stacker. The mechanism which removes and stacks the paper after the printing operation.

The Inking Mechanism. Rollers which apply ink to the plate.

The Dampening Mechanism. A device which feeds dampening solution from a storage fountain to soft flannel-like rollers which dampen the plate.

Due to the complexity of the feeding and receiving mechanisms, and the presence of several ink and dampening rollers, the offset press seems an incredibly complex apparatus. However, its basic principle—the incompatibility of oil and water—remains the same as in the original stone lithograph.

Offset lithographic presses are described in a manner similar to letterpress presses—in terms of their maximum size capacity. When the press is discussed in terms of "number of colors," it refers to the number of printing units—ranging from one to six colors in capacity. Litho presses are either sheet- or roll-(web-) fed. Because of the flexibility possible in the arrangement of the printing units, a press can be set up to perform a great variety of printing combinations, either printing one side or perfecting (printing both sides simultaneously). For example, the six-color, sheet-fed press—which consists of six individual printing units—can print six colors on one side of the paper, or can be arranged as a web-perfecting press, printing four colors on one side and two on the other.

THE SHEET-FED PRESS. Sheet-fed offset lithographic presses deliver from 4,500 to 7,500 impressions per hour and are capable of printing from one to six colors. They range in size from 14″ x 20″ to 54″ x 77″.

THE SHEET-FED PERFECTING PRESS. Perfecting presses print both sides of sheets, ranging in size from 17″ x 22″ to 52″ x 77″, in a single printing operation. Speeds from 6,000 to 7,000 impressions per hour are possible. These presses can print from one to four color combinations. Standard-size web presses range in size from 17" x 26" up to 35" x 39" and are capable of producing up to 10,000 impressions per hour.

THE WEB-PERFECTING PRESS. There are three types of web-perfecting lithographic presses.

Blanket-to-blanket. The blanket-to-blanket is the most common variety of web-fed press. A plate cylinder and its blanket cylinder are arranged in pairs. Each blanket cylinder acts as the impression cylinder for its mate. The paper passes between them and is perfected simultaneously. The web travels from the roll stand to the delivery mechanism in a straight line, and is kept in lateral and directional control by various tension units.

Drum Type. The drum type press represents an attempt to maintain better web tension control than the blanket-to-blanket. Individual printing units (plate cylinder, blanket cylinder, inking, and dampening systems) are mounted in circular fashion around a large impression cylinder. The tension of the web around the large cylinder resists any tendency for it to follow the blanket cylinder. The web is completely printed on one side, fed through a drying unit, and onto a second drum for perfecting.

The Unit Type. The unit type is similar to the blanket-to-blanket except that the web is perfected in a different unit. It is referred to as an "open" unit, signifying that each individual plate-printing unit can be handled separately and need not be paired, as in a blanket-to-blanket press.

THE SINGLE-PLATE JOB PRESS. The single-plate job press is used for high-speed printing of small, standard-sized handbills, throwaways, etc. which are printed on one side.

THE MULTILITH. The multilith is a small, one-color offset press that works on exactly the same principle as the larger ones. It is used primarily for office work—letters and business forms—and for small job printing from postcard size up to 9¾" x 14". Somewhat larger models are available. The "multi" utilizes presensitized aluminum, plastic, or paper plates. The plates may be prepared photographically, drawn by hand, or typed in much the same manner as a mimeograph stencil. They are available with basic business forms or letterheads already printed on them in reproducing ink. The machine's inking mechanism cannot handle a large flow of ink, and it takes a highly skilled operator to produce good halftone reproduction.

THE PREPARATION OF THE LITHOGRAPHIC NEGATIVE

In modern usage, the terms "offset," "photo-offset," and "offset litho" appear interchangeably. There is no practical distinction among them, since the photographic process is the key to modern offset lithographic printing.

In order to produce the offset plate, *all of the material which is to appear on the plate* must be assembled in the form of a photographic (film) negative. This assembly process is known as "stripping."

The film negative is produced by photographing the mechanical art. There is no possibility of incorporating cast type or existing engravings into the flat litho plate; mechanical art *must* be utilized. Although litho platemakers would prefer it, it is not always practical to have all of the art elements positioned, in proper size, directly on the mechanical. Photographs and illustrations, in their original form, may require enlargement or reduction in order to conform to the requirements of the layout. In this instance, they are supplied separately; their size and position is indicated on the mechanical by means of *key lines*.

The mechanical art is photographed, producing a film negative. The *separate art*—all art that is not pasted in position on the mechanical—is individually photographed, in negative form, to the required size and is stripped (mounted with cellophane tape) into position on the negative of the mechanical art. This operation produces a *single negative assembly* which will be used to produce the litho plate.[1] The stripped-up assembly of film sections is called the *flat*.

The flats are assembled on a light-table, utilizing various devices for accurate alignment. Negatives can be taped together to form a flat, taped to a transparent plastic sheet, or mounted on a *"goldenrod"* supporting sheet. The goldenrod sheet is an opaque, orange-colored sheet which serves to block the light from the nonprinting areas. Openings are cut in the goldenrod and the negatives are taped in position. All specks, imperfections, etc. are opaqued at the time of stripping. If several pages are to be printed simultaneously on the same sheet, the negative assemblies are positioned side by side (imposed) in negative form.

The litho plate is a thin, flexible sheet of metal, of insufficient thickness to provide any relief of the printing surface. Because of its minimal thickness, it is extremely inexpensive and therefore expendable. The

---

[1] It is often inferred that stripping is a process unique in offset lithography. This is not the case. Any printing process that relies on a photomechanical platemaking process utilizes this method. The unique feature of the photomechanical litho plate is that it must be produced from negatives assembled in this manner.

thinness of the plate and the nonrelief of the printing surface defy any attempts at alteration. Should the plate prove defective or be found to contain an error, the plate is discarded. The correction is rephotographed and stripped *into the negative.* A new plate is then produced. Thus, the correctness of the negative becomes the critical element in lithographic printing.

Since the correctness of the negative is the critical factor, proofs of one- or two-color work are made directly from the negative. These proofs are produced by exposing the negative to a light-sensitive paper, similar to the architect's blueprint. These *blueprints* are characterized by the fact that everything appearing on them, even the background, appears as some value of blue. *Van Dykes* are similar prints which are brown, rather than blue. Though giving no indication of the actual color of the printed piece, these prints still afford the opportunity to check copy, positioning of illustrative matter, etc. before the plate is made.

LITHOGRAPHIC PLATES

Types of lithographic plates

There are four types of lithographic plates:

Surface. The surface plate is used for short press runs. The light-hardened printing image is photomechanically deposited on the surface of the plate. The plate is grained in order to hold the necessary moisture provided by the dampening mechanism.

Deep-etch. The deep-etch plate is used for long runs and color work. The image is held in acid-etched areas *slightly* (.0005 in.) below the grained surface.

Bimetal. The bimetal plate is used for extra long press runs. A copper image-bearing layer is electroplated to a nonprinting base of aluminum, stainless steel, or chromium. The metals of bimetallic plates are so selected that the image-bearing metal is ink-receptive, under the same conditions that render the nonprinting metal water receptive. These plates are always made from film positives.

Presensitized. Presensitized plates have already been sensitized when purchased. Coated with a thin layer of diazo light-sensitive compound, they are available in positive or negative form. Made of ungrained aluminum, plastic, or paper, they are especially adaptable for short runs. Paper plates permit direct use of the typewriter for producing the printing image. Presensitized plates will keep from six months to one year.

The surface lithographic plate is produced in the following manner:

1. The printing side of the aluminum or zinc plate is "grained" in order to render it capable of retaining moisture.
2. The plate is coated with a light-sensitive emulsion. This consists of a mixture of a protein such as egg albumin, casein, or soybean protein, together with ammonium bichromate. This coating is done in a centrifugal "whirler" which spreads the emulsion uniformly on the surface. The coating is then dried with warm air.
3. The plate is placed in a vacuum printing frame and the negative flat is positioned over the plate. The image is contact-printed frontwards on the plate by exposing it under arc lamps.
4. The exposed plate coating hardens and becomes waterproof. The coating on the nonprinting areas remains water soluble and is washed off.
5. The remaining image is treated and developed with ink. This leaves a black, greasy, visible image on the plate, which is now ready for the press.
6. Offset plates may be saved for reruns; they require little storage space. If the plate is not retained, the negatives generally are kept on file. Both plates and negatives are easy to mail. Plates can be salvaged for reuse by grinding off the image and regraining them.

The deep-etch plate

Years ago, offset printing could be readily recognized by a characteristic softness or fuzziness, caused by the transfer of the dot pattern onto the soft rubber blanket. This gave rise to the inference that good, sharp color printing was accomplished best by letterpress. Modern lithographic technology has eliminated this distinction so that now, if quality is the criterion, both processes compare favorably.

One of the technical problems of offset lithography was the inability of the printing area to withstand long press runs. The thin printing surfaces—especially if halftone dots were involved—had a tendency to wear away, causing the dots to become ragged or smaller. In order to compensate for this, and to increase the sharpness and durability of the plate, the *deep-etch* litho plate was developed.

Slightly recessed areas can retain more ink than a surface plate and are more sharply defined. Softness is no longer an identifying factor. The deep-etch plate has lengthened running time to a point where it can compete favorably with letterpress plates.

In this process, the area *underneath* the printing surface is etched in order to prolong its ink-retaining qualities. This requires the use of a

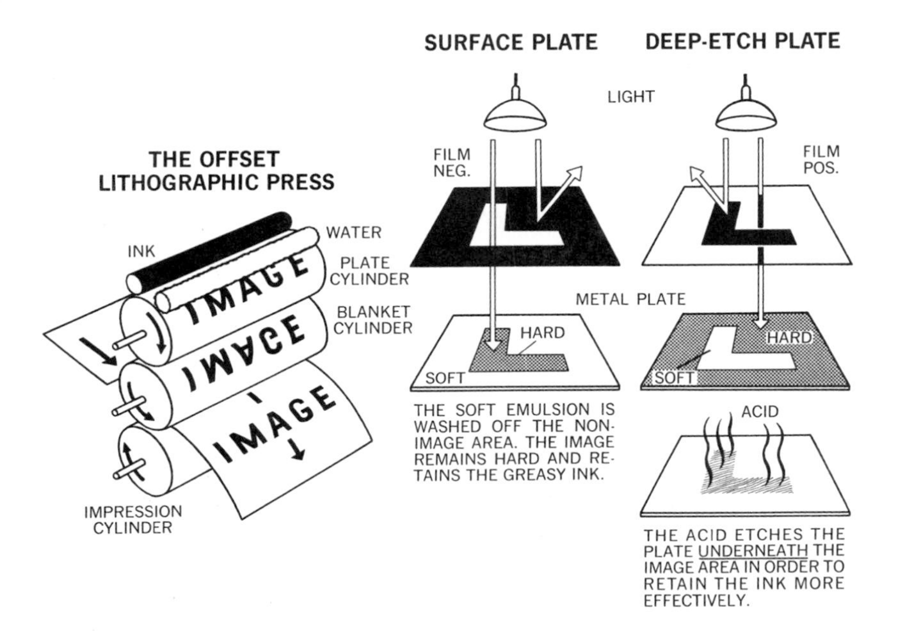

LITHO PLATEMAKING

film positive rather than a film negative, exposing the *nonprinting* areas in order to protect them with a light-hardened coating while the printing surface is being etched.

The deep-etch lithographic plate is produced as follows:

1. The plate (zinc, aluminum, or stainless steel) is grained in order to make it moisture retentive.
2. A *continuous-tone* film negative is made from the artwork.
3. A *screened film positive* is made from the film negative.
4. The film positive is exposed to the light-sensitized (bichromated gum) plate. The use of the positive protects the emulsion *underneath* the printing area, while the light hardens the emulsion in the nonprinting areas.
5. The plate is developed. The emulsion in the image area remains water-soluble and is washed off, leaving bare metal where the etching is to occur.
6. The image area is etched slightly. This is not a "bite," as in the engraving process, but a shallow etch of less than .0005 in.

7. The light-hardened coating over the nonprinting area is removed. The remainder of the process is identical to the treatment of the surface plate.

Dot-etching

As in the photoengraving process, continuous tone art must be screened in order to be reproducible. The halftone screens used in lithography are the same as those used in letterpress. They vary in fineness in proportion to the quality of the paper to be utilized. Unlike photoengraving, lithography cannot go to the plate in order to enhance halftone reproduction. In lithography, the alteration of the dot size must be accomplished on the film.

Dot-etching is a process similar in effect to the re-etching process in letterpress, utilized to chemically reduce the dot in certain areas in order to provide greater contrast. It relies more upon photographic control and less upon handwork than does re-etching. Attempted etching directly on the litho plates can endanger the image.

Dot-etching is a chemical process that can be very accurately controlled. It is effected on the film positive rather than the film negative. This is in keeping with the deep-etch process where positives are required for platemaking, and is especially applicable in color lithography. It is possible to effect dot alteration on halftone negatives, but positive dot sizes match the actual printing values and are thus easier to work with. For surface plates where negatives are required, the negatives are contact-printed from positives which have already been dot-etched. Intensification (enlargement of the dots) has limited usefulness, but it can be effected chemically by staining with light washes of dye, or by using a spatter technique with the airbrush.

Dot-etching is accomplished with the following steps:

1. If surface plates are to be utilized for low-cost halftone reproduction, *screened negatives* are produced for dot-etching.
2. If deep-etch plates are to be used, because better halftone or color reproduction is desired, a *continuous-tone* negative is made from the art.
3. A *screened positive* is made from the continuous-tone negative. Brushed on the positive, the chemical solution attacks the exposed emulsion of the film. Therefore, any work on the positive will *reduce the size of the dots.*
4. Acceptable dot areas are staged (protected) with asphaltum or lacquer so that they will not be altered by the chemical action.

5. The positive is immersed in a tray of Farmer's reducer, a solution which reduces the dot size by chemically attacking the emulsion on the perimeter of the dot.
6. Local tone lightening may be done by hand; generally little handwork is required.
7. Intensification is effected on the positive by the use of chemical intensifiers, dye staining, or spattering with the air-brush.
8. The film image is contact-printed onto the metal plate. If deep-etch plates are to be made, the positive is used. If surface plates are required, the positive must be reverted to negative form.

Combination plates

There is no counterpart of the letterpress combination plate in offset lithography, although the same effect can be readily accomplished.

In photoengraving, the halftone area is processed in a slightly different manner than the line area. As a result, there is an additional charge for all halftone work in terms of the cost of the plate, over and above the necessary camera work. The generous use of halftone art can appreciably increase platemaking costs. In the lithographic plate there is no difference between the line and halftone areas, since there is no depth of etch to be considered. The area of the plate that is occupied by halftone has no bearing on the cost of the plate. Exclusive of the cost involved in screening and stripping the negatives, a plate entirely covered by halftone costs no more than one with only a small halftone area in one corner.

Additionally, the litho plate is capable of accepting copy that *has been previously screened.* A screened proof from a magazine or other printed source can be pasted on the mechanical. The existing dot pattern will be accepted by the litho plate. There will be some percentage of quality loss, but this method is often feasible in instances where the original art is not available.

Surprints, drop-outs, and mortises are produced by combining film in the same manner as in the letterpress process. However, once the proper combination has been made, no special attention to the plate is required. The plate will accept anything that is on the film—line, halftone, or a combination of both—without discrimination.

Considerable economies can be effected due to the inexpensive nature of the lithographic plate, particularly in work that requires the combination of line and halftone. However, this saving can be dissipated by improper preparation of the mechanical art. The platemaker, so long as he understands what is wanted, can and will produce it (at additional charge), even if the art has been improperly prepared. Production of the desired result in such cases may require the shooting of additional negatives, positives, or both, which would not have been required had the art been prepared properly. As a result, a thorough understanding of the intricacies of combination art is recommended for the artist who becomes involved in the preparation of art for offset printing.

DUPLICATE LITHOGRAPHIC PLATES

There is no counterpart of the electrotype or the stereotype in offset lithography. Duplicate plates are not made from original plates, but rather from film negatives (or positives). Once the stripping operation has been accomplished, it is a simple matter to produce any number of plates.

Both the film and the plate are sufficiently light in weight to pose no problem in mailing. Few magazines are printed by offset lithography, but if an advertisement is destined for a publication which is, the film should be sent, since there is no method for locking a small litho plate into a large press plate. If the film is submitted, it may be readily stripped into position on the page flat.

The step-and-repeat machine

The step-and-repeat machine is a specially calibrated device equipped to produce the multiple-image plates required for small packages, labels, stamps, stickers, etc. The film negative (or positive) is placed in the machine. After exposure to the photo-sensitized plate, the film holder is moved, in perfect alignment, to the next position, and so on, until the desired number of exposures have been made. Any number of images may be produced from the original film. This machine is not limited to lithography; it can also be used effectively in the production of multiple letterpress plates.

LITHOGRAPHIC CONVERSIONS

There is no method in the lithographic process for printing directly from letterpress plates, nor is there any means of incorporating all or part of a letterpress plate into a litho plate. However, it is possible to rephotograph *proofs* of letterpress plates and deposit their image on the surface of a litho plate. This method of adapting letterpress for lithographic printing is known as *conversion.*

The simplest example of conversion is the reproduction ("repro") proof utilized on the mechanical art. The reproduction proof is an impression of cast metal type—the simplest form of letterpress plate. These proofs are pasted in position on the mechanical art and are photographed to become the line negatives used by the litho platemaker. Proofs pulled on transparent sheets or translucent paper can be used in converting to lithography. Cold type (photo-typesetting) machines produce typography on transparent film, both in positive and negative form, which may be used directly in litho platemaking.

As previously discussed, any halftone proof may be copied with some degree of success by the litho camera. If care is taken and special proofs are pulled for the purpose of litho conversion, good results may be obtained. A typical example of conversion would be the reuse, in a lithographed sales-promotional piece, of a four-color letterpress advertisement. Each of the four plates utilized in the advertisement is proofed *in black ink* on special proofing paper. Each proof is then photographed (without further screening) by the litho camera, preparatory to the platemaking process. This use permits distribution of the cost of the original color plates over several jobs, and provides for the economical use of color in sales-promotional advertising.

Reduction from the original letterpress size is not practical, since a 50-per-cent reduction of a 110-line screen would produce a 165-line screen, too fine for normal advertising purposes. Enlargement presents no problem. The dots become enlarged—noticeably so at close range—but it can be safely assumed that sales-promotional advertising will normally be viewed at a greater distance than the magazine advertisement.

The Brightype method

Letterpress *plates* can be converted for lithography by the Brightype method, which functions as follows:

1. All enamel is removed from the original letterpress forms (these can be either type, line, or halftone) and the surfaces are tin plated with a small electroplating hand brush.
2. The form is sprayed with a fast-drying, nonreflective black lacquer.
3. The printing area is gently polished with a soft rubber eraser to remove the lacquer. Only the top surface is polished, so that rounded serifs and worn dot shoulders do not show.
4. The form is clamped to a camera board, illuminated frontally by a special light arrangement, and the shiny plated surface is photographed.
5. The resulting negative is used to produce the litho plate.

METAL LITHOGRAPHY

Offset lithography is especially suitable for printing on metal, due to the softness with which the blanket roller lays the image on the unyielding metal surface. The metal sheets are printed flat and dried in special ovens before being formed into the desired product. Metal lithography is waterproof, rendering it suitable for beverage cans, bottle crowns, and screw caps—any container or closure which is subject to moisture due to freezing or refrigeration. Other typical applications are: metal toys, decorated trays, metal signs, cans, and large drums.

The metal decorating press is similar in principle to the offset lithographic presses used for printing on paper. The only difference lies in the arrangement of the cylinders, in the mechanisms which feed the sheets to the press, and in the drying apparatus. Precision requirements are very high. There is no difference in the plates utilized, other than that they must be produced to withstand extremely long press runs. The mechanical art and the stripped film flat are prepared in the same manner that would be employed for paper printing.

A SUMMARY OF THE LITHOGRAPHIC PROCESS

Lithography is printing from a flat surface, based in principle upon the incompatibility of oil and water.

The design is deposited on the printing surface, either by hand or photographically. Printing may be accomplished directly from plate to paper, or by the intervention of an offset or "blanket" roller. The use of the blanket facilitates printing on less expensive paper. Offset lithography is the most prevalent modern method of printing.

Offset lithographic plates are one-piece, inexpensive metal plates, which are not easily corrected. These plates are readily curved to fit rotary presses. They are easy to store and mail. Deep-etch plates rival letterpress plates for long press runs.

Mechanical art must be prepared for offset lithography, with the exception of nonillustrated book printing, where film negatives and positives produced by phototypesetting machines are utilized. Phototypesetting machines are finding increased use in lithography.

The offset plate is produced by exposure through photographic film, which deposits a frontwards-reading image on the plate. Assembly of the elements of the design is accomplished by stripping the film together to form a "flat." Necessary corrections are stripped in a similar manner. Blueprints, made from the film, are submitted for client approval.

Due to the level, even nature of the plate, makeready does not pose a serious problem in lithography.

Duplicate plates are inexpensive and easy to produce. Multiple images are economically projected onto the printing plate by the step-and-repeat machine.

Because offset presses are rotary presses, they are faster than flat-bed letterpress presses. It takes less time to produce plates, duplicate plates, and multiple images.

It is possible to reprint previously printed material with the lithographic process. Letterpress plates can be converted for litho use by various methods.

Lithography is especially adaptable for large-sized work. It is easily applied to materials other than paper, since the plate lays down an ink film of uniform thickness.

5 THE GRAVURE PROCESS

Simultaneously with the development of the wood engraving, another method of printing illustrative matter was becoming popular—the *intaglio* method. Intaglio means "cut-in" or "incised." In this form of printing, the ink is held in an incised area *beneath* the surface of the plate. Paper, placed upon the plate, draws the ink from the incisions by capillary action.

This method enables the artist to cut his design—either with a tool or with acid—directly into the plate, rather than having to cut away the areas around the line, as in the black-line wood engraving. Although cut into the plate, as in the white-line wood engraving, the ink is held in the incisions, rather than on the surface. This produces a black-line positive image.

Since the recessed (intaglio) printing surface is incompatible with the raised printing surface of type, it is not acceptable to the letterpress process. As a result, intaglio printing was reserved for the production of individual prints which were used for decorative purposes, or pasted in books on blank pages inserted for their mounting.

There are five methods of hand-producing an intaglio printing plate.

The etching

Etching originated in the shops of the armorers. It appeared as a printing process in the latter part of the fifteenth century, and was practiced by Dürer and others in the sixteenth century. Lines are etched (eaten) with acid into a polished metal plate—usually copper—which has been covered with a protective film called the *etching ground*. Steps in the execution of an etching are:

1. The acid-resistant ground, a wax composition, is rolled onto the plate with a roller.

2. The plate is smoked so that the artist can see his drawing as he scrapes through to the bare metal. The drawing is done with a sharp etching needle, or any other tool capable of cutting through the wax and baring the metal. The image is drawn backwards-reading.

3. The back of the plate is sealed with wax in order to protect the metal while it is immersed in an acid bath.

4. The plate is placed in an acid bath. The depth of the lines—which will control their darkness—is controlled by the length of time the plate is kept in the acid bath.
5. The ground is removed with a solvent.
6. The ink is forced into the incised lines.
7. The surface of the plate is wiped clean with tarlatan—a stiff, transparent muslin—leaving the ink remaining in the lines. The ball of the palm also may be used.
8. Damp paper is placed on top of the plate and subjected to heavy rolling pressure. The damp paper sucks the ink from the incised lines, resulting in a black line or positive image being imprinted on the paper.

Etching achieved its highest development in the seventeenth-century works of Rembrandt. It declined in the eighteenth century, but was redeveloped in the nineteenth century through the work of Whistler and the Frenchman, Meryon. It is currently enjoying considerable popularity as a graphic art medium.

Drypoint engraving

In drypoint, the lines are scratched, backwards reading, into the metal plate with a diamond or a pointed piece of steel. The tool is *drawn* across the plate, rather than pushed. The point raises a burr which is not removed. In printing, the burr, which holds ink, imparts a rich velvety effect to the line. Drypoint is often used to reinforce an etched plate.

The aquatint

The aquatint is an etching process which combines line and tone. The tone, or tint, is produced by etching through a porous ground of resinous powder which is sprinkled evenly on the surface of the plate. The acid finds its way through the porous ground, effecting tonal variations in the plate.

The mezzotint

In executing the mezzotint, the artist works from a dark base to the highlight areas. Using a tool called a "cradle" or a "rocker," he roughens the entire surface of the plate. If printed, this burr would produce a uniform black surface. The picture is made by removing the burr with a mezzotint scraper. In the highlight areas, the plate is burnished so that no ink can be retained. The resulting print is characterized by its rich velvety tones, rather than by a line effect. The mezzotint process is identified with eighteenth-century England.

Metal or line engraving

Metal engraving consists of cutting into a polished plate of copper or steel with a burin or an engraving tool which is *pushed* by the hand. The intent of line engraving is extreme clarity of line; as a result, the burrs are removed with a scraper. No acid is involved. The image is transferred to the paper, under pressure, in the same manner as etching and drypoint. Steel engraving attained a high degree of perfection in the United States in the nineteenth century.

It is important that this type of engraving should not be confused with the term "engraving" as it is applied to letterpress photoengraving. Steel engraving finds modern use in the printing of currency, postage stamps, letterheads, business cards, and formal announcements. This is an intaglio process, wherein the design is *cut,* backwards reading, into the plate by hand or by an engraving machine. Photography's part in the operation may be to introduce the design onto the plate in order to serve as a guide for cutting, but there is no acid involved in the process.

Genuine steel engraving, which has come to symbolize the highest quality of printing, is characterized by the slightly raised or embossed effect of the image. It can be readily identified by the indentation (debossing) of the blank image on the reverse side of the paper. This debossing is due to the printing pressure to which the paper is subjected, forcing it slightly into the recessed areas of the plate.

The status accorded the steel engraving, with the distinctive quality of its raised letters, has given rise to the less expensive process of *thermography,* sometimes known as "fake engraving." Thermographic printing is accomplished with a relief plate or type, using a dense ink. After printing, the surface is dusted with a low-melting powdered resin. Application of heat causes the resin to fuse and the image to raise above the surface of the paper. Thermography is shiny and less delicate than genuine engraving; it can be readily detected. The image is easily scraped off, and there is no characteristic debossing on the back of the paper.

THE GRAVURE PROCESS

Gravure, the "intaglio" printing method, is a commercial printing process in which the printing area is incised photomechanically beneath the surface of the plate. Gravure is characterized by its soft, velvety appearance, by the subtlety of its tonal values, and by the apparent absence of the halftone dot. This is accomplished by the combined use of a fluid ink and a highly absorbent paper. Gravure can be printed on a cheaper grade of paper (newsprint) than is normally used for fine-screen letterpress or lithography.

Definitions

Photogravure. The original gravure process, executed by hand, except for the necessary original photography, and effected without the use of the halftone screen. Commercially too slow, it is utilized only to a limited degree in modern times.

Sheet-fed Gravure. A gravure process in which individual sheets of paper are fed to a rotary press. This process is employed for the printing of high-quality color reproductions, utilizing 150 to 200 line screens. Sheet-fed presses are limited in the number of hourly impressions they can produce, and are used for short runs from 10,000 to 100,000. The sheet-fed presses can accommodate a wider variety of printing papers than the faster, web-fed rotary presses.

Rotogravure. A gravure process in which a continuous web of paper is fed to a high-speed rotary press. Rotogravure can turn out four-color pages, printed on both sides, at the rate of 15,000 to 20,000 impressions per hour. This process is utilized for the printing of newspaper supplements, magazines, and folding boxes.

Conventional Gravure. Both monotone and a few color-gravure plants utilize the conventional gravure process which employs the 150-line gravure screen. "Conventional" refers to the screen arrangement. Conventional gravure is still rotogravure because rotary presses are utilized. The screen breaks up the plate into "pits" which do not vary in size—only in depth. Conventional gravure printing produces an effect of continuous tone, characterized by a softness, especially in the extremities of the value range. Plates are made from continuous-tone positives and the gravure screen.

The News-Dultgen Process. In conventional gravure, the darker the tone, the deeper the ink-retaining pit formed by the gravure screen. In the News-Dultgen process, the continuous tonal effect of conventional gravure is combined with the halftone process. Thus, the pits formed by the Dultgen process vary in *both* size and depth, permitting more subtle variation of light, shade, and color. In the finished product, the halftone dot is more evident than in conventional gravure, but not nearly so much as in letterpress or lithography. Plates are made from continuous-tone positives, superimposed over halftone positives.

Coloroto. Rotogravure, printed in color.

Pit. The recessed area, below the surface of the plate, that holds the ink in the gravure process.

Glass Negative. A photographic negative where the light-sensitive emulsion has been deposited on glass, rather than upon gelatin film. It is utilized because film negatives have a tendency to shrink.

Film (or glass) Positive. A transparent image where the values are the reverse of the negative. These values, though transparent, are positive, as in the actual image. Any print from a transparent positive—on paper or on metal—results in a negative image.

Carbon Tissue. A light-sensitive, paper-backed gelatin tissue used in the gravure platemaking process.

Four-color Process. Four-color process is the printing of a full-color image by superimposing the impressions of halftone plates inked in the three physical secondary hues; magenta, yellow, and cyan—plus a black plate. Color printing will be fully discussed in a later chapter, but this basic fact should be understood at this point.

Color Separation. In order to produce the necessary plates for process printing, the original full-color art (or photograph) must be photographically separated into the four basic components.

Register. A printed image is "in register" when it is in its correct position on the sheet of paper. Color impressions are in register when they are correctly positioned on top of each other in order to produce the desired combined effect. Register is a critical factor in color printing. It is accomplished by the alignment of crosshair register marks located in exactly the same position on each plate.

In the gravure process, exclusive of photogravure, the *entire* printing surface is screened. There is no counterpart of the line engraving or the combination plate. A 150-line gravure screen is generally utilized—one in which the *lines* are transparent and the *spaces between them* opaque. The image is transferred to a copper plate which is etched by acid. The deepest etched areas, or *pits,* correspond to the darkest areas of the original copy and the shallowest areas to the lightest.

The etched plate is mounted on the cylinder of the press. The cylinder is enclosed in the ink fountain and, as it revolves, it receives a spray of fluid ink. A thin steel blade—the *"doctor"* blade—wipes the surface of the cylinder, leaving ink deposited in the pits but not on the surface. A rubber roller feeds the paper against the cylinder and capillary action transfers the ink to the paper.

Gravure was invented in 1879 by Karl Klic (or Klietsch), a Viennese photographer, in order to provide a satisfactory method for reproducing works of art. He also developed rotogravure, which was introduced in England in 1895. The process was brought to the United States in 1903, and was first utilized by *The New York Times* in 1914, to print its Sunday supplement section. These early Sunday supplements were printed in a single color—dark brown—and came to be known, colloquially, as the "brown papers." In 1924, the *Chicago Tribune* was capable of printing four-color rotogravure.

Modern Sunday newspaper supplement sections are printed in four-color rotogravure. Several popular consumer magazines now utilize the process. The effect of a continuous tone—with its minimization of the halftone dot—is a characteristic of the gravure process. As a result, most motion picture "fan" magazines use gravure, since pictures of the stars can be printed to closely resemble photographic prints. Food and home decoration magazines often rely on gravure because of the rich, almost photographic quality it imparts to pictures of culinary creations and room settings.

Gravure plates are very expensive. One justification for the expense lies in the saving in paper costs that can be made on an extremely long run. Consequently, many manufacturers, especially of cigarettes, are printing their packages or boxes in rotogravure.

Photogravure

Photogravure, as originally developed by Klic, is a hand process, except for the necessary photography. Its output is a mere 500 sheets *per day*. The following steps are involved in the production of a photogravure print:

1. A thin layer of powdered resin is deposited on a polished copper plate, much as with the aquatint.
2. The art is photographed and a film positive is made.
3. The positive is printed onto a carbon tissue—a light-sensitive, paper-backed gelatin surface. The action of the light hardens the gelatin, rendering insoluble the portions which receive the most light. The darker areas, having received less light, remain water-soluble. After washing, an image formed in varying thicknesses of gelatin remains on the paper-backed surface.
4. The gelatin is squeegeed onto the plate on top of the layer of resin; then the paper backing is soaked off. The plate is etched with acid (perchloride of iron). The acid eats through the thin (dark) areas of gelatin more readily than through the thicker (light) areas. Thus, deeper pits will be etched in the darker areas.
5. *No screen is used.* The etching acid finds its way between the par-

ticles of the resinous ground. This breaks the tonal areas into minute, irregular shapes, not perfectly aligned as are halftone dots, but nevertheless just as effective.

6. The plate is inked by hand, forcing ink into the depressions. Multicolor photogravure is seldom, if ever, attempted.
7. The surface of the plate is wiped clean by hand.
8. Dampened paper is positioned on the plate and capillary action draws out the ink. Since the pits in the dark areas are deeper, they contain more ink. The ink in these areas floods onto the paper, obliterating the pattern of the resin particles and producing the effect of smooth, continuous tone. Photogravure is utilized for the fine printing of photographs and works of art.

Rotogravure

Rotogravure is essentially the mechanical version of the photogravure process. The 150-line is considered sufficient for most commercial purposes, but finer screens may be utilized for high-quality printing. The plates are curved in order that they may be used in the faster rotary press. The press may be sheet- or web-fed. The following steps are employed in the production of positives used to make a rotogravure plate:

1. Film negatives of the artwork are made and developed. In the monotone (one-color) process, film negatives are used, since there is no problem of color register. Color rotogravure requires the use of glass negatives. Tone and line work are developed on separate negatives.
2. The negatives go to the retoucher. These are continuous-tone negatives—they have not been screened. Tonal values are *added* with dye or *reduced* with cyanide. At least 75 per cent of the retouching is done on the negatives.
3. Negatives of individual elements of the artwork are stripped together to form a complete assembly.
4. Continuous-tone positives are made from the negatives. A continuous-tone positive print is also made for the purpose of examination. The positives are returned to the retoucher for the retouching of defects too slight to be observed on the negatives. The positives—glass or film—are used for platemaking, and the positive prints are submitted to the client for approval.

If the plates are to be made by the Dultgen process, a *halftone screen positive* must be made. This is made from the artwork in the photoengraving process.

THE GRAVURE PLATE

Etching

The gravure service provides etched plates for the printer. Newspapers, however, print from cylinders containing the plates for sixteen pages; these must be etched simultaneously *on the cylinder*. For this purpose, continuous-tone glass positives are supplied to the newspaper by the gravure service. The positives are utilized for the production of the plates in the following manner:

1. The positives are contact-printed onto the light-sensitive carbon tissue. In the conventional gravure process, the 150-line gravure screen has been previously contact-printed onto the carbon tissue. This screen provides for the structure of the pit—the lines form the walls and the squares form the pits themselves. The intensity of the color value will be regulated by the depth of the pit.

   In the Dultgen process, the *halftone screen positive* is printed onto the carbon tissue. This provides the structure of the pits, which will vary in *both* size and depth. This process eliminates the need for the conventional gravure screen.

   The continuous-tone positive is then surprinted, in exact register, onto the screened carbon tissue.

2. After exposure, the carbon tissue is squeegeed onto the copper plate and the paper backing is soaked off. This process is similar to the adhesion of a decalcomania. Where the gelatin of the tissue has been exposed to much light, it has hardened and become water-*in*soluble. The gelatin under the darker portions has become relatively more soluble since the unhardened gelatin has been washed away with hot water. Adhesion to the plate forms a relief image, in gelatin, which is thickest in the highlights and thinnest in the shadows.

3. The etcher paints the nonprinting areas of the plate with black asphaltum, as further protection against the acid. The acid (perchloride of iron) is then applied. Where the gelatin is thinnest, the etch is deepest. The etch is shallower in the thicker areas. This variation in depth of etch (or variation of size *and* depth in Dultgen) of the pits accounts for the tonal gradations of the printed image.

   The curved plate is now ready for the sheet-fed press. In large newspaper presses, a cylinder accommodating sixteen pages may weigh as much as a ton. In such presses, the carbon positive is squeegeed onto the copper-surfaced cylinder and etched by pouring acid directly

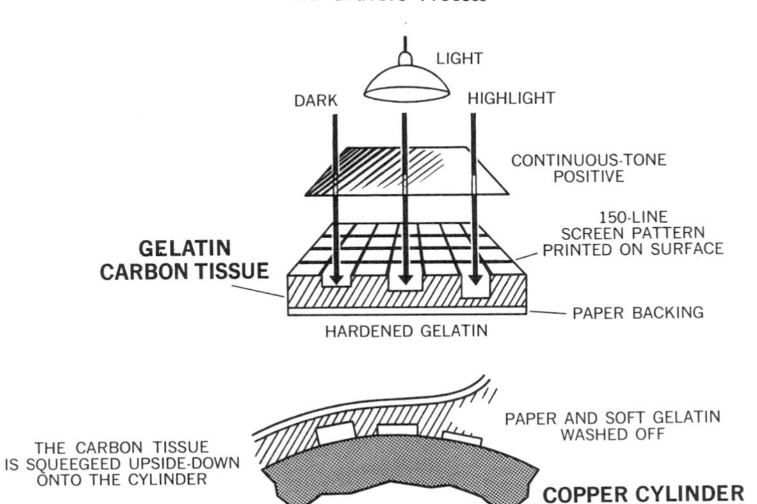

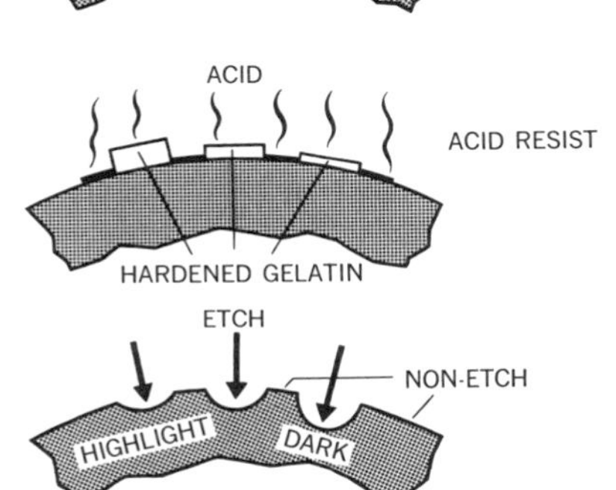

THE GRAVURE PLATE

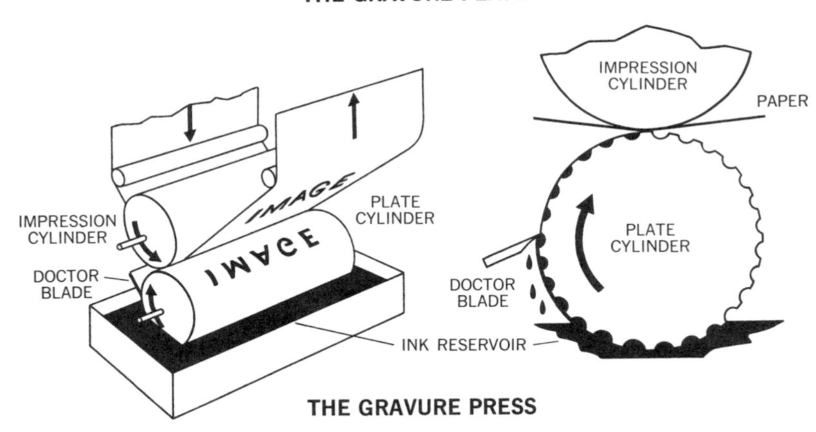

THE GRAVURE PRESS

over the surface. After the press run, the cylinder can be stripped and replated by immersion in an electrolytic copper bath.

4. The plate, mounted on the press cylinder, is sprayed with ink. As the cylinder rotates, the doctor blade wipes the nonprinting surface clean, forcing the ink into the pits. The ink, which is very fluid, is held in each pit in a varying quantity, depending upon the depth of the pit. In the Dultgen process, ink retention is dependent on both the depth and the size of the pit. The paper is soft and absorbent; its capillary action sucks the ink out of the pits and floods it onto the surface.

This surface flooding obliterates the impression of the individual pit, producing a printed proof that has the appearance of continuous tone. Since the Dultgen pits are *smaller,* as well as shallower in the lighter areas, there is less tendency to flood and the pit (dot) pattern is more evident. This tendency toward lesser flooding is capable of producing a more subtle tonal range, which is the characteristic quality of the Dultgen process.

Combination plates

There is no combination plate in the gravure process—all of the copy, even the typography, is screened. In gravure, if a letter image were to consist of a single pit for the entire letter, it would contain too much ink and the resultant flooding would obliterate its original shape. Consequently, the selection of type for the gravure process is a critical factor, since type that is too small or too thin tends to have a fuzzy-edged appearance and becomes difficult to read. This characteristic fuzziness of the type, caused by the screen, is one of the first indications for determining if a piece has been printed by gravure. Some publications print partially in letterpress and partially in gravure in order to overcome this problem.

Duplicate plates

In gravure, there is no counterpart of the electrotype or the stereotype—one gravure plate cannot be used to produce another gravure plate. The problem of running an advertisement simultaneously in several newspapers has been solved by the Intaglio Service Corporation. This service produces a set of master negatives from which the required number of positives can be made. A preliminary set of plates is prepared so that proofs may be submitted for client approval, as well as for guides to the various publications. A set of carbon-tissue positives, in either conventional or Dultgen screen, is sent to each publication that will print the advertisement. In some cases, the continuous-tone positives may be shipped to the publication.

Conversions

There is no method of converting halftone letterpress and lithographic plates or proofs to gravure, because continuous-tone positives are necessary for gravure platemaking. Also, commercial letterpress and lithography seldom employ the 150-line screen. Proofs, pulled from *line* letterpress or litho plates, can be utilized for gravure art. For example, the mechanical art for a gravure advertisement necessarily contains pasted-up type proofs—which are line letterpress proofs. In practice, it is often less complicated to make individual mechanical art for the gravure advertisement.

A SUMMARY OF THE GRAVURE PROCESS

Gravure is printing from an incised surface in which the ink is held in pits beneath the surface of the plate.

In the gravure screen, the lines are transparent and the spaces between the lines are opaque.

In conventional gravure, which utilizes the 150-line gravure screen, the depth of the pits controls the darkness of the tone. In Dultgen gravure, which utilizes the 150-line halftone screen, the size *and* depth of the pits controls the darkness of the tone.

Gravure plates are expensive. The paper (newsprint) used in gravure is comparatively inexpensive. The saving in paper costs in a large press run compensates for the extra cost of the plates.

There is no counterpart of the electrotype or the stereotype in gravure. If additional plates are required, additional carbon tissues or additional continuous-tone positives must be produced.

Once a gravure cylinder is etched, it is impossible to make any but the most minor changes.

Makeready does not pose a serious problem. It is difficult to maintain hairline register in gravure, due to the method of transferring the carbon tissues to the plates and to the high speed of the rotary web presses.

Rotogravure is an unexcelled medium for the reproduction of the color photograph, due to the minimization of the dot pattern. It is also an excellent medium for the production of monotone halftone when speed is a requisite—as in the newspaper supplement—or when high-quality reproduction is desired.

Rotogravure is an economical process when an extremely long press run is involved. It is poor economy to utilize gravure for line reproduction, unless a particular publication prints only in gravure. Many publications printing gravure also contain sections printed in letterpress, so that existing one- and two-color letterpress plates can be utilized.

The use of gravure for short press runs is neither practical nor economical.

6 THE REPRODUCTION OF COLOR

Definitions

Color. Color is a visual response—both physical and psychological—to the wave lengths of visible light. Color is the inclusive term for this phenomenon, and is so used in this chapter.

Spectrum. The spectrum is that area of visible radiant energy whose wave lengths fall between 3,800 and 8,000 Angstrom units. Varying wave lengths within this range evoke different color sensations. When white light is passed through a prism, it is decomposed into a band of its varying component hues. The sequence in which these hues occur is commonly known as the color spectrum.

Hue. The descriptive name given to a spectrally pure color in order to distinguish it from the remainder of the color spectrum. Hue is the first characteristic of color that the eye detects.

"Hue" is the spectral characteristic to which most persons refer when they say "color." Thus, red is not a *color,* it is a *hue*—the common name of a specific visual sensation falling within a specified wave length.

In this chapter, the word *hue* is used when reference is made to a specific color.

Value. Value is the lightness or darkness of a hue, noted in terms of the light it is capable of reflecting.

The Value Scale. The value scale is a series of ten recognizably graduated tones, ranging from black to white. Value is noted by comparing a given hue to this scale. In the Munsell system of color notation, value "10" represents white and value "0" represents black. Conversely, the platemaker uses a percentage scale in which 100 per cent represents black and 0 per cent represents white. In this volume, values are represented in terms of platemaker's percentages.

In painting, value is changed by the addition of either white or black pigment. It may also be altered by the addition of a complementary hue.

Chroma or Intensity. Chroma is the strength or weakness of a color. In painting, *chroma* is *increased* by the addition of pure color; *decreased* by the addition of a transparent medium.

Primary Hues. Primary hues are the basic components of color which, when combined, are capable of producing the remaining hues of the spectrum. The hues which are considered primary vary with the manner in which color is produced.

Physical or Light Primary Hues. These are the primary hues of the physicist, who produces color by means of *light*. When light is decomposed by prismatic analysis, the resulting primary hues are red, green, and blue—with wave lengths of 650, 550, and 460 millimicrons, respectively.

Pigment Mixture Primary Hues. These are the primary hues of the artist, who produces color with *pigment*. When pigments are mixed and deposited on a white background, the three primary hues are considered to be red, yellow, and blue—or, more specifically, crimson lake, gamboge, and Prussian blue.

Psychological Primary Hues. The psychologist considers the primary hues to be *four* in number: red, yellow, green, and blue. These primaries are derived from observations of the spinning color wheel, and are dependent upon the degree of the observer's visual acuity for their perception. These will not be discussed further in this volume.

Physical Secondary Hues. These are hues produced by any combination of two of the physical primary hues. The secondary hue magenta (pinkish-red) is a combination of red and blue; yellow, a combination of green and red; cyan (cyanine blue), a combination of blue and green.

These secondary hues more closely resemble the primary hues of the artist than the primary hues of the physicist; therefore, they are the ones used by the color printer. In color printing, these secondary hues are known as *process colors*.

Although these hues represent primary hues as far as the printer is concerned, they will still be considered *secondary hues* in this chapter in order to maintain a consistency of terminology in the discussion of both physical and printed color.

Complementary Hues. Complementary hues are hues which differ the most radically from each other. The complement of a primary hue is the resulting secondary combination of the two remaining primary hues. To the artist, whose primary hues are red, yellow, and blue, the complement of red is the combination of yellow and blue—green. To the printer, who utilizes the physical primaries red, green, and blue, the complement of red is the combination of blue and green, or the secondary hue, cyan. The mixture of a hue and its complement will produce either white or black, depending on the method by which it is mixed.

Additive Color Mixing. Additive color mixing consists of adding, by the superimposition of light rays in equal proportions, the three physical primary hues in order to produce white light. In the additive process, utilized by the physicist, the primary hues are red, blue, and green; the secondary hues are magenta, yellow, and cyan. The complement of any additive primary hue is the secondary hue composed of the two remaining primaries:

Hue	Complement
Red	Green and Blue, or *Cyan*
Green	Red and Blue, or *Magenta*
Blue	Green and Red, or *Yellow*

Subtractive Color Mixing. Subtractive color mixing produces a visual sensation by subtracting light from the whiteness of the paper. For example, magenta, when placed on the paper surface, *subtracts* cyan and yellow from the reflected light, allowing the eye to perceive only the sensation of magenta. In the subtractive process—utilized by the artist, printer, and the modern color photographer—the primaries of the subtractive process are the *secondary hues* of the additive process—magenta, yellow, and cyan. Any two of these will combine to form one of the additive primaries. The combination of all three will produce black. The complement of any secondary hue is the primary hue composed of the two remaining secondaries:

Hue	Complement
Magenta	Yellow and Cyan, or *Green*
Yellow	Magenta and Cyan, or *Blue*
Cyan	Yellow and Magenta, or *Red*

Transmission Copy. Copy which is viewed by light passing *through* it; for example, the positive color-film transparency.

Reflection Copy. Copy which is viewed by light which is *reflected* from the copy; for example, the color photographic print, the painting, the printed image.

Color Separation. The separation of a color image into its component primary hues, in order that it may be reproduced by either the additive or subtractive process.

Register. The accuracy with which separated colors are superimposed over each other when reproduced—either photographically or photomechanically. Colors which are accurately superimposed are said to be in perfect register.

Filter. A piece of colored glass which, when placed over the lens of the camera, will remove unwanted color from the image recorded by the film.

Panchromatic. Sensitive to all colors. Panchromatic film records all colors with equal sensitivity, and is thus able to differentiate between colors which would appear to be similar on other types of black and white film.

Screen Tint. A chromatic reduction of a solid color, produced by reducing it to a uniform dot pattern. A screen tint differs from a halftone in that there is no tonal variation. Screen tints are measured in percentages of the solid tone.

Moiré. Derived from the textural pattern characteristic of watered silk, the term "moiré screen" denotes the result of two photomechanical screen patterns which have been improperly superimposed. The resulting wavy effect is considered objectionable in both screen tints and halftones, since it produces an irregular tonal appearance.

MULTICOLOR PRINTING

The first thing that should be understood, in order to develop a knowledge of color printing, is that a printing plate is capable of being printed *in any color suitable for inking.* With modern printing inks, it is possible to ink a plate in almost any conceivable color. It is not essential that a plate printed in black must continue to be printed in black. The plate can be washed, then printed in red or any other hue. It is the ink that controls the color, not the plate.

When one-color art is printed, the only problem encountered is the mixing of the desired hue of ink. When two solid colors appear simultaneously in the same design, a different situation occurs. It is impossible to ink a plate in more than one color. Since both colors cannot be printed by the *same plate,* there must be an individual plate for each of them. The parts of the image which are to be printed in the first color—and *only* those parts of the image—must appear on the first plate, while those which are to be printed in the second color—and *only* those—must appear on the second plate. The division of the two colors—the process by which the proper part of the image becomes incorporated in the proper plate—is known as *separation.*

The simplest type of line-color separation is the instance where neither of the colors in the design touch or overlap each other. This type of separation is accomplished photographically. Two identical film negatives are made from the original art. On the first negative, everything which is *not* to print in the first color is opaqued out by hand. On the second negative, the parts of the design which were *not opaqued* on the first negative are, in turn, obliterated. Thus, the design has been separated into its two components, the nonopaqued parts representing an individual negative for each plate. It is important to understand that *the negatives are not colored;* they are black—identical in appearance to any other film negative. It is merely that the component color areas of the design have been disassembled on negative photographic film.

A plate is made from each negative in the normal manner of the printing process. Obviously, both plates cannot impress the paper simultaneously. The color press must have a separate plate cylinder for each plate, and the feeding mechanism must be so arranged that the paper comes in contact with each plate in perfect register. Each plate can be inked in any color that is desired. It is important to note that in printing terminology, *black* is considered a color. A black and red impression is as much a two-color job as a red and green impression.

It is possible to use a one-color press by printing the first color on all of the sheets, mounting a second plate, and running all of the sheets through the press again. In the case of long runs, this is an extremely inefficient method.

A more complex situation arises when the colors in the design overlap each other. If the art is prepared in two colors, one superimposed over a background of another, the colors will appear superimposed on the negative and it will be impossible to separate them by hand opaquing. If the colors are too close in value, the second color may not even be apparent on the negative; it may prove impossible to differentiate it from the background. When this is the case, the colors must be separated photographically by using a transparent, color *filter* placed over the lens of the camera. This is known as camera separation. In order to separate a color photographically, a filter of the complementary color is used. For example, to filter the *red* from a design, a *green* filter is used. The resulting negative will contain all of the elements of the design necessary for the production of the red plate.

The alternative to this process is *preseparation* by the artist. The artist produces the design by placing all portions of the art that involve the second color on a transparent overlay, registered accurately in position on top of the "key" art. The key art contains all of the first color. The key art and the overlay are photographed separately and the resulting negatives are used to produce the plates. No opaquing or filtration is required of the cameraman. Accurate registration of the colors necessitates a high degree of skill on the part of the artist, but the cost of camera separation is eliminated.

If halftone art is drawn in two colors by the artist, it is normally separated with the camera. There are special art processes for the preseparation of halftone art in the event that this proves desirable. These methods will be discussed in another chapter.

It is important to understand the difference between value and chroma in order to visualize how a color will appear when it is photomechanically reproduced. To alter the printing characteristics of a particular hue of ink, the plate must be either screened, surprinted with a screened plate of another color, or both. The halftone screen reduces the chroma of the ink by lessening the intensity of the hue deposited on the paper. Surprinting with a black screen increases the value. The surprinting of another hue may both alter the hue and increase the value.

Technically speaking, there is no means of photomechanically reducing the *value* of any ink other than black. For example, suppose a red artist's pigment and a red printing ink are identical in hue. A halftone screen will reduce the *chroma* of the ink by weakening its intensity; a light red will result. If white pigment is mixed with the red pigment, the *value* of the pigment is reduced. The result will be a pink, completely different in character from the screened ink. A pigment hue, which has been reduced in value by the addition of white pigment, cannot be matched by screening an ink of the same original hue. In order to effect a match, the ink itself must be altered.

This is complicated by the fact that the platemaker, or the printer, seldom speaks in terms of chroma; to them, screening means a reduction in value. Since reduction in value is a reduction of grays, their terminology is correct when it applies to black and white halftones. When the same terminology is carried over into color printing, a discrepancy occurs which should be realized by all concerned.

When printing in a single color, the printer is capable of mixing ink to produce any desired hue. Often a one-color job will contain both solid and screened areas of the color. Obviously, the nature of the tonal areas will be governed by the hue used to print the solid areas. It is the job of the artist to anticipate this effect. Since screening reduces chroma, he must reduce his pigment with a transparent medium rather than with white.

When printing in more than one color, variation is achieved by screening, surprinting, or both. *The variations which may be produced are limited by the nature of the hues with which the plates are inked.* Since the artist is hampered by no such limitations, he must learn by experience to compensate for the limitations of the photomechanical processes, rather than expecting them to be capable of reproducing anything he may choose to create.

When two colors of the same chroma overlap, a third color results. In areas where blue and yellow overlap, a green hue will result. However, if the inks are opaque, and the blue is particularly strong, the overprinting will not produce a true green; the blue will bear a greenish tint. In order to *surprint* solid color, solid blue on top of yellow, or vice versa, the second color underneath must be *dropped out* of its plate in order to prevent discoloration of the surprint. This is not necessary when black is used, as black will surprint any other color. Dropping out behind fine-line detail is a problem of such critical registration that it is best handled by the cameraman. Specific instructions to drop out an underlying color should be given to the platemaker.

In Order to:	Artist	Printer
Alter hue	Adds additional hues to pigment.	Superimposes screened patterns of basic hues.
Increase chroma	Adds pure hue.	The printer does not increase chroma. His ink is mixed to its full chroma.
Decrease chroma	Adds transparent medium to pigment.	Uses screen pattern.
Increase value	Adds black or a complementary hue.	Surprints with a second screen of black or a complementary hue.
Decrease value	Adds white pigment.	Changes value of ink, and prints as a solid color.*

* In order to print *light red* (low-chroma red), the printer screens a solid red. In order to print *pink* (low-value red) he mixes pink ink. Once mixed, the pink ink is printed as a solid, full-chroma color. If *light pink* is required, the solid pink is reduced in chroma by screening.

The tendency for two overlapping colors to form a third can be used to great advantage. If the solid colors are opened up by means of a dot formation (screen), and the screen angles turned to prevent superimposition of the dots, the resulting overlap will mix optically, forming a third color of equal clarity and intensity. In this manner, screen patterns of two colors can be combined to form a third color—three colors for the price of two. If the percentages of the screen patterns are knowledgeably varied, an infinite number of combinations can be obtained. For example: an 80 per cent (almost solid) screen of yellow and an 80 per cent screen of blue combine to form a solid green. A 50 per cent yellow and a 50 per cent blue produce a green of a similar, but lighter, hue. However, an 80 per cent yellow and a 50 per cent blue will produce a *yellow green,* while an 80 per cent blue and a 50 per cent yellow will form a *blue green.* The possibilities are endless.

In this method of printing, there is no necessity for a third color plate; therefore, there is no charge. The extra color can be obtained for the cost of stripping the screen patterns into the proper areas of the two negatives.

Similar results may be obtained by overprinting solid areas of *transparent* ink. The production techniques of these methods will be discussed later.

The duotone halftone

It is often effective to print halftones in two colors—black and a second color—in order to enhance their appearance and give them extra "life." This two-color process is known as the duotone. Obviously, the artist cannot attempt to preseparate a photograph; this is a job which requires camera separation. Two halftone plates are made from a single black and white original photograph. A separate screened negative is made for each color. Each negative is identical, except that when the negative is made for the second color, the lines of the screen are turned at a 30-degree angle from those of the first negative, so that the dots of the second color will appear *between* those of the first color (black) rather than becoming obliterated by falling directly *underneath* them. The key (black) halftone is etched for detail, while the second is flat-etched. The impressions are printed, in register, on top of each other, the resulting image producing a two-color effect. If each plate were to be proofed separately, the image would be visible in the impression made by each color. This process is also known as the duograph process, although the term duotone persists in common usage.

The "fake" duotone

A similar, but more lifeless, effect can be obtained by printing a colored screen tint behind a black halftone. The screen tint is merely a uniform tone, carrying none of the image detail. One negative bears the halftone image; the other the screen tint pattern. The screen angle of the tint is turned, in order to avoid a moiré effect. The result appears as a tinted photograph, lacking the clarity and contrast of the duotone. This process, known colloquially as the "fake" duotone, is considerably less expensive than the duotone.

FULL-COLOR PRINTING

It does not require much imagination to conjure up the infinitesimal range of hues and values suggested by the term "full-color." If one were to develop a press to print each of these colors, its size would be incomprehensible. But when the variations that can be obtained by the combination of various screen tints are considered, duplicating "full-color" with a minimum number of impressions becomes feasible.

The artist uses three *primary* hues—red, yellow, and blue—which can be combined, in varying percentages, to form every other hue. Mixed on paper, red-yellow, red-blue, and blue-yellow combinations form, respectively, the *secondary* hues: orange, violet, and green. The *three* primaries, mixed in strength, form brown. Each secondary color, mixed with its adjacent primary, forms the intermediate, or *tertiary* hues: red-orange, yellow-orange, yellow-green, blue-green, blue-violet, and red-violet, respectively. In this manner, the three primary hues, mixed in appropriate percentages, can be combined to produce all the colors of the spectrum. The mixture of any two complementary colors will produce black.

It has already been noted that a printed color, when screened, will mix optically with another color that is superimposed over it. It follows logically that if three primary colors can be screened to the proper component percentages, and superimposed, the full color range of the spectrum can be produced. This method of printing, using three plates, each inked with one of the three primary hues, is known as *three-color process printing*. A fourth plate, *black,* is generally added to produce strength of detail and neutral values of gray. The black ink can also be employed to print the accompanying typography. This process of printing full color with the three primaries and black is known as *four-color process printing*. This is the most prevalent method of full-color printing, whether in letterpress, lithography, or gravure.

It is important to realize that every color wheel is an arbitrary affair. The traditional red, yellow, and blue primaries of the artist provide much latitude of interpretation. In the development of process printing, it was necessary to scientifically determine *which* red, yellow, and blue would most effectively combine in *printing* full color, as well as to provide standard inks which would be used consistently by the industry.

Spectrum red and spectrum blue do not provide the answer. Spectrum red, overprinting yellow, will still produce red. Spectrum blue and yellow are complementary and will combine to produce black. Red and blue are spectrally exclusive colors and their overprint will produce black. The primary hues of the artists are not the same as those utilized in process printing.

The artist must become aware of the scientific aspects of color in order to understand color printing. To the physicist, who is concerned with color in terms of light rays, the primary hues of the spectrum are *red, green, and blue.* He finds that when beams of red, green, and blue light are added together in a darkened room, the result is *white* light.[1] This is the method of color combination known as the *additive process.*

The additive color process

The additive color process depends upon the fact that the addition of light rays of the three primaries—red, green, and blue—will produce white. It takes equal parts of all three to produce white. If lesser combinations occur, intermediate hues will result. In this manner, the combination of red and green light produces *yellow;* red and blue produces a pinkish-red known as *magenta;* and blue and green produces a blue-green called *cyan* (cyanine blue). In the additive process then, red, green, and blue are the primaries, and *yellow, magenta, and cyan* are the *secondary* hues.

The secondary hue, magenta, composed of red and blue, is the complement of green; yellow, composed of green and red is the complement of blue; cyan, composed of green and blue is the complement of red.

The physicist and the artist/printer are dealing with two different aspects of color. The physicist is concerned with *light;* the artist/printer with *pigment.* The physicist *adds* color, proceeding from black (no light) to white. The artist/printer *subtracts* from the white of the paper, superimposing color upon color until he finally achieves black (no light), indicating that he has *subtracted* all of the light that the paper is capable of

---

[1] The experiment may be performed in a darkened room, using three flashlights. Cover the lenses with red, green, and blue Zipatone or Bourges transparent sheets and superimpose the beams of colored light on a piece of white paper.

reflecting. The process of mixing pigment on paper (assuming for the purposes of this explanation that the paper is white) is an example of the *subtractive process.*

The subtractive color process

Subtractive color processes depend on the *subtraction* of unwanted colors from light in order to reproduce, in the eye, the colors of the original subject matter. When white light reaches the eye, no color is perceived. It is not until some of the color is subtracted from the totality of light that the eye perceives color. It perceives the color which has *not* been subtracted.

White paper is a reflective surface, a source of *reflected* white light. The very nature of its manufacture was designed to make it so. When this surface has been altered by the addition of color, it no longer reflects white light—some of the color has been subtracted. This subtraction is accomplished in the following manner.

In order to subtract colors from light, one must move in the opposite direction from the additive process, proceeding from white *through the secondaries* in order to produce the primaries, which are their complements. The true secondary hues are, as has been noted, magenta, yellow, and cyan. If magenta ink is printed on the paper, it subtracts, or eliminates, the other two secondaries—yellow and cyan—from the white, allowing only the color sensation of magenta to reach the eye. If magenta and cyan are superimposed, they subtract the yellow. Since the subtracted yellow is composed of green and red, the remaining complementary primary, *blue,* is the only hue remaining for the eye to perceive.

The primary hue, blue, composed of magenta and cyan, is the complement of yellow; red, composed of magenta and yellow, is the complement of cyan; green, composed of cyan and yellow, is the complement of magenta.

In this manner, the physical secondary hues magenta, yellow, and cyan can be combined to produce the physical primaries red, green, and blue. Magenta, yellow, and cyan have become the standard hues utilized throughout the industry for color-process printing. Because these are somewhat close to the artist's primary hues of red, yellow, and blue, it is often erroneously stated that process printing is accomplished with the primary hues red, yellow, and blue. This is a fallacious statement, and professionally inexcusable.

Summarizing, one-color printing requires merely the inking of the plate in the desired color. Two-color printing requires a printing plate for each color, and the art must be separated into its components by camera separation or by preseparation. Any number of colors can be printed in this manner, as long as there is a plate for each color and a cylinder in the press to accommodate each plate. Or it may be done, if time permits, by running the sheets through the press several times. *Multicolor* printing is distinguished from full-color (process) printing in that there is no attempt to reproduce the full range of the spectrum. The inks need not be process colors, but can be mixed to the individual requirements of the job. Multicolor art may be camera-separated or preseparated. Process printing is the printing of a full-color impression utilizing three or four plates, inked in the three process hues, plus black. Process inks are the physical *secondary* hues, magenta, yellow, and cyan. Full-color art for process printing must be camera-separated.

Color of Light	Add	Produces Sensation of:	
Red	—	Red	*Primaries*
Green	—	Green	
Blue	—	Blue	
Red	Blue	Magenta	*Secondaries*
Green	Red	Yellow	
Blue	Green	Cyan	
—	Red, green, & blue	White	

Color of Ink	Subtracts	Produces Sensation of:	
Magenta	Yellow & cyan	Magenta	*Secondaries*
Yellow	Magenta & cyan	Yellow	
Cyan	Magenta & yellow	Cyan	
Magenta & cyan	Yellow	Blue *	*Primaries*
Magenta & yellow	Cyan	Red	
Cyan & yellow	Magenta	Green	
Magenta, yellow & cyan	All light	Black	

* This color is described as violet in many sources.

COLOR SEPARATION

Color separation involves the extraction of the component hues of a full-color image in order that each of these hues can be recorded on photographic emulsion—an emulsion capable of ultimately producing a positive image—either by the additive or the subtractive process. Separation requires the extraction of not only the solid areas of a hue, but also the percentages of the hue that are found in other hues. As a result, a separation negative will carry a great variety of tonal areas, some of which will print in the hue itself, and others which will be contributing factors of different hues.

This extraction or separation is accomplished by photographing through a filter, making a separate exposure through a different filter for each component hue. Colored light, rather than white light, is being reflected from the subject. The filter *subtracts* all of the light reflected by a particular hue.

An additive image is produced by a combination of the physical primaries—red, green, and blue. In order to produce an additive transparency, each primary hue must be recorded as an *exposed* area (black) on the film negative, so that when a positive is made, the hue will be represented as a *transparent* area through which light of the same hue may be projected. Three hues of light, superimposed and passing through the separated positive, *add* to form a full-color image.

In order to filter for the additive primaries, filters of the desired hue are used. Thus, red is separated with a red filter. The filter *subtracts* the green and blue from the reflected light. Only red light passes through the filter, exposing the corresponding areas of the negative as desired.

Modern color transparencies, color prints, and process printing plates are a result of the subtractive process. As such, the image is produced with a combination of the physical *secondaries*—cyan, magenta, and yellow. In this case, each secondary hue of the subject must produce an *unexposed* area on the negative. In the photographic process, this area will be positively reversed and replaced with a dye. In process printing, it will produce a printing area on the plate which will be inked with the appropriate hue.

A secondary hue is separated from the original image by *filtration through its complement*. The complement of any secondary color is the primary color which is the combination of the remaining two secondaries.

Filter	Subtracts from Copy	Separates from Copy
Green	Cyan & Yellow	Magenta
Blue *	Magenta & Cyan	Yellow
Red	Magenta & Yellow	Cyan

* Many sources state that yellow is separated with a *violet* filter. The standard set of three-color separation filters are the Kodak Wratten filters: No. 25-red, No. 58-green, and No. 47-*blue-violet* or No. 47B-*blue*. *The Lithographer's Manual* recommends the use of No. 47B. Reference to this as the blue filter is consistent with the color terminology which is used in this chapter.

The green filter is a combination of cyan and yellow. Magenta light, reflecting from the copy, combines with the cyan and the yellow and is completely subtracted. *No light* from the purer magenta areas passes, and only *partial light*—gray—passes from the partial percentages found in the other hues. The reflected magenta light is represented by *unexposed* areas on the film negative.

Black is a separation used solely by the process printer, and has no counterpart in the photographic process. It is separated either with an amber filter, which subtracts the primaries but allows certain gray values to pass, or by a split-filter exposure. The split filter separates black by a varied exposure through all three of the primary filters.

In order to print in three- or four-color process, the negative separations must be screened and halftone printing plates produced from them. A screen of less than 110 lines per inch is seldom utilized, except in the case of newspapers which run color. Halftone separations are produced by the direct or the indirect method.

Direct method separation exposures are made directly through the halftone screen, using high-contrast film. Halftone negatives are produced in one step. Plates are made directly from the screened negatives. Screen positives for deep-etch lithography are made by contact-printing the negatives.

In the *indirect method,* halftone negatives or positives are made from intermediate continuous-tone separations. Retouching can be accomplished on the continuous-tone images with either retouching pencils or dye. The indirect method provides a greater degree of tone and color control.

Screen Angles. When color is reproduced photographically, the image is produced by the superimposition of *transparent* dyed layers. In the photographic print, the combined layers of the transparent emulsion subtract from the white of the paper in order to form a full-color image. In printing, the component hues are deposited on paper as dots of ink. The ideal situation would consist of dots of perfectly transparent ink, superimposed exactly over each other. However, some dots, due to their pattern and size, print partially either on top of or alongside the dots of the first-printed hue. Printer's ink is necessarily more opaque than photographic dye; as a result, some of the lighter dots will be obliterated by the darker ones. This conflict of dot pattern produces an undesirable effect known as moiré. This effect can be readily examined by superimposing two identical sheets of dot-patterned Zip-A-Tone and rotating the top sheet.

The moiré pattern is minimized by changing the screen angle at which each separation is made, forming a mosaic pattern of the dots which, when viewed at any distance, creates the effect of continuous-tone color. The ideal condition is achieved when the screen angles of the separations are 30 degrees from each other. Thus, in three-color process, the cyan screen is shot at 45 degrees, the magenta at 75 degrees, and the yellow at 105 degrees. In four-color process, it is impossible to include four 30-degree intervals within the 90-degree range of the cross-ruled screen. Therefore the yellow—the weakest hue—is shot at a 15-degree interval, between either the black and magenta, or the magenta and cyan. A typical screen-angle variation for four-color process would be: black—45 degrees, magenta—75 degrees, yellow—90 degrees, and cyan—105 degrees.

Often, in order to avoid a moiré pattern, a different screen ruling may be used for the yellow separation. For example, if a 133-line screen is used for magenta, cyan, and black, a 155-line screen will be used for the yellow.

Color correction

There is a loss of color fidelity in photomechanical reproduction, due to the inability of the filter to compensate for ink and printing deficiencies, and because the photographic negative does not record the exact ratios of the color densities of the original subject. Consequently, there is a considerable amount of effort expended by the platemaker in an attempt to "correct" his color—to bring it to a point where it most closely duplicates the color of the original.

Color correction has been traditionally accomplished by the hand work of etchers—either on the letterpress plate or dot-etched on the litho-film positive. Color areas are corrected by dot enlargement or reduction, in the same manner as the black and white halftone.

Suppose, for example, that a red area on a color proof does not match the hue or the value of the original copy. This red area is composed of dots which appear on the magenta and the yellow plates plus, in all probability, light dot patterns on the cyan and black plates. If the printed red appears too orange, the yellow dots must be reduced in size or the magenta dots enlarged. If the red appears purplish, the cyan dots must be reduced and perhaps the yellow and the magenta dots enlarged. If the value of the red is too light, the black dots may require enlarging; if too dark, reduction may be necessary. It is the skill of the etcher in visually determining *how much* on *which* plates or negatives must be corrected that makes him a valued craftsman.

While handwork has always been the basis for color correction, photographic masking techniques are currently eliminating a good deal of such work. A *mask* is a photographic image which, when superimposed over another photographic image, will improve its reproduction characteristics. A mask may be negative or positive, and may be employed to alter either a negative or a positive image. Simply stated, the continuous-tone mask is a device for holding back unwanted colors so that the wanted color may be recorded in its proper density. There is a wide variety of masking techniques whose use depends on the nature of the original copy. Masking is an integral part of color separation. Used with the indirect method of separation, masking improves the quality of color reproductions and reduces the work of the color retoucher.

THE KODAK MAGENTA CONTACT SCREEN. The magenta contact screen consists of cross-lines ruled in magenta, rather than black, enabling the opacity of a color to be manipulated with the use of filters. It cannot be used in direct separation, as its use will interfere with the separation filters. Use of the magenta screen improves the sharpness of highlight detail and simplifies contrast control.

THE KODAK GRAY CONTACT SCREEN. The gray contact screen, due to its neutral gray color, may be used for direct separation in order to effect some degree of color correction by strengthening dot formation. Filters cannot be used for contrast control; this is effected instead by standard procedures, such as controlled flash exposure.

THE DENSITOMETER. The densitometer is an electronic device which is used to measure tonal values accurately. It is especially useful in color separation and correction. *Transmission densitometers* are used to examine negatives and transparent copy, while *reflection densitometers* are used to measure opaque copy.

Printing in color

Process color is printed either dry or wet. In dry printing, each color is allowed to dry before receiving the next impression. This is accomplished in the press by having a separate impression cylinder for each plate cylinder. Thus, the ink is given a short interval in which to dry before proceeding to the following pair of cylinders. The ultimate result in color printing is accomplished in this manner. In dry printing, the platemaker makes heavy-printing magenta, cyan, and yellow plates, and a light accentuating black plate.

Wet printing better meets today's requirements for high-speed press runs. Colors are printed wet—impressions of each color follow so rapidly that there is no appreciable drying time between them. This is accomplished by arranging the plate cylinders around a single large impression cylinder. This allows for a much faster press run, but does not equal the quality of dry printing. In wet printing, the plate must use as little ink as possible, avoiding excessive overprinting which would cause the colors to bleed. In order to accomplish this, black is substituted for the magenta, cyan, and yellow in the darker areas of the subject, thus creating a dark value with less ink. Wet printing almost necessitates the use of four-color process.

Accurate register of the succeeding impressions is a critical factor in both methods.

Progressive Proofs. Progressive proofs, known as "progs," are color proofs submitted by the platemaker or engraver for the client's approval, prior to the actual press run. They are made from the separation plates, and show the impression of each plate and the resulting effect of each successive color as it is applied. Progressive proofs are pulled on the type of paper that will ultimately be utilized; publications supply samples of their particular paper for this purpose.

Not every lithographer has proofing facilities. Litho proofing, due to the necessity for dampening, etc. is not as readily accomplished as color letterpress proofing. If color is a critical factor, a lithographer with proofing facilities should be employed. If litho proofs cannot be pulled and checked, it may be advantageous to print the job in letterpress.

COPY FOR PROCESS PRINTING—COLOR PHOTOGRAPHY

Process printing was an accomplished fact even before a commercially practical method of color photography was perfected. Full-color illustration, executed by hand, could be filter-separated into its three component colors. From these, halftone plates could be made. The first reproduction of color art was made from black and white photographs which had been tinted by hand. The development of a practical color photographic film was the final link in the chain of processes which contribute to printing as we know it today.

There are two types of copy from which platemaking negatives are made—*transmission copy* and *reflection copy*. Transmission copy is copy that is photographed with light passing *through* the copy; for example, the color transparency. Reflection copy is copy that is photographed with light that is *reflected* from the copy; copy such as artwork and the photographic print—black and white or color. One looks *through* transmission copy and *at* reflection copy. Both transmission and reflection copy are submitted to the platemaker in positive form.

Transmission copy—the additive process

Early transparencies were produced by the color additive process. This process, as mentioned previously, depends on the addition of the primary hues of light—red, green, and blue—to produce the desired image. The additive process functions in the following manner:

1. The subject is photographed on three sheets of panchromatic film. Each sheet is exposed through a different color filter—red, green, or blue. Each filter passes its own hue and records it as an exposed black image. The resulting negatives separate the colors of the subject into its three primary hues. There is no counterpart of the black process plate in color photography.
2. A film positive is made from each separation negative. The separated hue is now represented by a clear or light gray area on the positive.
3. The positive is projected onto a screen, using a light of the hue represented by the positive. The light passes through the transparent areas of the positive, and is blocked by the opaque areas. If the three positives are projected simultaneously, each with its own hue of light, the overlapping primaries will *add* to form a full-color image.

Commercial applications of this principle are known as screen-plate processes, representing an attempt to produce a positive color transparency on a single photographic plate or film. These processes employ microscopic red, green, and blue filtering particles, superimposed over a panchromatic film emulsion. These particles pass or reject the colors of the subject, resulting in a patchwork of negative separations on a single surface.

This image is converted to positive form by the reversal process—bleaching, re-exposing, and redeveloping—or by making a print on another plate. In the reversal process, the emulsion which has been affected by the image is bleached out. This leaves nonaffected areas of emulsion remaining behind the filter particles. The film is re-exposed to light and these newly-affected areas are developed. Light will now pass through the bleached areas of the first exposure and will be blocked by the areas affected by the second exposure. The values of the emulsion layer have been reversed—converted from a negative to a positive image.

When viewed through the color screen, the positive serves as a mask. It allows the light to pass through only the appropriate primary particles of the screen, which will *add* visually to produce the desired color.

The principal disadvantage of this process is that the color screen pattern is noticeable and becomes objectionable when enlarged. The screen patterns are dense; it is difficult to get enough light for projection. Plates and films are not easily manufactured.

The following are commercial applications of the additive color process, none of which find current usage.

LUMIÈRE AUTOCHROME. The Lumière Autochrome was the first practical commercial process, introduced in 1907. It used heavy, cumbersome, glass plates. It consisted of a screen of dyed orange, green, and blue-violet grains of potato starch, .0024 in. in diameter. These grains were first passed through a sieve in order to obtain a uniform size. They were then mixed in a ratio of four green to three red to two blue, and dusted onto a glass plate. The interstices were filled with an opaque powder and the mixture was rolled smooth under heavy pressure. The screen particles were covered with a layer of waterproof varnish, over which was spread a panchromatic emulsion.

Exposure was slow. The emulsion was developed by the reversal process to produce a black and white positive which, when viewed through the dyed filter particles, gave a color reproduction of the subject.

AGFACOLOR. Agfacolor, a German process twice as fast as Autochrome, employed a screen of dyed particles of gum arabic rolled out flat in collodion. The sizes of the particles were more uniform than in Autochrome. The screen transmitted nearly twice as much light, due to the higher transparency of the colored grains and the absence of black filling between them. The color elements completely covered the plate; no filler was required. Agfacolor permitted exposures of a fifth to a tenth of a second in brilliant sunshine, using a large-aperture lens. The plate was developed by the reversal process.

FINLAY COLOR. The Finlay process utilized a 175-line checkerboard screen of red, green, and blue elements 1/300 in. square. The screen was made by printing dyed bichromated albumin with a black and white cross-lined screen. The plate was first coated with a green-dyed collodion. It was then coated with a bichromated (light-sensitive) albumin and exposed beneath the cross-ruled screen. The unprotected areas were then bleached and dyed with a red dye. Coated a second time and re-exposed beneath the screen, the remaining unprotected areas were bleached and dyed with blue dye. A protective layer of collodion was applied over the entire screen.

The process required no emulsion layer; the pattern itself was light-sensitive. Exposure speed was considerably faster than for its predecessors.

DUFAYCOLOR. The first process to utilize a film base rather than glass plates, Dufaycolor employed a geometric screen, or *reseau*. The film base was first covered with a layer of blue-dyed collodion. It was then printed with a set of greasy dye-resistant ink lines. These parallel lines (20 to the millimeter) were printed with engraved rollers. The blue dye between the lines was bleached and the resulting clear spaces were colored with green dye. Removal of the greasy lines left parallel blue and green lines. A second set of lines was then printed at right angles to the first. A second bleaching removed the blue and green dye between the lines; the resulting clear spaces were dyed red. In order to achieve the proper color balance (the blue and green lines appeared as alternating squares between solid red lines) the red lines were made narrower than the blue and green squares. The screen pattern was then coated with varnish and panchromatic emulsion. Dufaycolor was developed by the reversal process.

Transmission copy—the subtractive process

The subtractive method has produced the most successful color processes from the standpoint of simplicity of use and quality of result. The subtractive process makes use of the three secondaries, cyan, magenta, and yellow, and their ability to subtract the unwanted colors of light in order to produce the colors of the original subject. The following applications of this process find widespread use in the production of copy for process printing.

KODACHROME. Kodachrome is a subtractive color film which was first marketed in 1935 and further improved in 1938. It is based upon the coupler principle: the emulsion (silver bromide) is reacted upon by a developer which reduces it to silver. The resulting oxidized developer will then react with certain compounds to form dyes. Thus, any light-sensitive layer of emulsion which has been exposed to a primary hue can be coupler-developed into its complement, forming the secondary hue necessary to produce a subtractive image.

In Kodachrome, the film negative consists of three emulsion layers superimposed on a transparent gelatin support (film). The top layer is blue-sensitive. Beneath it is a yellow filter layer used to prevent the blue light from reaching the lower layers, which are green-sensitive and red-sensitive in that order.

In order to produce a transparent positive image, each layer must be developed and dyed with its complementary color. Kodachrome processing consists of chemically assigning the dyes to their proper layers. In processing, the blue-sensitive layer is dyed its complement, yellow; the green-sensitive layer is dyed magenta; the red-sensitive layer is dyed cyan.

These resulting secondary hues are subtractively combined, either by projection or by viewing over a light source, to produce a full-color positive image. Kodachrome transparencies are processed by the manufacturer.

There are two types of Kodachrome film available, one for artificial (tungsten) light, and one for daylight.

Ektachrome. Ektachrome film, also manufactured by Eastman Kodak, is similar to Kodachrome but can be processed by the photographer. Ektachrome permits a greater latitude of exposure than Kodachrome, resulting in an improvement of highlight and shadow detail. Preference between Kodachrome and Ektachrome is usually a matter of the photographer's personal discretion. It is important that halftone separation negatives made from Ektachromes be masked in order to take advantage of the increased photographic qualities inherent in the film.

Ektachrome film is available in high-speed, tungsten, and daylight types.

Ansco Color Film. Ansco film is similar to Ektachrome; three emulsion layers are superimposed on a film base. In processing, these are reversed and dye-coupled, producing a positive color transparency. Ansco film may be processed by the photographer's own facilities. It is available in tungsten and daylight types.

Kodachrome, Ektachrome, and Ansco color are *color reversal films*. In developing, the negative layers of the emulsion are reversed to the positive and dye is substituted for the silver in the appropriate layers. Kodachrome is coupler-developed by the manufacturer. In Ektachrome and Ansco color, coupler particles are contained in each emulsion layer. After exposure, the film is processed with a developer which reacts with the couplers, producing the proper dye image in each layer—complementary in hue to its exposing light.

Reflection copy—color prints

Color prints are positive color images which have been processed on white cellulose paper in order that they may be viewed without recourse to the projector or the light-table. A result of the subtractive process, they are made from color transparencies.

Most types of color print have a tendency to lose some of the color quality and fidelity of the original. As a result, separation negatives for process printing are preferably made *directly from the original transparency*. The prime reason for utilizing a color print for reproduction purposes occurs when some form of color retouching is required. Obviously, it is quite difficult to retouch a color transparency. Color prints are also used when it is necessary to produce a montage or a paste-up assembly.

There are two types of color prints used for reproduction—the indirect and the direct print. *Indirect prints* consist of chemically dyed separations which have been superimposed in exact register on a white base. They are expensive, and represent the highest quality of print available for reproduction purposes. The most commonly used varieties are the Carbro and the Dye Transfer.

THE CARBRO. The Carbro is a positive color print, consisting of three layers of dyed carbon tissue which are mounted in register on an opaque white cellulose base. As in the gravure process, the carbon tissue is photosensitized gelatin. The name Carbro is a combination of "carbon" and "bromide." In order to produce a Carbro, a bromide print of each separation, treated with a special bleach, is contact-printed onto colored gelatin. A value-related hardening occurs. The unhardened gelatin is washed out with hot water. The resulting print consists of three physical layers of carbon tissue—magenta, cyan, and yellow.

Due to the delicate nature of the tissue layers, the Carbro must be handled with extreme care. With the highest fidelity to the original, it is used when color retouching is required, but it is too fragile for paste-up purposes. The Carbro is extremely expensive, and duplicate copies are as costly as originals.

THE KODAK DYE TRANSFER. Less expensive than the older Carbro method, dye transfers find widespread use as reproduction copy. The original print is expensive, but once it has been produced, additional copies may be ordered at a far lesser cost.

Since the dye transfer consists of three layers of dye, rather than carbon tissue, it is more durable than the Carbro and may be readily cut apart for paste-up assembly.

In the dye-transfer process, three separation negatives are exposed to three sheets of matrix film, forming a gelatin-hardened relief image. The matrices are then dyed magenta, cyan, and yellow. Registered with punched holes that position on pins, the dyed images of the matrices are transferred to white photographic paper. The matrices may be redyed and retransferred for the production of additional prints. The cost of a single dye transfer includes the production of the separation negatives and the matrix films. Once these have been paid for, additional copies may be had for merely the cost of the transferring operation.

Direct Prints. The direct print requires no separations; as a result, it is not nearly so expensive as an indirect print. Direct prints generally result in a color loss from the original transparency. There is further loss in the printing process; consequently, they are not preferred as copy for color separation. However, they can be readily color-retouched in an attempt to compensate for this tendency, making them an often-acceptable medium in view of their relatively low cost.

The Kodachrome Professional Print. The Kodachrome Professional Print consists of Kodachrome emulsion coated on a white cellulose base. It is produced from positive transparencies, its quality depending upon the quality of the transparency utilized. Eastman Kodak also produces paper for the printing of Ektachrome transparencies.

The Ansco Printon. The Printon is a three-layer tripack emulsion on a white base, similar to Ansco Color film. Developed by the reversal process, prints may be made by contact or projection from original transparencies. The Printon is probably the most widely-used inexpensive print for color reproduction.

Gasparcolor. Gasparcolor is a multilayer photoprint, made either by contact or enlargement from an original transparency. There is no reversal, second development, or subsequent dyeing. The dyes are already in the emulsion and are chemically bleached in proportion to the light acting upon each layer.

Any number of copies of this type of print may be readily produced.

This makes the direct print a suitable medium for short runs of color copy, in which the expense of producing printing plates is not warranted.

Kodacolor prints and Polaroid color prints are amateur media and have limited use as copy for process reproduction.

Full-color illustration, rendered in any color medium, is used as reflection copy for three- or four-color process printing.

THE KODAK FLEXICHROME. The Flexichrome, while not a color print, provides an economical method of producing full-color copy for process reproduction. This process produces a black and white positive gelatin relief image on white base paper, utilizing a black and white negative as original copy. The gelatin image may be dyed by brushing over it with a suitable color. Since the thickness of the gelatin governs the acceptance of the dye, each color area becomes dyed in a tone value corresponding to the original.

The disadvantage of the Flexichrome is that there are no color variations in any particular color area. The area will lack the subtleties of color variation to be found in a color photograph or a well-executed illustration.

7 SCREENLESS PRINTING: THE PHOTOGELATIN PROCESS

The principle of photogelatin printing, commonly known as *collotype,* was discovered about 1858 by the Frenchman, Poitvin. He found that when a bichromated (light-sensitized) colloid such as gelatin is exposed to light passing through a film negative, a reaction takes place that is in direct ratio to the exposure. The light tans (hardens) the gelatin where it has received much light; the areas which have received less light remain relatively untanned. When the exposed plate is placed in water and the sensitizer is washed out, an image composed of hard and soft gelatin is left on the plate. This gelatin image will absorb glycerin and water in the same proportion as the tanning action, determining the amount of ink it will accept. The darker, less glycerin-impregnated areas are capable of accepting more ink.

In the collotype process, no halftone screen is required. It is a true screenless printing method.

The first collotype printing, which was done in Europe, employed glass plates—necessitating the use of a flat-bed press. The process was introduced in this country about fifty years ago, and no significant technological developments occurred until the 1930's. At that time the direct rotary press came into use, increasing the output from 500 to 5,000 impressions per day. In the late 1930's printers attempted to use collotype plates in the offset press, but the results were unsuccessful.

Modern direct-rotary collotype presses have a large size capacity, ranging up to 44″ x 64″. Their speed remains about 5,000 impressions *per day*. Plates cannot be rerun, but have been run continuously up to 15,000 impressions when treated properly.

COLLOTYPE PRINTING

Collotype printing is produced in the following manner:

1. The copy is prepared in the same manner as for offset lithography.
2. The copy is photographed. A continuous-tone negative is made for the tone art; a line negative is made for line art. No halftone screen is used.

3. The negatives are retouched and opaqued. They may be exposed to the plate separately or stripped together as a combination negative.
4. Aluminum plates are coated in a whirler in a similar manner to lithographic plates. The light-sensitive coating consists of a mixture of gelatin, potassium bichromate, water, and ammonia.
5. The negative is contact-printed onto the plate.
6. The light action tans the gelatin. The lighter areas of the negative, which will become the dark-printing areas of the plate, harden the emulsion. The emulsion hardens little in the light-printing areas. In developing, the gelatin is washed from the underexposed areas of the plate. The grain of the gelatin is much finer than the halftone screen and is capable of producing a continuous-tone image.
7. The plate is soaked in a glycerin-and-water solution. The light areas of the plate containing the softer gelatin swell, absorbing much glycerin. The dark, harder areas absorb little glycerin. This leaves the printing areas of the plate slightly below (.006 in.) the nonprinting areas. This makes no difference, since it is the chemical capability of the area to accept ink, rather than its height, that governs its printing ability. The presence of glycerin lessens an area's ability to accept ink.
8. The plate is inked. The nonglycerin areas (dark) accept the ink, while the glycerin areas (light) tend to repel it. The middle tones accept a proportionate amount of ink. A stiff, slow-drying ink is used, and clean sheets (slip sheets) must be inserted between the impressed proofs in order to keep the backs clean. Make-ready consists of preparing the plate to accept necessary moisture, which will be absorbed from the air of the humidity-controlled pressroom.
9. The printing is done on firm, uncoated paper. A photogelatin reproduction coated with lacquer is difficult to tell from a glossy photograph. Collotype plates cost considerably less than letterpress or gravure plates. Their ability to reproduce photographs makes them substantially cheaper for use where a run of only a few thousand impressions is involved.

THE OPTAK PROCESS

Optak is an improved photogelatin process which was developed by Edward Stern and Company. Originated in the 1920's, it was formerly known as *Aquatone*.

Optak, unlike collotype, employs a screen, which can be as fine as 400 lines per inch. No etching or mechanical treatment of the plate is required, as in the photomechanical processes. Platemaking and printing are accomplished in the following manner:

1. A plate is prepared, consisting of a sheet of Monel metal coated with a light-sensitive gelatin emulsion.
2. A *screened* photographic negative is contact-printed onto the plate. The action of the light tans the gelatin under the transparent areas of the negative, while the gelatin composition under the dark areas remains unchanged.
3. The plate is curved and placed on the plate cylinder of an offset press. The plate is dampened. The tanned printing areas reject the water, while the untanned nonprinting areas absorb it. The plate is then inked with greasy ink, which is repelled by the wet non-printing areas in a similar manner to a lithographic plate.
4. As in lithography, a blanket cylinder is used. This enables printing on practically any type of paper. The Optak process is especially suited to the fine reproduction of halftones. Use of the halftone screen enables the plates to withstand longer press runs—a speed of 4,000 impressions *per hour* can be attained.

OFFSET COLLOTYPE

Aware of the fact that continuous-tone photogelatin plates had possibilities for use on an offset press, collotype printers attempted this technique in order to increase their output. However, due to the short-wearing qualities of the nonscreened gelatin plate, the experiment had been abandoned by the 1940's. The offset press was blamed for the failure.

Experimentation with high-speed, long-wearing continuous-tone plates was begun during World War II, due to the demand for screenless reproduction of maps and aerial photos. The 5,000-impression maximum of the conventional photogelatin plate was far from adequate. These experiments produced a longer-wearing offset collotype plate, suitable for use in a high-speed offset press and capable of press runs in excess of 25,000 impressions. This plate has also proved useful in conventional direct-rotary collotype. As a result, the whole concept of collotype is being re-examined; experimentation intended to render offset collotype a practical printing process is in progress.

A SUMMARY OF THE PROCESS

Photogelatin printing is an ideal process for the reproduction of fine photographs, paintings, photographic posters, displays, and picture post cards. Collotype reproductions may be enlarged to any practical size. Since there is no screen pattern, the enlargement will still effect continuous tone. In quality booklet printing, it is possible to print the illustrations with photogelatin and then run the sheets through a letterpress in order to print the copy.

There is no method of obtaining a proof in advance of the press run. Corrections are not readily made (although some areas of the plate can be lightened or darkened by the pressman), nor is there any method of duplicating plates. New plates can be so rapidly and economically produced that correction is accomplished by remaking the plate. Since each plate is produced by an individual chemical process, *exact* duplicates are impossible to achieve, although any number of reasonably similar plates can be readily produced.

8 WRAP-AROUND PRINTING: DIRECT AND INDIRECT

Printing technology is on the verge of another major breakthrough—a dual process which takes advantage of the best properties of both letterpress and offset printing. It has been felt by many that offset lithography is the more advantageous process, due to the economies inherent in litho platemaking and the higher speeds of the rotary presses. Others have held that letterpress is superior for color work. Wrap-around printing, although coming into use in the offset plant and the letterpress plant in slightly different manners, is essentially a marriage of the two processes.

The wrap-around process attempts to retain the color control and low waste of letterpress, while gaining the low make-ready time and higher speed of offset. It also attempts to eliminate the often troublesome dampening system of offset.

The plate

The essential ingredient of wrap-around printing is the plate, which is utilized in both the direct and indirect methods. The photomechanical copy preparation and the platemaking process are identical for each system. The thin, flexible, wrap-around plate is a *shallow relief* plate. It is made of zinc, magnesium, or Dycril (photopolymer plastic), ranging from .025 in. to .032 in. in thickness, with an etching depth of from .006 in. to .020 in. Standard letterpress plates are .152 in. or more in thickness, with a depth of .130 in. or more. Offset lithoplates have an overall thickness of .010 in. to .025 in. Zinc and magnesium plates are powderless etched, while Dycril plates are washed out like offset plates. Copper has been utilized to some degree. As in offset, it is important to have a good film negative, since corrections cannot be made in the metal.

Some technical problems have been encountered in the platemaking process—mostly limitations in halftone quality, and certain difficulties of precise press adjustment—but as wrap-around printing comes into more widespread use, solutions to such problems are anticipated.

DIRECT LETTERPRESS

The direct letterpress process utilizes three cylinders: the plate cylinder, the impression cylinder, and the inking cylinder. It is difficult

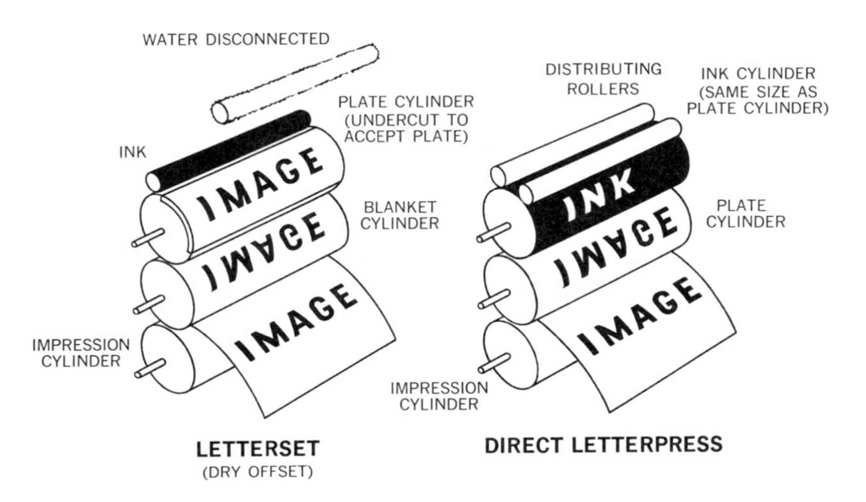

WRAP-AROUND PRINTING

to adapt existing letterpresses for the process. The cylinder arrangement is similar to that of the offset press, suggesting that existing offset presses can be converted to this use. The flexible plate is wrapped around the plate cylinder and receives its ink from a cylinder of the same size, which inks the plate in one revolution. This type of inking system provides exceptional ink coverage in solid areas. The ink is distributed to the inking cylinder by means of rollers.

The plate image is backwards-reading and is transferred directly onto the paper, which is brought into contact with the plate by means of the impression cylinder. The first wrap-around letterpress was introduced in 1959, and a two-color press was developed shortly afterward. The single-color press produces 7,500 impressions per hour, while the two-color press produces 6,000. Wrap-around printing has been successfully employed for such items as packages, labels, cartons, greeting cards, and magazine inserts.

LETTERSET (DRY OFFSET)

Letterset is the indirect method, utilizing the blanket roller without recourse to the dampening system. It is an offset, nonlithographic process. A greater future is predicted for this system because of the possibility of converting existing offset presses to its use. All that is required is the undercutting of the plate cylinder so that it can accommodate the thin, flexible, shallow-relief plate.

The dry-offset press has a triple-cylinder arrangement identical to the conventional offset press. The three cylinders are: the plate cylinder, the blanket cylinder (which the direct letterpress does not utilize), and the impression cylinder. The plate cylinder is undercut from .030 in. to .035 in. to receive the plate, which is inked with a series of rollers. The dampening system is either disconnected or removed entirely; there is no limitation on the type of ink which can be used. Litho ink, as will be remembered, must be essentially greasy in nature.

The "frontwards-reading" plate image is transferred to the blanket roller. The nature of the blanket is critical. If it is too soft, the lines may spread; if it is too resilient, they may stretch. The "backwards-reading" image is transferred from the blanket cylinder to the paper, which is delivered to it by the impression cylinder as in the litho press.

Advantages claimed for the dry offset process are:

1. The complete elimination of water and all its inherent difficulties.
2. The elimination of water increases the variety of papers that can be run in the press.
3. The plates are almost indestructible.
4. There is less ink consumption, since only the image areas receive ink. (In offset, the ink, although it is not held by the dampened areas, must be applied to the entire surface of the plate.)
5. The plate cost is less than for the standard letterpress, but more than for the standard litho plate. In dry offset, the economies found in the endurance of the plate, the higher printing speeds, and the ink savings tend to overcome the higher plate cost.

Flexible electrotypes for wrap-around

Flexible electrotypes, ranging in thickness from .050 in. to .090 in., have been produced for wrap-around printing. These are electrotype shells supported by a flexible plastic backing. This material is lightweight, with a high impact strength. The electros are mounted with pressure-sensitive double-sided tape.

The development of these electros affords certain possibilities for the conversion of existing letterpresses to direct letterpress. The electros are mounted on a precurved aluminum saddle. The saddle, .100 in. thick, the .005-in. tape, and the .075-in. flexible electro combine to make a

.180-in. plate—standard letterpress thickness. This results in a considerable economy of make-ready time. The next step would be the conversion of the conventional cylinder to a wrap-around cylinder, thus utilizing the full advantage of the process.

9 THE SILK-SCREEN PROCESS

The silk-screen process differs radically from other printing processes. Letterpress, lithographic, and gravure printing are accomplished with a plate; silk-screen printing is accomplished with a stencil.

The principle of the silk screen is a simple one. Silk, or other finely woven fabric, is capable of supporting ink unless it is forced through the interstices between the threads. If the nonprinting areas are blocked with some nonporous material, the stretched silk fabric provides a surface through which pigment can be forced onto a desired printing surface. In this manner, the screen functions as a stencil.

In the conventional stencil, any free-standing, nonprinting area—such as the center of the letter "O"—must be connected to the surrounding nonprinting area in order to secure it in place. These connecting lines are the characteristics of stencilled lettering. With the silk-screen stencil, it is not necessary to connect such free-standing areas; the silk fabric holds them in position. Because of this, silk screen is a stencil medium not subject to the artistic limitations of the conventional stencil.

Silk-screen printing is accomplished in the following manner:

1. The silk is stretched on a wooden frame having sufficient depth to serve as a reservoir for the ink. The frame is hinged to a flat surface upon which the material to be printed will be placed.
2. The stencil design is applied to the silk. It may be applied by painting directly on the screen with a liquid capable of blocking the pores of the silk; it may be cut from prepared stencil film and attached to the silk; or it may be produced photographically. The stencil blocks out the nonprinting area; the printing areas are the untouched silk.
3. The silk, stretched across the underside of the frame, forms a shallow receptacle into which the ink (or paint) is poured. Silk-screen frames have permanent blocked-out areas on all sides. It is in one of these areas that the ink resides when the frame is lifted. Normally, the ink will not pass through the exposed silk in the printing areas unless it is forced through, but thin inks will run through the silk mesh if allowed to stand.
4. The frame is lowered into contact with the surface to be printed.

5. The ink is forced through the mesh of the silk with a squeegee. This is a rubber blade similar to a windshield wiper or a window-washer's tool. The ink is scraped with the squeegee held at a 45-degree angle. The motion of the squeegee covers the entire length of the frame; a single "pass" is sufficient to transfer the image onto the printing surface. Little pressure is required.
6. The frame is raised and the printed image is removed and racked for drying.

The silk screen is not to be confused with the halftone screen. Although the pigment is forced through the spaces between the fibers, no dot pattern results. The silk-screen stencil prints *solid* areas, similar to the line plate.

There is no record of the origin of silk-screen printing. The Egyptians have been credited with having used some form of stencil printing. The early Japanese developed a cut-paper stencil in which the free-standing areas of the design were held in position with strands of human hair. This can be considered the ancestor of the modern silk-screen stencil, in which finely-woven fabric is used to hold the free-standing areas in place.

Woven silk was used in Europe for this purpose during the 1870's. The silk used, known as *bolting cloth* in the sugar refineries, was made originally for the sugar industry. A patent for a silk-screen printing process was granted to an Englishman, Samuel Simon, in 1907; but it was not developed commercially. Full-scale commercial development of the process came about in the United States in the 1920's.

Silk-screen printing is basically a hand operation. Its great advantage as a commercial process lies in the fact that it can be applied on almost any surface. Silk screen can print on paper, metal, or glass, of any thickness. It can print on flat or curvilinear surfaces. Due to this versatility, the process has come into wide use. Since wide use implies volume production, special equipment has been designed to facilitate the printing of specialized applications.

The commercial development of the process has hinged upon the solution of two problems: the sharpness of the stencil image, and the drying of the resulting prints.

Early silk-screen printing was characterized by ragged edges, caused by the inadequacy of the materials used to block out the nonprinting areas. In 1929, a knife-cut stencil tissue was developed. This tissue, known as Profilm, eliminated the unsharp quality of the stencil image.

A more easily cut version, called Nufilm, was developed several years later.

Early silk-screen inks dried too slowly to keep up with the output of the printing equipment. Drying is one of the inherent problems of the process. Printing equipment is compact; most of the available space in the silk screen shop must be utilized for drying the prints. If the ink dries too fast, it will clog the pores of the screen and render it useless. If it dries too slowly, the shop will become overrun with drying prints and production must be halted until there is room for more. Since silk-screen printing has become a large enough industry to warrant the attention of paint and ink manufacturers, formulas have been developed that are capable of being air dried in minutes or mechanically dried in seconds.

Traditionally, silk-screen stencils are cut by hand. The development of the photographic stencil—in which the stencil material is photographically deposited onto the screen—has widened the scope of the process. The photographic screen makes possible the printing of designs—especially type—too small to be cut practicably by hand.

Silk-screen printing, practiced as a fine-art medium, is known as *serigraphy*. The word is a combination of *seri,* meaning silk, and *graph,* meaning print. The process attracted public attention as an art medium in 1938, when Anthony Velonis organized a group of serigraph artists under the auspices of the New York City WPA. Through the work of such modern artists as Harry Sternberg, Adolph Dehn, and others, serigraphy has attained a high degree of prominence as a medium for the graphic artist and the printmaker.

THE SCREEN

SCREEN FABRICS. Traditionally, silk is the fabric of the process. It has great strength and its weave is uniform and durable, enabling it to last for many thousand impressions. The finest grade is imported from Switzerland; less expensive but nevertheless practical fabrics are produced domestically and in Japan. In modern use, silk is not the only fabric employed. Organdy, nylon, dacron, and wire cloth screens can be used effectively.

Organdy is an inexpensive substitute for silk, but it does not have the durability, nor the uniformity of weave. It may not remain as tightly stretched on the frame as does silk, especially under damp conditions.

The synthetic fibers, nylon and dacron, possess excellent tensile strength, but their high polish does not provide as effective an anchor for the stencil as does silk.

Wire thread, particularly stainless steel, can be woven into an extremely fine, uniform mesh which will last indefinitely. Such screens are used for the printing of glass, electrical circuits, and many varieties of packaging where a large run is required. Metal screens are not easily stretched on the frame, nor do hand-cut stencils adhere to them as well as to silk.

Stretching the Screen. The silk, or other fabric, must be stretched drum-tight across the frame. It is tacked to the wooden frame with tacks or staples; the edge of the silk is often faced with cloth tape in order to prevent the tacks from ripping the silk.

The fabric is bound to the edges of the frame in order to prevent leakage of the ink. This is accomplished by lacquering the tacked edges and covering them, when dry, with gummed paper tape. The tape is then coated with lacquer to protect it during the printing and the washing out of a glue stencil.

Several mechanical screen-stretching devices, and special frames that require no tacking, are available.

New fabric generally has a surface deposit of wax or other sizing agent. This is removed after the screen has been stretched by scrubbing the fabric with a pumice-type detergent. The scrubbing roughens the fibers, causing better adhesion of the stencil.

Cleaning the Screen. In order to prepare the screen for reuse with a new stencil, all of the leftover ink and the previous stencil must be removed with an appropriate solvent. The reusability of the screen is governed less by the nature of its fabric than by the thoroughness with which it has been cleaned; proper cleaning will prolong its life.

THE STENCIL

There are four methods of preparing the stencil. The first two are more applicable as art techniques than for commercial printing.

The Blocked-out Stencil. In the blocked-out stencil method, the nonprinting area of the screen is masked with lacquer, shellac, or glue. After the design has been traced onto the screen, the liquid is applied to the screen with a brush. The liquid is painted around the outline of the design. When dry, the liquid blocks the pores of the screen, preventing the passage of ink. A reverse image may be obtained by coating the design itself with the blocking liquid.

Since the blocking liquid is difficult to manipulate with a brush, particularly when intricate detail is required, this method has little application commercially. After printing, the screen is cleaned with a solvent capable of dissolving the particular blocking liquid.

THE TUSCHE-GLUE STENCIL. The tusche-glue method is, like lithography, based upon the incompatibility of oil and water. Tusche is a black, free-flowing, oily liquid, soluble in kerosene or turpentine. The design is painted onto the screen with the tusche. When the tusche sets, the entire screen is covered with a solution of equal parts of glue and water. When the glue dries, it forms a hard covering over the screen, trapping the tusche underneath. The screen is then washed down with kerosene. The kerosene has no effect upon the glue alone, but it loosens the tusche and causes the glue coating over it to wash off. This leaves a hard glue stencil, with openings in the areas that were formerly occupied by the tusche.

The tusche-glue stencil is generally employed by serigraphers, since it allows the use of drybrush and other textural effects. The No. 2 litho pencil can also be used for this purpose. The edges of the printed image are too rough to meet commercial standards, and delicate detail is often difficult to achieve. Sharper image edges may be obtained by sizing the screen with a starch and water solution before applying the tusche.

THE HAND-CUT STENCIL. The hand-cut stencil is made from a layer of Profilm or Nufilm laminated to the surface of a transparent backing sheet. An advantage of this type of stencil is that the design may be cut while it is laid directly over the artwork; there is no need to trace or transfer the design onto the screen. The backing sheet holds the free-standing areas in position until the stencil can be transferred to the screen.

The stencil is placed over the artwork and the design is cut on the stencil with a knife. There are several types of swivelling knives, parallel-blade knives, and cutting compasses manufactured to facilitate this operation. Care must be taken that the knife does not cut through the paper backing; only the laminated layer is cut. When the design has been cut, the film in the printing areas is removed, leaving all the non-printing areas held together with the backing sheet. The stencil is cut in positive form.

When the stencil has been cut and the printing areas peeled away, it is placed, face up, on the underside of the stretched fabric. The upper side of the screen is rubbed with a rag soaked in thinner. The thinner softens the film sufficiently to cause it to adhere to the screen. When the film is properly attached, the backing sheet is peeled off and the screen is ready for printing.

The hand-cut stencil produces an image with a clean, sharp edge. Glue may be used in conjunction with the hand-cut stencil in order to obtain soft edges in desired areas. It is painted directly onto the screen after the stencil has been attached.

A well-cut stencil is good for several thousand impressions. It may be retained for reprinting or may be cleaned with a solvent in order that the silk may be reused for a new stencil.

THE PHOTOGRAPHIC STENCIL. In the photographic stencil method, the stencil is produced with an emulsion that is sensitive to light. There are two methods of producing the photographic stencil: the *direct* and the *transfer* method.

In the direct method, a coat of the sensitized emulsion is put directly on the screen. As in the other photochemical processes, the action of light causes the emulsion to harden. It is necessary to harden the nonprinting areas so that they will block the passage of ink through the screen. As a result, a *film positive,* photographed from the original design, is employed for photographic stencils. This positive is contact-printed onto the emulsion.

When the nonprinting areas have been hardened by the light action, the soft emulsion remaining over the printing areas is washed off. This leaves bare screen in the printing areas of the design.

The transfer method employs a sensitized transfer sheet which must be attached to the screen after it has been exposed. There are two types of transfer film; one type is sensitized by the operator, the other is presensitized by the manufacturer.

The steps for the preparation of a transfer film stencil are as follows:

1. A photographic film positive is made from the original art.
2. The transfer film is sensitized. This process varies with different types of film. It involves coating the film with an applicable light-sensitive solution, using a tray or a brush. Presensitized film eliminates this step.
3. The positive is contact-printed onto the sensitized film. A frontwards-reading image is produced on the film emulsion.
4. The film is developed by immersion in hot water. The printing areas, represented by the unhardened gelatin, will wash away. Presensitized transfer films are developed with chemical developing solutions.
5. The transfer film stencil is fastened to the screen. The stencil is placed underneath the screen and the excess moisture is blotted up

with sheets of newsprint. The blotting process causes the emulsion to adhere to the fibers of the screen.

6. After adhesion of the stencil, the backing sheet is removed.

There are several types of sensitized stencil.

THE CARBON-TISSUE STENCIL. The carbon-tissue stencil requires a double transfer of the stencil image. The operator-sensitized emulsion tissue is placed on a plastic backing sheet during exposure. After exposure, the backing sheet is removed and the carbon tissue is placed on a sheet of glass. After washing, it is fastened to the screen. The gelatin of the carbon tissue is colored black in order to make the image readily visible after wash-out.

THE ULANO WET-SHOT STENCIL. The wet-shot film stencil is a simplified operator-sensitized stencil, requiring little knowledge of photographic technique for its use. An advantage of this method is that the film may be used immediately after it has been sensitized. During the sensitizing operation, the film is placed on wrapping paper which serves as a backing sheet. After contact exposure and adhesion to the screen, the backing sheet is peeled off.

DUPONT PRESENSITIZED STENCIL FILM. DuPont presensitized film requires no film positive. The speed of the emulsion is sufficiently fast to enable exposure by direct photographic projection from the art. Because of the film's high light-sensitivity, it must be processed in the darkroom.

KODAK EKTAGRAPH FILM. Kodak Ektagraph film is presensitized by the manufacturer. The emulsion of this film is sensitized silver—ready for immediate exposure. Although possessing a high exposure speed, it can be processed under ordinary incandescent light. The manufacturer claims that excellent results can be obtained with both halftone and full-color copy.

Although the method is free from the artistic limitations of the conventional stencil, designs created specifically for silk screen are best handled in a flat-color poster technique. Considerable progress has been made in the development of a stencil capable of reproducing halftones, and creditable results have been obtained by those firms willing to put forth the effort. However, the ability of the average screen shop to produce good halftone work is still questionable. The use of silk screen to print process color is also a questionable practice. It might be practical to use color-corrected lithographic positives in an attempt to produce stencils, but separation solely for the purpose of silk-screen printing leaves much to be desired in terms of color quality.

Situations may arise wherein it is absolutely essential to reproduce a halftone design with silk screen. In this event, firms capable of handling the job can doubtless be found. However, it is still ill-advised to design a halftone silk-screen job if it can possibly be avoided. Good artistry implies the selection of the proper printing process for the art or for the execution of art to take advantage of the intrinsic nature of the printing process required.

PRINTING

The screen frame is hinged to the printing surface—either a flat table or some supporting device designed to hold a three-dimensional object in the proper printing position. The object to be printed will be placed in the printing position by hand. If this object is paper, corner guides are employed to make certain that it will be inserted in proper register with the stencil.

The hinged screen is brought into contact with the paper. The ink or paint is poured into a corner of the tray formed by the frame with the

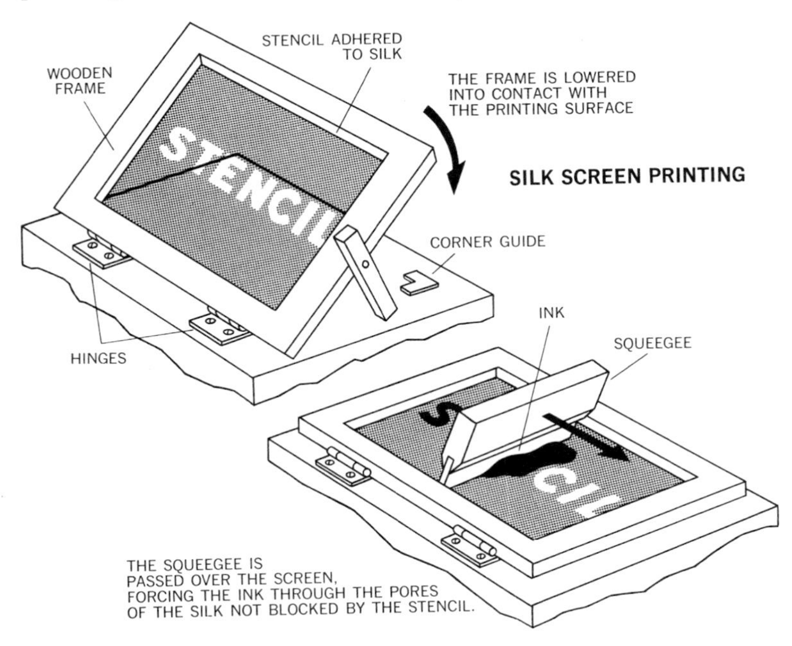

screen on its underside. The ink need not be replenished after each impression, but is used until the supply is almost exhausted.

The paint is scraped across the screen with the rubber squeegee. The squeegee should be wider than the design, so that one "pass" will be sufficient to force the ink through the pores of the screen.

The screen is lifted and the printed piece is removed. Most screen frames are equipped with some device that will cause them to remain in the "up" position while the next sheet is being inserted.

In multicolor printing, there must be a separate screen for each color. There is no limit on the number of screens—thus, the number of colors—that may be printed. Accurate registration, both in the screens and in the positioning of the paper, must be maintained.

As previously mentioned, silk screen may be used to print on almost any surface. It may also use any color, in any of a great variety of inks and paints. Colors may be opaque, transparent, glossy, or matte. Lacquers, enamels, fluorescent paints, plastic colors, and textile colors are all readily used with the silk-screen process. Silk-screen printing produces a heavy layer of ink. This heaviness is responsible for the hand-painted appearance of screen prints. This heaviness contributes to the coarseness of attempted halftone reproduction and poses considerable drying problems, but some of these have been overcome by mechanical printing developments.

Except in the case of small type, or other intricate detail, most stencils are hand cut. The experienced cutter can cut anything the artist can draw, usually with a higher degree of precision. As a result, it is generally wasted effort to preseparate silk-screen art unless photographic screens are to be used. The stencil cutter will probably cut and register his separations with greater accuracy than can be expected of the average mechanical artist.

Automatic printing equipment

It is possible to go into the silk-screen printing business with less capital outlay than for any other area of the graphic arts. All one needs are screen frames, a printing surface, and an adequate arrangement for drying the prints. Plus, of course, silk, stencil material, and the necessary inks. As a result, many screen shops are small, two-man operations, even though the quality of their work may be excellent. One of the advantages of the process is that it may be economically used for extremely short runs. Small shops are ideal for this purpose.

The versatility of the process, with its ability to print on almost any surface, has brought it into widespread use. No longer is silk screen used solely to print signs and displays. Bottles, glasses, souvenir ash trays, cans, metal drums, and numerous other containers are printed with silk screen. Printed electrical circuits are silk screened. The metal signs used in the cockpits of aircraft and spacecraft are silk screened. Decalcomanias, wallpaper, and textiles are printed with the process.

Such popularity has necessitated automated production. Three types of automatic equipment are available for the silk-screen process: (1) automatic equipment for printing cylindrical objects, (2) automatic equipment for printing flat objects, and (3) automatic drying equipment. Larger silk-screen shops are equipped to perform die-cutting. This is usually accomplished with a steel die mounted in a small platen letterpress. Equipment for applying flock (finely cut cloth fibers), and tinsel may also be employed.

A SUMMARY OF THE SILK-SCREEN PROCESS

Silk-screen printing is a stencil medium in which a woven screen is used to hold the elements of the stencil in place. The stencil may be hand-applied to the screen, hand-cut separately and then fastened to the screen, or produced photographically. The printing pigment is forced through the mesh of the screen onto the printing surface.

Silk screen, known as serigraphy, enjoys considerable popularity as a fine art medium.

The screen cutter applies considerable personal skill to his craft. His judgment and accuracy with regard to color separation and registration is probably more reliable than that of the average artist.

The process can print any number of impressions, in any color, in a wide variety of pigments. It can print on a great variety of three-dimensional objects. However, it is not able to compete with the long runs of letterpress and lithography.

As a line medium, the process is unexcelled. Halftone and process-color work, although possible to some degree, have not attained a quality comparable to other printing processes.

Due to the simplicity of the printing equipment, and the fact that once the stencil has been produced there is little preparation of the printing equipment, silk screen is an ideal medium for printing in small quantities.

10 THE PREPARATION OF ILLUSTRATIVE MATTER

When the layout has been approved and work on the finished art commences, it is the illustration—drawing or photograph—that is begun first. The illustration may take a longer time to execute than any other element of the job. The artwork should be undertaken as far in advance of the job deadline as possible, in order that the client may evaluate it and any necessary changes or corrections may be accomplished. It is important to produce illustrative matter which satisfies the client, as this is the element of the finished art on which the greatest profit can be realized.

It may be necessary to photograph the illustration for inclusion on the mechanical art. The illustration should be finished before the mechanical is begun so that time may be allotted for photography, as well as to make sure of proper fit.

LINE ART

Line art may be produced by a variety of methods and techniques.

The line drawing

The simplest form of illustration to reproduce is the one-color line drawing. Such an illustration results in a printing plate which does not require the use of the halftone dot. In order to provide copy of maximum intensity for the platemaking camera, a dense black drawing ink is used. Each line is drawn in full value; there is no dilution of the pigment. There are five types of line drawing:

THE OUTLINE DRAWING. The outline drawing is rendered with pen or brush and ink, utilizing lines of uniform or varying thickness, without recourse to any solid or tonal areas. The character of the line is dictated by the type of pen or brush that is used and by the surface texture and absorbent qualities of the paper on which it is drawn.

THE LINE AND SOLID AREA DRAWING. The use of line and solid areas produces a drawing of strong contrast. There are no middle values. This type of drawing is usually rendered with brush and ink, since an attempt to fill in large areas with a pen results in the destruction of the paper surface. The dark areas in such a drawing should be well organized, so that the eye can make the difficult transition from white to black without the assistance of middle values.

THE LINE AND TONE DRAWING. A line and tone drawing is one in which intermediate tonal areas are used to form transitions between white and black areas, thus heightening the illusion of form or texture. Tonal areas may be produced by patterned pen or brush strokes, or through the use of special shading films or papers which have been designed to aid in the rendering of such tonality. Although each line in the tonal area is full-value black, the eye measures the totality of white and black in these areas and visualizes them as gray tones, in the same manner as it perceives the halftone dot.

There are various techniques for artist-produced tone:

Pen strokes provide a great variety of tonal and textural effects. The pen strokes may be free and loose, or precise and mechanical. Ranging from closely-spaced parallel lines to cross-hatching, stippling, and scribbly effects, they constitute a part of the vocabulary of the individual artist.

Brush strokes are bolder than the pen stroke and artistically more sensitive. The brush may be utilized for a wide range of tonal effects. The nature of the pen and brush stroke is left completely to the imagination and discretion of the artist, thus affording him the complete freedom of his medium.

Dry brush technique provides an interesting effect when a brush from which most of the ink has been wiped, is dragged across the surface of rough textured paper. This technique deposits pigment on the irregularly-shaped spots of the paper surface, creating a stippled, feathery effect that lends character to both line and tonal areas. The resulting texture is determined by the speed of the brush stroke and by the roughness and absorbency of the paper surface. The paper utilized may range from rough illustration board to water-color paper, Japanese rice paper, and blotting paper.

Stipple or spatter may be used for tonal or textured effects. This is done by stippling directly on the drawing with a stiff brush, by applying the ink with a sponge, or by applying it with a swab of cotton or cloth twisted around the end of a stick or a brush handle. Spatter areas may be produced by rubbing an ink-filled toothbrush with a small stick, by rubbing a toothbrush over a fine-mesh screen, or by spraying ink directly from the bottle with a fixatif sprayer or an atomizer. Care must be taken to keep the texture coarse.

Stipple or coquille board is commonly known as Ross board—after a well-known manufacturer. It is Bristol board whose surface has been embossed with thousands of tiny raised patterns. These boards are available in a variety of pattern styles, ranging from dots to irregular shapes. A tonal effect is accomplished by rubbing the surface with litho (grease) pencil. This deposits pigment on the high spots of the embossed surface pattern. The harder the pencil pressure, the more the pigment is forced into the intervening depressions and the darker the tonality becomes. Used for cartoons and newspaper illustrations, where speed is a critical factor, stipple boards produce a texture that is somewhat cliché in character, since the nature of the texture is determined by the pattern embossed on the board rather than by the discretion of the artist.

THE LINE AND MECHANICAL TONE DRAWING. Mechanical tone is textural tone that is produced either with prepared shading sheets, which are cut out and fastened to the illustration, or by drawing on an impregnated paper whose tonal pattern may be made visible by the application of a developing fluid. A line and solid-area drawing is made first. This drawing is always rendered in black ink, so that the mechanical tone will not appear in the solid areas. After the line drawing has been rendered, the mechanical tone is applied. The areas which will contain the tone should be carefully planned in advance, so that they will assist the eye in making the transition from white to black areas. There is little to be gained by covering the entire drawing with a tonal pattern.

Mechanical tones are uniform in their over-all texture; each pattern produces a single tone which does not vary. The tones are available in a wide variety of patterns. It is not considered good practice to include too many tone patterns in a single drawing, and care should be taken that those used are compatible. Mechanical tone, as is any other type of tonal rendering, is utilized in an attempt to introduce clarity and illusory dimension to the drawing, not to decorate it to the point of confusion.

Since mechanical tone produces a regimented, rather than a random pattern, its use imparts a precise appearance to the work. Therefore, the line drawing should be executed with similar precision. It is an ideal medium for the rendering of hard goods, technical illustrations, and similar work. Mechanical tone finds widespread use in the production of black-and-white charts; it serves as a means of differentiation where the use of color is prohibited. There are several methods of applying mechanical tone:

Shading film consists of uniform tonal patterns, which are printed on transparent, adhesive-backed sheets. It is available in over 200 textures—parallel lines, dots, cross-hatching, stipple, etc.—in both positive and negative form. Each variety of texture is produced in different weights of line or dot, so that different values may be obtained with similar patterns.

The film is removed from its protective backing sheet and placed over the line drawing. It is cut to the desired shape with a razor blade or a frisket knife; the adhesive back will cause the shape to remain temporarily in position while the remainder of the sheet is being removed. The film may be of the pressure-sensitive (self adhering) variety, or may be coated with a wax adhesive which can be activated by burnishing the film with the edge of a triangle or the back of a comb. Once burnished, the film becomes difficult to remove. Some of the more popular types of shading film are known as Zip-A-Tone, Add-A-Tint, Contak, and Transograph.

Craftint engraver's top sheet is a transparent shading film, printed with opaque patterns which may be scraped off where not wanted. This type of film is especially useful for creating highlight areas, but care must be taken not to scrape off the pattern accidentally.

Craftint board is three-ply Bristol board, impregnated with an invisible tonal pattern which may be brought out by applying a colorless developer with a brush or pen. As in the mechanical tone drawing, a line drawing is made first. Available in over fifty textural patterns, "Singletone" board contains one tone. "Doubletone" contains two patterns on the same board; one a light and one a dark tone, which may be brought out with the use of two developing solutions.

Engraver's tint patterns may be added to illustrations by the engraver (or the litho platemaker), in accordance with the artist's instructions, either by the Ben Day process—which prints and etches textured patterns on the plate—or by stripping transparent pattern sheets onto the film negatives. This method is especially practical when necessary enlargement or reduction prevents the use of shading film on the original art. When the engraver or platemaker is to add the tint, the desired pattern is specified and the tonal areas are indicated on the original drawing with a light blue wash or with blue pencil. The blue will not photograph—thus will not appear on the negative—but its presence on the original art will serve as a guide to the proper location of the tonal areas.

SCRATCHBOARD. Scratchboard represents a unique art technique which may be utilized to duplicate the effect of wood engraving. The board is Bristol, coated with a thick, white clay surface. The artist covers it with black poster paint or drawing ink and, with a scriber, scratches white lines into the black areas. The scribed line cuts through the black surface coating into the white clay layer, producing a line which is crisp and precise. Correction may be accomplished by re-inking and rescribing, provided the original lines have not been scratched too deeply. If the surface is coated with drawing ink, care should be taken that the ink does not crystallize; this will cause the ink to flake off, resulting in unclean, ragged lines. A wide variety of scribing tools is available, including ones which produce multiple lines.

Scratchboard is a crisp, precise medium which, in skillful hands, can duplicate the technique of the black-line engraver. Beginners in scratchboard tend to blacken the entire surface and work in a white-line technique. The novelty of scratching the lines becomes too tempting and soon the whole work becomes covered with tonal values, with little regard for solid blacks or whites. If a white-line technique is desired, it is simpler to execute the drawing on ordinary board in either pen or brush and ink, then make a reverse plate or order a photostat negative. The accomplished scratchboard artist generally works in a positive, black-line technique, even when he desires the background to be black. This approach requires a bit more advance planning, but its mastery is well worth the effort.

Scratchboard is an ideal surface upon which to execute precise hand lettering—either positive or negative. The fact that the black pigment may be scraped away enables the letterer to clean his edges to a razor sharpness.

The line drawing is produced by means of a line plate—there is no recourse to the halftone screen. It is considerably less expensive than the halftone plate. In letterpress, zinc plates are used for short runs, while copper is utilized for longer runs for finely detailed work. Standard lithographic plates are employed for that process. Unless the line drawing represents a minor element of the layout, line reproduction should not be attempted with the gravure process, since each line will necessarily bear a screen pattern.

If the plate is made from a film positive, rather than a negative, the printed image will be in reverse values from the original art. If it is necessary to evaluate a reverse drawing before platemaking, a photographic negative may be made both for examination purposes and for mounting on the mechanical art. It is, of course, possible to produce the original drawing in reverse, but it is generally easier to draw in the positive and reverse photographically.

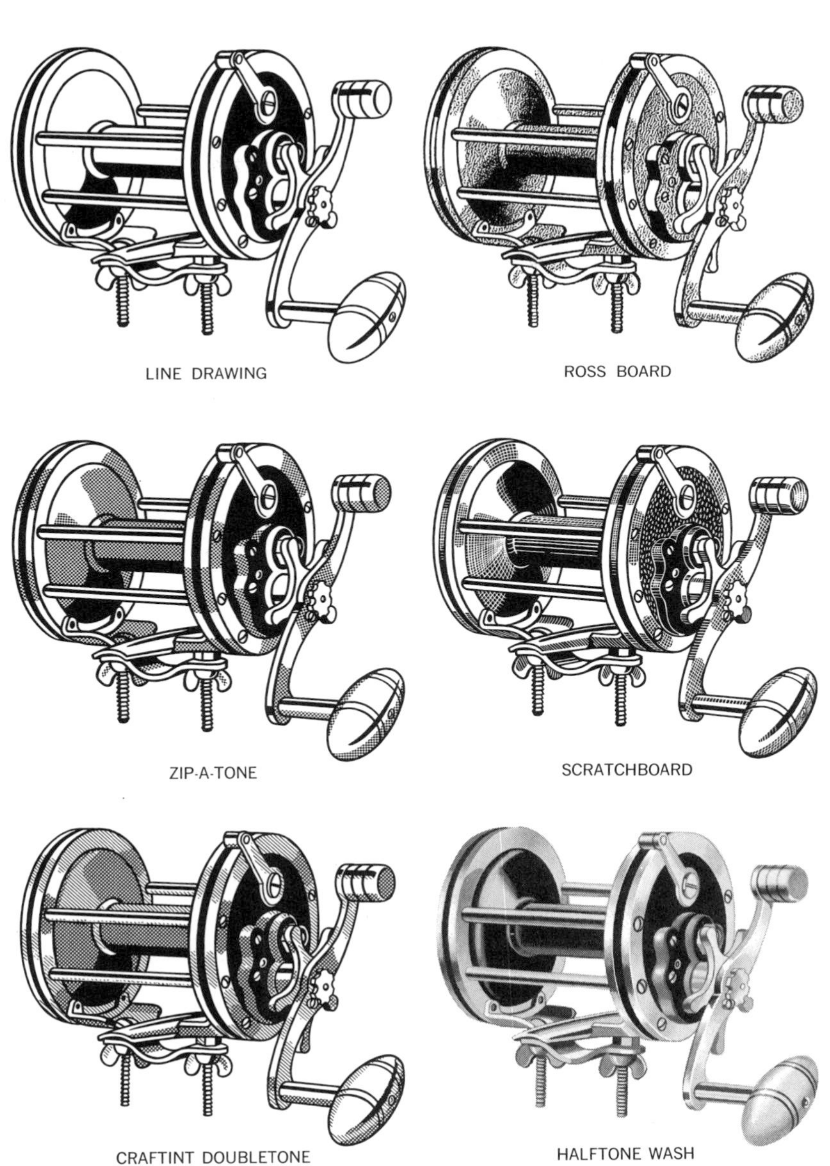

VARIOUS BLACK-AND-WHITE RENDERING TECHNIQUES

The criterion of good line drawing for reproduction is that the lines be spaced far enough apart so that there is no danger of fill-in, and that they be substantially thick so that they will not disappear on the film negative or break away during the press run. Excessive areas of solid color tend to retain ink and eventually flood. Sizeable solid areas should be avoided.

Line art should always be prepared in black, regardless of the color in which it is to ultimately print. Care should be taken that the ink does not become diluted; nor should it be allowed to bleed because the paper is too porous. Fuzzy line edges, dirt, and fingerprints should be avoided. All preliminary pencil lines should be carefully erased. An artgum eraser is best for this purpose, since a kneaded rubber eraser tends to dull the luster of the ink. All artgum residue should be carefully brushed away.

Line art is preferably executed one-and-a-half or two times the finished size, for the convenience of the artist. Reduction tends to minimize imperfections, but it is reasonable to expect that there will be no imperfections in professionally executed artwork. The final size of the art which is to appear should always be kept in mind. This is especially important where tonal effects are present—either those drawn by the artist or produced with shading film. Too much reduction will cause these areas to fill in. Most shading film manufacturers provide charts which show their patterns in various reductions, enabling the artist to foresee what will happen to the artwork when it is reduced. Viewing the drawing through a reducing lens will help the artist to anticipate troublesome platemaking problems. Enlargement poses no problem of fill-in, but lines that are too greatly enlarged may appear ragged and cumbersome.

When ordering plates, the desired size of each illustration should be carefully specified, with an arrow between perpendicular lines drawn at each horizontal or vertical extremity. Blue pencil should be used in order to prevent these instructions from appearing on the film negative; film used for platemaking is not sensitive to blue. The type of metal required should be noted. The number of plates, duplicate originals, electros, or mats should be specified. Even if duplicate plates are not to be made until a later date, they should be noted, so that the engraver will etch to the proper depth.

In some illustrations, especially spot drawings, the vertical axis is not always obvious. Since the angle at which the plate is squared off or "blocked" will determine its verticality in the press, an indication of the desired vertical should be given and the engraver instructed to block at a particular angle.

Illustrations produced on thin paper should be mounted before shipment to the engraver. All original art should be covered with a tissue overlay and a paper flap for protection.

Line reproduction from continuous-tone art

It is possible to convert halftone art into line art through the use of various photographic techniques. Such methods will produce the effect of a black-line engraving or the mezzotint, while eliminating the laborious techniques of the original processes. Photographic line illustrations are finding widespread use for newspaper advertising. They may be photographically produced from continuous-tone original art in the following ways:

1. A contrasting photograph is made in which all tones will appear as either solid blacks or whites. Contrasting developer is used. The subject matter must be appropriate; it must be capable of retaining its identity when reduced to this form.
2. The copy is photographed through a single-line screen. This screen consists of etched parallel lines, running in one direction only. They may be horizontal, vertical, wavy, or may be arranged in concentric circles. There are no crossed lines; therefore, no dot pattern is produced. The resulting effect is a linear pattern which varies in thickness as value changes occur in the image, similar to the appearance of a black-line wood engraving.
3. The negative may be contact-printed through any irregular texture that is capable of transmitting light through the interstices. This breaks the image into tiny, irregular shapes, as in the mezzotint. The resulting photoprint is photographed as line copy by the platemaker. A wide variety of textural effects may be obtained by printing through a loosely woven texture such as cheesecloth, a silk stocking, or wire mesh screening. Sheets of shading film may be used.

It is possible to make a line conversion of halftone art by placing acetate over the negative and tracing the image with black drawing ink. The line acetate tracing is then contact-printed onto photographic paper.

HALFTONE ART

Definitions

Halftone Art. Any continuous-tone positive art (black and white, or color) that will require reproduction by means of the screened halftone dot. Pencil and pastel drawings, wash and opaque drawings, oil paintings, and photographs all fall in this category.

Square Halftone. A halftone whose entire area has a tonal value and whose edges have been finished off in either a square or a rectangular shape. A ruled border may or may not be utilized.

Silhouette Halftone. A halftone whose background has been removed, leaving the image in silhouette form. The silhouetting may be performed with white paint on the original copy, by opaquing the film negative, or by etching away the dot formations on the engraved plate or on the film positive. An outline is seldom utilized—the shape of the image is considered to be self-containing. Care should be taken that the values at the edges of the image are strong enough to provide a differentiation from the background on which it is to be printed. The silhouetting process is most effectively accomplished by the artist on the original art, since at this stage he can readily determine if any of the edges need strengthening. It is easier to observe minor details of the silhouette shape on the original art or photograph—details which might be obliterated when silhouetting on film or plate.

Vignette Halftone. A halftone whose outer edges fade off gradually into the background. This effect is accomplished by airbrushing the edges of the original to blend into the background, or by chemical (acid) reduction of the sizes of the outermost dots on the film positive or the engraved plate in order to achieve the desired tonal gradation.

Drop-out Halftone. Also known as a highlight halftone, this is a halftone in which certain areas are highlighted—the halftone dot is eliminated in order to permit the paper to show through as a contrasting or "highlight" effect. This is accomplished by dot etching the film positive or re-etching the engraved plate. The *magenta contact screen,* which contains dyed magenta rather than black lines, can be manipulated with filters in order to produce drop-out areas on the film negative. Drop-out halftones are considerably more expensive than regular halftones.

The drop-out is much more effectively utilized for the reproduction of the artist's drawing than for the photograph. Drop-outs in photographs, unless carefully handled, have a tendency to look contrived and artificial. Several manufacturers produce processes by which illustrations may be prepared for an automatic drop-out and silhouette. The highlight areas are rendered with a medium which will fluoresce under ultraviolet light, eliminating dot formation on the film negative.

The black-and-white halftone drawing

Any drawing utilizing a medium in which the value of the pigment becomes reduced—either by less pressure, dilution, or the addition of white pigment—is a halftone drawing. Such a drawing must be printed by the halftone process. In order to reproduce well, the pigment must be strong enough to record its tonal value on the film negative with a minimum of value loss. As a result, opaque pigment reproduces more faithfully than transparent pigment or pigment which has been smudged over the paper.

THE PENCIL DRAWING. Pencil drawings are seldom used commercially because the pencil is incapable of producing a black that compares with the strength and opacity of ink. With pencil, the value scale is condensed; the darkest pencil areas seldom represent more than an 80-per-cent value, and the highlight areas tend to become smudged, thus increasing their value. This gives the pencil rendering a flat, lifeless appearance which will appear even more so when screened. If the job requires a pencil rendering, its value range should be spread as wide as possible in a deliberate attempt to obtain maximum contrast. The blackest areas may be reinforced with drawing ink and the highlights painted white. There is no point in making a pencil drawing for line reproduction—the value of the pencil line is not strong enough to insure good reproduction.

It is possible to produce charcoal, crayon, or litho pencil drawings in either line or halftone. The choice is dependent on the paper used—this governs the texture of the tonal areas. If the tonal texture is coarse, black, and has not been smudged, line reproduction is possible. Otherwise, a halftone plate must be ordered. In a line reproduction, some of the darker areas will fill in and some of the finer specks in the tonal areas will be lost. Charcoal and litho crayon drawings give better results than pencil drawings, since the blacks tend to be stronger.

THE BLACK-AND-WHITE WASH DRAWING. A wash drawing is a water-color rendering that has been executed in a single hue. It is painted with transparent color in which the values are reduced by the addition of water. When so diluted, the color becomes more transparent, thereby allowing the paper to show through and reduce its value. It is possible to make a wash drawing using diluted drawing ink, but water-color pigment is more finely ground and generally produces better results. The more diluted the color, the weaker it becomes and the less its ability to properly expose the film negative. Gray wash areas can be expected to lose 10 per cent in value when screened. As a result, a wash drawing should be deliberately executed in a full value range so that it will not weaken too much when reproduced. If the lower-middle values are too subtle, the cameraman must overexpose to retain them and the upper-middle values will fill in. If the upper-middle values are too dark, the cameraman will lose his lower values if he attempts to lighten them. Properly executed wash drawings have a tonal subtlety which is ideal for the rendering of fashion drawings and soft-goods illustrations.

Wash drawings should be rendered on water-color paper. Many artists make the mistake of attempting to render them on illustration board. Such board is mounted Bristol, and it does not have the capacity for absorbing the excessive water required for the rendering of a light wash area. As a result, the paper surface is destroyed; the wash becomes difficult to manipulate and takes on a scrubbed or muddy appearance.

Wash drawings must be reproduced in halftone. The more subtle the tonal values, the finer the screen that should be used. Newspaper advertisers utilize a good many wash drawings, due to the speed with which they can be executed. Since newspapers require a coarse screen, strong values are desirable. One-color wash drawings should be executed in black, regardless of the color in which they will ultimately print.

THE BLACK-AND-WHITE OPAQUE DRAWING. The most suitable medium for the rendering of halftone art—from a reproduction standpoint—is opaque or "poster" color, also known as "designer's color." Poster color is often referred to as "tempera," which is inaccurate. Tempera is an opaque pigment which employs a colloidal medium, such as egg white, as a vehicle. Poster color uses water as a vehicle. Its values are reduced by the addition of white pigment. This assures a strong deposit of pigment, even in the lighter areas, producing the necessary strength for good reproduction.

Tubes of standardized opaque grays are manufactured for the retoucher and may be conveniently used by the illustrator. In the absence of these, black and white poster paint will suffice. Opaque color is more difficult to handle than transparent color. Care must be taken that solid areas remain flat and do not streak. This is accomplished by mixing the pigment to a proper consistency—approximately that of heavy cream. Edges, especially those of a high value contrast, are more difficult to soften or blend than with water color. It is often necessary to introduce an intermediate value in order to produce a smooth blending of color; such blending requires a high degree of skill and patience. Opaque paint is normally used for airbrush rendering. Use of the airbrush permits an extremely subtle blending of tonal values.

Opaque drawings are reproduced in halftone. Since stronger values are usually produced with opaque pigments, opaque renderings reproduce well with a coarse screen. Airbrush rendering should not be reproduced in coarse screen unless it has been executed with considerable contrast.

The drop-out processes

When continuous-tone original art is photographed through the halftone screen, *every* area of the negative receives a dot pattern, even in the lightest portions. In the normal halftone, the dot pattern present in the highlight areas can be minimized, but the pattern seldom disappears completely. Thus, there are no pure white highlights.

Even a white background will produce a minimal dot pattern when screened. When halftone art is to appear as a silhouette, it must either be drawn on a white background, masked with a paper mask, or outlined with white paint. This will still produce a faint dot pattern which must either be opaqued on the negative or be etched out by the platemaker. The platemaker may produce pure white highlights by opaquing, etching, or filtering with the magenta contact screen. This requires additional work on the part of the platemaker, and results in considerable more expense than the normal halftone plate.

Drop-out processes are a method of preparing halftone art in such a manner that the whites will automatically drop out when photographed, causing a complete absence of dot pattern in the corresponding areas of the negative. In most cases, this is accomplished by the addition of a fluorescent material to the artist's pigment. When photographed under ultraviolet light, often through a special filter, the dots close up in the highlight areas of the negative, thus becoming nonprinting or pure white areas.

The Fluorographic Process. The Fluorographic process offers the artist a choice of four different fluorescent media: a solvent to replace water in the execution of wash drawings, drawing pencils, a set of standard-hue water colors, and flat retouching grays in five values. Artwork prepared with these media looks like any other drawing to the naked eye. The solvent in the media strongly absorbs ultraviolet light, so that when the art is photographed through an ultraviolet filter, it will reflect only visible light. This visible light produces a normal dot pattern. The non-painted areas of the background and the highlights reflect ultraviolet light onto the film negative, causing additional exposure which closes in the dot pattern. These become pure white nonprinting areas. In this manner, drop-out highlights and silhouettes are automatically achieved with this process.

THE KEMART PROCESS. In the Kemart process, the artist works on illustration or Bristol board which has been especially treated to fluoresce under ultraviolet light. The fluorescence is in the paper fibers and is not a surface coating, permitting the use of erasers and scratching techniques. A fluorescent white paint is available for highlighting purposes. Any convenient drawing medium may be used—pencil, wash, or opaque grays.

The white areas of the drawing—the white, unworked areas of the board and the painted highlights—fluoresce under ultraviolet light. This fluorescence causes additional exposure of the film neagtive and produces unscreened, nonprinted areas.

Photographs may also be used. They are cut out in silhouette shape, mounted on the Kemart board, and highlighted with the fluorescent white paint.

THE KROMO-LITE PROCESS. The Kromo-lite process is widely used for the rendering of drop-out illustrations for newspaper advertisements. The artist mixes a solution called Hi-lite with his black pigment instead of the usual water. He then proceeds to execute a wash drawing in the normal manner.

The platemaker sprays the art with Kromo-lite spray, which turns the gray washes greenish yellow. Blacks and highlights remain unaltered. In photographing the copy, two shots are taken. The first uses a filter to neutralize the yellow so that the negative carries an overall screen. The second, shot through a different filter, registers the yellow as a solid black, producing a transparent area on the negative. Since no screen is used for the second shot, only the whites will appear on the second negative, appearing as unscreened black nonprinting areas. When sandwiched together for contact printing onto the plate, the black areas on the second negative mask out the dot patterns in the corresponding areas of the first, completely eliminating the dot pattern in both the background and highlight areas.

Obviously, if any of these techniques is employed, it will require the services of a platemaker equipped with the appropriate ultraviolet equipment.

Multicolor and full-color drawing

Media for color drawings include pastel, water color, opaque poster (designer's) color, and oil. As in black-and-white drawing, the more opaque the pigment, the better it will reproduce.

It is possible to produce multicolor art in line. Line color may be preseparated by the artist, or camera separated by the platemaker. Preseparation entails few difficulties other than accurate registration of the color overlays. The number of colors which may be used is limited only by the patience of the artist and the budget of the advertiser.

Preseparation of continuous-tone art represents a considerably more difficult problem. Although there are methods by which this may be accomplished to some degree, continuous-tone color art is generally camera separated. It is always printed in halftone. Fake color process will give a full-color effect but without any continuous tone; the various color areas will be flat, except for some modeling which may be attempted with the black plate.

Full-color illustration, destined for process printing, may be prepared in any number and combination of colors desired. The purpose of the printed result will be the deciding factor between the use of three- or four-color process.

Most illustration which is found undesirable is so because of inept execution and failure to serve the purposes of the advertiser, rather than from any nonreproducible qualities.

The work of an artistic genius is worthless if he has missed the job deadline.

A common cause for the rejection of an illustration is the fact that it has been executed in an incorrect size. When reduced, it will not fit into its allocated area.

Good halftone art should have a maximum definition between values. It is easy to be fooled by contrasty art. This may appear to be most dramatic, but the middle values, which should be clearly defined, succumb to the opposite ends of the value scale. Detail, which should be present in the middle values, is lacking.

Flat art is the opposite of contrasty art. It is characterized by a loss of detail which should be expressed with darker areas. This is an undesirable situation and should be corrected by the introduction of greater contrast.

Paper has a strong influence upon tonal reproduction. The grayer the surface, the weaker the highlight area. Hard, glossy paper produces the best highlight areas. The highlights become duller as the paper texture becomes coarser. Coarse paper will also cause black areas to become grayer.

KODAK FLUORESCENT WATER COLORS. Kodak fluorescent water colors are colored pigments which fluoresce under ultraviolet light. This fluorescence produces an increased density on the separation negatives, greatly reducing the amount of color correction required.

The colors are available in a set of eighteen hues, plus white and opaque gray. The brighter hues have been grayed by the manufacturer to better match the process inks. The artist can work with the assurance that his drawing will not present difficulties in reproduction. The colors are applied in the same manner as normal water colors, except that black is used in conjunction with another color to produce a dark area. Many artists have been taught to darken a color by introducing its complement, rather than black. In the Kodak process, the black separation is made by photographing the drawing under infrared light. The use of red to darken green will disturb the infrared balance of the hues, causing improper exposure of the black separation negative. As a result, some artists using fluorescent water color will find it necessary to alter their color mixing procedures.

THE COMBINATION DRAWING

There is one predicament into which the illustrator may inadvertently stumble; one from which no cameraman can extricate him. This is in the execution of the combination drawing—the drawing which is to appear partially as line and partially as halftone. An example is the line illustration which has been supplemented with modeling or a tonal background.

The artist seldom encounters serious difficulty in the combination of type and halftone. Type is alien to halftone art, and can hardly be positioned elsewhere but on an overlay. However, it is almost second nature to draw with pen or brush over a wash background, or to model a line drawing with gray washes.

If such a drawing is to reproduce as line superimposed over halftone, the art must be separated. The wash must be painted on the illustration board with the line drawing registered over it on a transparent overlay. The wash rendering and the overlay will be photographed separately; one as halftone, the other as line. The resulting halftone positive and the line positive will be used to produce a combination plate.

If the line and halftone are not executed as separate art, but are drawn on the same board, the entire illustration will reproduce in halftone;

the lines as well as the background will bear a dot pattern. In many cases, the screening of both line and wash is acceptable. However, some line work is so delicate that a dot pattern would destroy its character; retention of the line work as line is an absolute necessity.

If the artist unknowingly prepares such a drawing as one-piece art, he cannot be rescued by the cameraman. It is impossible to separate a black-and-white combination drawing. A black-and-color combination drawing may be camera separated with an appropriate filter, but there is no method of filtering black from black.

Registration of line and halftone by the artist is easier to accomplish if the halftone is rendered on an overlay on top of the line drawing. Unfortunately, there are few overlay materials which accommodate tone well—especially wash. Because of this, the tonal rendering is usually done on some suitable drawing surface and the line work is drawn on an acetate or vellum overlay. It is left to the ingenuity of the artist to devise a method of accurate registration.

In combination drawings, the line overlay is usually rendered with drawing ink. The halftone may be rendered in transparent wash, opaque gray, pencil, crayon, or charcoal. The tone must be kept light enough so that the overprinting line will not be obliterated.

It may often be desirable to drop out the halftone background behind the line art. If accurate registration is a problem for the artist, the drop-out can be accomplished on the halftone film negative. Using the line positive as a guide, the opaquer can determine exactly where to obliterate the dots on the halftone negative. If such work is required, it should be carefully specified in the instructions to the platemaker.

PHOTOGRAPHY

Photographs, unless intended for some special linear effect, are printed with a halftone plate. Photographs intended for reproduction should be taken by a professional photographer. The "snapshot," except under unusual circumstances, is considered inadequate for the purpose. Sharply focused, well-lighted photographs reproduce best. The halftone process rarely improves the quality of a photograph. It compresses the value range and a certain amount of detail is lost. If the original photograph does not contain sufficient detail, it will certainly not be brought out by the halftone process. As a result, areas lacking in detail must be clarified by the retoucher.

Lighting

Lighting is an important factor governing the suitability of a photograph for reproduction. The detail of an object, especially the definition of its texture, is seen in its middle-value areas. The eye resists making an abrupt transition from light to dark or vice-versa. Middle values provide the eye with a comfortable means of moving from one extreme of light to the other.

FLAT LIGHTING. Flat lighting is the direct frontal illumination of the subject. The large tonal masses are either too dark or too light. As a result, much detail is lost.

SIDE LIGHTING. Side lighting gives more illusion of depth, but the tones normally occur in large masses. The shadow edges merge with the background and the light side of the subject tends to lose its detail.

BALANCED LIGHTING. In balanced lighting, the subject is illuminated from the front quarter and the shadow areas are "filled in"—illuminated with a less brilliant light. This produces a photograph containing the full tonal scale. Light areas and adjacent shadow areas are properly separated by middle values, and there is sufficient detail present to identify the nature of the subject.

When a photograph is to be silhouetted or retouched, the subject should be distinct from the background. This eliminates guesswork as to the precise location of the edges. Important parts of an object are often eliminated by the silhouetter because they have become lost against the background.

If left to his own devices, the photographer tends to print his work on photographic paper that will look well. Sepia-toned, matte finish, or textured paper is not necessarily the best from the standpoint of reproduction. Glossy, white, 8" x 10" prints reproduce best and are the easiest to handle. Since the professional photographer generally shoots his pictures on 4" x 5" cut film, this represents a twice-up enlargement.

When producing a halftone from a photograph, it is better to reduce than to enlarge; reduction makes any retouching less apparent.

Photographic prints should be kept in the same scale, whenever possible. This enables the platemaker to gang up his halftone art and reduce it all in one shot, rather than having to reduce each photograph separately to a different camera focus.

In order to prevent damage, photographs should be immediately mounted by the recipient. They should be rubber-cemented or dry-mounted (a process where dry-mounting tissue, cut to the size of the photo, is placed between the photo and the backing and pressed down with an electric iron or a dry-mounting press) on a durable mounting board. Once mounted, photographs should be covered immediately with a protective tissue flap.

All information written or stamped on the back of a photograph should be copied on the back of the mounting board before the photo is mounted.

Photographs received in a torn or cracked condition should be photocopied (if the negative is not available), so that the defect can be retouched.

Retouching

Retouching is not, as is sometimes implied, a method of misrepresenting or misleading, but rather the enhancement of a photograph in order to obtain maximum quality and efficiency from the various reproduction processes.

Retouching is accomplished with the airbrush, dyes, bleaches, or other chemicals. It is done directly on the positive photographic print. Retouching includes the removal of photographic imperfections, the removal of undesirable or extraneous elements, the sharpening of contrast, and the accentuation of highlights. The retoucher may clarify detail, lettering, etc., and may restore lost edges. He may add extra area to the photograph in order to alter its overall proportions.

Color prints

Color photographic prints are utilized when color retouching is required, when lettering must be done on the photograph, or when some paste-up combination must be made. If none of these operations is necessary, color printing plates are produced directly from color transparencies.

Photoprints

Also known as copy prints, photoprints are photographic copies of existing art or photographic prints. The photoprinter does not take original photographs. He may be called upon to duplicate a photographic print for which there is no existing negative, or to make contact prints—in any quantity—from a negative. He may also produce screened Velox prints.

As previously mentioned, halftone proofs can be utilized as art for lithography. This is not so in letterpress. An occasion may arise when the only available art is a screened proof. It is possible for the photoprinter to copy this proof by keeping his camera slightly out of focus, or moving the copy a fraction of an inch. This will cause the dots to merge and form some semblance of continuous tone which can be used as letterpress copy. There is a considerable loss of quality in this process, but it provides a possible solution for an emergency situation.

The stock-photo service

Most photographs used for advertising purposes, especially color photographs, are taken expressly for their required purpose. A photograph taken by a competent professional is as expensive as a good illustration. There is an inexpensive source of black-and-white photography upon which the producer of advertising art relies heavily. This is the stock-photo service.

The stock-photo service maintains a file of photographs of almost every conceivable subject. These range from photographs of historical landmarks to posed scenes of housewives in the supermarket. Large photo services publish catalogs of their available material. Reproduction rights to these photos are granted to the advertiser for a modest fee. The fee is further reduced if the advertiser agrees to credit the source of the photograph.

Obviously, the stock photo will not suffice for every occasion, but it may well save the advertiser the expense of sending a photographer afield to photograph a well-known landmark. In return for the savings involved, the advertiser runs the risk that the same photograph might be used by another advertiser, since no exclusive rights to stock photos are granted.

Photographers' models

Photographers' models are hired from model agencies. Their services are retained for an hourly fee; the best may command upwards of fifty dollars per hour. Models submit photographic "composites" of themselves in various poses, together with pertinent information concerning age, clothing sizes, etc. These are kept on file by the persons involved with their selection.

The model may be selected by the client or by the art director. It is the responsibility of the production manager to schedule the photography so that expensive model time will not be expended needlessly.

Model releases

No advertiser may use the face of any person in his advertising without the express *written permission* of that person. This includes the faces of professional models. As a result, models are required to sign releases granting permision to use their picture, upon the completion of each assignment. These are kept on file by the advertiser or his agency. Stock photographs involving models should bear the imprint "Model Release on File" on the back of the photograph.

If *any* photograph of a crowd or other persons of unknown identity is used by an advertiser, *every face must be retouched to a point* beyond recognition. Disregard of this practice may result in serious legal consequences.

11 PHOTOSTATS

The photostat is one of the most useful items employed by the advertising artist, serving a multitude of functions in the preparation of both preliminary and finished art. Photostats enable the artist to enlarge and reduce line art at will, and provide him with a means of reversing the values of original art. They can be used as copies of continuous-tone art which—while not suitable for reproduction—may be used to indicate the appearance, cropping, and positioning of halftone on either comprehensive or mechanical art. They can be used to make duplicate copies of line art for future use; they may be colored by hand or dyed for displays and exhibits. They represent an inexpensive method of clear duplication when a minimal number of copies are required.

The photostat machine is a large copying camera which utilizes paper negatives. The machine photographs the subject matter through a lens which has a prism mounted in front of it. The prism prevents the lens from recording a backwards-reading image, producing, instead, a frontwards-reading image on sensitized paper contained within the machine. This image is in negative form. The paper negative is developed and dried. In order to obtain a positive image, a *second* photostat must be made from the paper negative; the negative is reshot as if it were the original art. This second shot, or *positive*—also paper—returns the values to those of the original subject matter.

The machine will enlarge up to twice the size of the original, or reduce to half the size in one shot. In order to make a further enlargement or reduction, the negative is enlarged or reduced to the maximum amount, and the positive is further enlarged or reduced to the desired size. Thus, if a negative is reduced to half the size of the original, and the positive is reduced to half the size of the negative, the result will be one-fourth the size of the original. Greater reduction requires additional shots.

Photostat paper is blue-sensitive; blue will photograph as white and red will photograph as black. In order to correct this tendency, a yellow filter must be employed. Its use should be specified by the person ordering the photostats, should the filter be required. Photostat paper comes in either matte or glossy finish. The paper is of the high-contrast type, designed to record near-white areas as white, and dark gray areas as black. Glossy paper gives the maximum contrast and should be specified when ordering copies of line art for reproduction. Good quality glossy photostats provide a sharp, perfect duplication of the original. Matte paper is more sensitive to tonal values, but lacks the sharpness of a photographic print. Matte photostats are used to provide visual indications of halftone drawings and photographs on comprehensive layouts, and to indicate cropping and positioning on the mechanical. A special photostat paper, called PMC, will accept water color without wrinkling. This is used for the fast production of color comprehensives by applying tints of color over a black-and-white PMC positive.

If required, a photostat may be "flopped"—photographed in a mirror in order to produce a backwards-reading image.

Photostats should be ordered carefully to make certain there is no misunderstanding on the part of the operator. The following items should be clearly indicated on the artwork:

1. *Whether the desired print is to be positive or negative.* To the photostat operator, a negative means one shot of the original; a positive two shots. If the photostatter is supplied with a negative photostat as original art, the first shot made from it will result in a positive image. If the specifier has requested a "positive," the operator has no way of being certain whether he wants a positive image or a duplicate of the original negative. In order to avoid confusion, many specifiers prefer to specify an "opposite" (one shot), or a "duplicate" (two shots). Others order "first prints" or "second prints."
2. *The type of paper desired.* Glossy paper is specified for line copy that is to be used for reproduction; matte paper is ordered for photostats used for the identification or positioning of halftone copy.
3. *The size(s) desired.* Size indication should be accomplished by marking lines at the horizontal or vertical extremities of the copy, and indicating the size within a double-headed arrow which touches each line. The lines should be accurately placed, since the operator uses them rather than the actual copy as a guide when he reduces or enlarges. If the photostat is to be made the same size as the original, it should be marked "S.S."

   The size indicator on the photostat machine is marked in percentages of enlargement or reduction, with 100 per cent representing the original size. If the specifier has a proportional calculator, it may be convenient to indicate enlargements or reductions in terms of percentages of the original.

Do not write photostatting instructions in blue pencil. If a great number of photostats are ordered, the fastest means of checking them for proper size is to measure between the lines that appear on the actual photostat and compare the result with the size indication which has been indicated there. If marked in blue pencil, the instructions will not appear on the photostat, and considerable time will be wasted in locating and referring to the original.

The exact appearance of a photostatic enlargement or reduction may be determined in advance with the Lacey-Luci, or if there is none available, the area may be calculated with the diagonal-line method. This should always be done in order to eliminate the possibility of incorrect size indication.

4. *The number of prints desired.* The job may require several prints, either the same size or in varying sizes.
5. *The job number.* The specifier's job number should accompany all photostat orders. This facilitates identification for billing purposes. The typographer or the engraver may attach a proof to his bill, but the photostatter has no visual evidence of the work he has performed.

The following procedures may prove helpful in the efficient utilization of the photostatic process.

All photostats should be checked for correct size and sharpness of focus immediately upon receipt from the photostatter. The messenger should be detained until this has been done, in order that he may return any that prove incorrect.

Common sense should be utilized when ordering photostats in order to avoid excessive costs. Indiscriminate ordering of photostats can wipe out the profit that is to be made on a small mechanical. For example, suppose it is necessary to photostat a line of lettering to five different positive sizes. A minimum size photostat might cost $.75; five negatives and five positives will cost $7.50. However, if the photostatter is given instructions to shoot five negatives to the required sizes, *gang up the negatives* and shoot a single positive from them, the resulting *six* stats will cost $4.50—a saving of $3.00 for exactly the same end result.

The cost of the photostat is based on the size of the paper required—not on subject matter. Material to be photostatted in the same focus should be grouped closely together so that it may be accommodated on a minimal-sized sheet of paper. If the subject matter is very small, extra material—logotypes, trademarks, constantly used items—may be mounted around it, and as long as they do not exceed the minimum paper size (8½" x 11"), they will be included at no extra charge.

Glossy paper costs slightly more than matte paper. It is poor economy to order glossy photostats when matte photostats will suffice.

Time is an important factor. Whenever possible, photostats should be ordered far enough in advance to be on hand when the mechanical is begun. Rush orders involving overtime charges should be avoided by proper job planning. Often, after the mechanical art is in progress, it is found that an element does not fit properly and must be photostatted to the desired size. If there is any error in sizing at this stage, it may delay delivery of the job. If there is any doubt as to size that will fit the layout best, it is often practical to order two or three photostats to slightly different sizes. One of them should certainly fit properly.

Original art—line drawings, logotypes, lettering, etc.—is the property of the client and should be returned to him. Photostat negatives of all such material should be kept on file. This eliminates the need for requesting original art from the client each time such material is needed. A client will tend to favor an art source which is known to have an ample photostat file of his advertising material. If a negative photostat is available, only one shot is required to make a positive image. This results in a considerable saving.

Material that is used continually for a particular account—logotypes, trademarks, slogans, address lines, etc.—should be ganged up on a master board. If several positive and negative logotypes of varying sizes are ganged up on a board, and a photostatic copy is ordered occasionally, there will always be a constant supply of such material on hand in a wide variety of sizes. This makes it unnecessary to send out to the photostatter every time such material is required.

It is easier to clean up enlarged type or hand lettering when it is in negative form, since the cleanup can be accomplished with black ink. If time permits, a negative photostat may be ordered, cleaned up by hand, and a positive photostat made from the cleaned-up negative. When appearing in reverse, the serifs and thin strokes of type or hand lettering may tend to fill in. A negative photostat affords the opportunity to appraise this possibility and to strengthen the offending lines with white paint before submission to the platemaker.

A minor paste-up assembly—the repositioning of elements of a line drawing, or the respacing of large lettering or type are good examples—can be accomplished in negative form and recopied as a positive. The positive will show no evidence of the alteration. When this is done—when any negative photostats are cut apart—the pieces should be mounted on black paper and the cut edges blackened so that the cut lines will not show in the positive.

Photostats are generally billed to the client at cost plus a 15 per cent service charge. It is possible for a skillful production man or an artist to effect considerable economies by the intelligent ordering of photostats. It is a matter of discretion whether or not to pass this saving along to the client.

12 TYPOGRAPHIC PRODUCTION

Prior to the twentieth century, there was little necessity for a knowledge of typographic production on the part of anyone not directly involved with the composition of type. Once the process of aesthetic selection was exercised, including perhaps, a suggestion of format, the resultant product was the sole responsibility of the typographer.

Today the methodology of typographic composition is so varied that the mere selection of type style and indication of the desired layout is no longer sufficient. The knowledgeable determination of *the method by which the typography will be produced* is of equal importance.

Modern typography is effected by hand composition, cast by machine, produced on positive or negative film or on photographic paper, printed by typewriters which have interchangeable type faces and proportional spacing mechanisms, or assembled by hand from letters printed on cardboard tabs or transparent adhesive (or transfer) sheets.

None of these processes are characterized by any lack of legibility when properly executed. Their specific advantages or disadvantages lie in the aesthetic desirability of the type styles available, the sizes available, their ability to produce spacing to a more critical degree, their speed (an influential factor in the cost), and their adaptability to the requirements of the various printing processes.

Good typographic production entails the ability to adapt the attributes of the various processes to the requirements of the job so that the finished product may be of the maximum quality attainable within the boundaries of sensible economy.

TYPOGRAPHIC MEASUREMENT

The unit of measurement for all type, regardless of the manner of its production, is the *point,* which measures .013837 in., or approximately one seventy-second of an inch. This measurement is applied to the distance between the edge of the type body that touches the line of type below and the edge that touches the line above.

The *height*—the distance from the feet upon which the type stands to the printing surface—is a constant .918 in.

Before the point system was introduced in 1878, there was little standardization and type sizes were known by name:

Great Primer	—	18 point
Columbian	—	16 "
English	—	14 "
Pica	—	12 "
Small Pica	—	11 "
Long Primer	—	10 "
Bourgeois	—	9 "
Brevier	—	8 "
Minion	—	7 "
Nonpareil	—	6 "
Agate	—	5½ "
Pearl	—	5 "
Diamond	—	4½ "
Brilliant	—	3½ or 4 point (seldom used)
Excelsior	—	3 point (seldom used)

The *pica,* the *nonpareil,* and the *agate* still persist in modern typographic terminology.

The units of type measurement

Point = 1/72 inch (.0138 in.)
Pica = 12 points, 1/6 inch
Nonpareil = 6 points, ½ pica
Em = a square of the type size
En = half an em
Agate = 5½ points, 1/14 inch

Definitions

The Point. The point is used for the measurement of type, leads (line-spacing materials), and rules (used for printing straight lines).

The Pica. A pica is equal to 12 points and is based for measuring line width (measure), margin width, depths of columns, paragraphs, etc. The *nonpareil* is half a pica, or 6 points.

The Em. The em is a square of the type size—the exact size depending on the size of type in question. For example, an 8-point em is 8 points x 8 points—8 points square. An *en* is one-half an em, divided vertically. Thus, an 8-point en would measure 4 points x 8 points.

The em is used to measure spaces, indentations, column sizes, and pages, and can be utilized in an area method of type estimation or cost determination. Prices are frequently quoted at a certain figure per thousand ems.

The Agate. The agate is 5½ points or ¹⁄₁₄ in. and is used as a unit of measurement of newspaper column depths.

TYPOGRAPHIC COMPOSITION

Definitions

Typography. The selection and arrangement, in printable order, of movable types and other related characters which have been cast in relief; or in the case of phototypesetting, assembled photographically. The resultant cast product is either utilized directly for printing or duplicated by means of electrotyping or stereotyping. Proofs (impressions) of cast type are utilized in the paste-up assembly for the photomechanical platemaking processes. Phototypography, in film negative form, can be used for the production of offset printing plates. In positive (paper) form, it can be utilized for paste-up assembly.

Type Face. The part of the type that touches the paper in printing. Also, the classification of a particular type style, based upon the characteristics of its design; often named after its designer. A type face may be distorted and still remain within the boundaries of its classification. Thus, the width of the character may be expanded or condensed. The weight—the thickness of the strokes—may be thinned or thickened. Some typical adjectives employed to describe such variations are:

Width	Thickness
Condensed	Light
Medium condensed	Medium
Extra condensed	Demi-bold
Wide	Bold
Extended	Extra bold
Expanded	Black
Open	Ultra bold

Serif. The cross stroke at the terminals of the letter. Type is classified as either a *serif* or a *sans* (without)-*serif* face.

Gothic. An American colloquialism for any upright, sans-serif type face.

Roman. A general term used to describe any upright, serif type face—though not necessarily Roman in its derivation. The term "Roman" is applied to all upright type faces when they are being differentiated from "italic" faces.

Italic. Any slanting type face; used to distinguish words for importance, emphasis, etc.

Body Type. Type faces, mostly Roman, used for paragraphs and running text. Body type comes in sizes of 14 points and smaller.

Display Type. Type faces used for headlines and other attention-getting elements, as distinguished from body type. Display type commonly comes in sizes from 14 to 72 points; however, sizes up to 144 points are available.

Composition. The selection of individual letters, and their placement (by hand or machine) in printable order, thus forming lines of words. These lines can be composed, or "set," in any desired length (measure).

Make-up. The process of *arranging,* by hand, the lines of type—headlines, subheads, text, captions, etc.—in the position in which they will appear on the printed piece, as specified by the layout. Most sources used the word "composition" to encompass the entire operation of *setting* the individual lines of type and *arranging* them into the desired format. This definition is based on the assumption that the actual type (or an electro) will be used for printing and that the lines of type, of necessity, *must* be arranged to coincide with the layout. This definition does not suffice when the mechanical assembly (paste-up) of camera-ready art is involved.

The mechanical artist has the choice either of accepting elements of the advertisement which have been proofed in random order and cutting them out and positioning them on the mechanical himself, or of instructing the typographer to make up elements furnishing a single proof with all the elements in their proper layout position. The latter operation makes less work for the artist, but it adds to the cost of the typography.

Consider, for example, a layout requiring a narrow paragraph of machine-set body type, centered under a wider, hand-set caption. The machine-set copy consists of a block of single-line slugs, while the caption is made up of two lines of individual hand-set letters. Both elements can be placed at random and quickly proofed, even though they do not appear on the proof in layout position. The process of locking up the caption and the body type so that they will appear on the proof in *exact layout position* is an *additional* operation and is billed as such.

For this additional operation, which must be specifically requested, an individual definition is required; thus the use of the term "make-up" as a separate and distinct function from "composition."

Letterspacing. The addition of thin spaces *between the letters* in order to avoid a crowded appearance and increase legibility.

Word Spacing. The spacing *between the words,* which may be increased or decreased in order to lengthen or shorten a line; accomplished with the use of *spaces* or *quads.*

Line Leading. The spacing *between the lines,* accomplished with the use of *leads.*

Spaces. Thin metal blanks used to separate letters or words in a line. The thinnest blanks range from the *hair* space (1 point wide) to the *3-em space* (1/3 of an em in width).

Quads. Metal blanks used for larger spaces. Sizes range from the *en quad* (1/2 of an em), through the *em quad* (a square of the type size), up to the *3-em quad* (3 times em).

Leads. Thin metal strips, furnished in thicknesses of 1, 2, and 3 points, inserted between lines of type in order to increase the space between them. A lead is considered to be 2 points, unless otherwise specified.

Slugs. (1) Leads that are more than 6 points in thickness. These are generally used for the spacing between paragraphs. (2) Lines of type that have been cast in one piece by an automatic typesetting machine.

Set Solid. Type that has been set without the use of leads.

Justification. The process of setting type so that the lines of type will be equal in width (measure), and so that both the left- and right-hand margins will be vertically aligned. This is accomplished by varying the spacing between words. A line may be well justified but poorly spaced, or vice versa. Typesetting machines will automatically justify to a measure determined by the operator, while justification of hand-set type must be accomplished by the manual insertion of spaces.

Flush Left. Type which has been set so that the *left-hand margin* aligns vertically and the right-hand margin is allowed to terminate normally, without any attempt at vertical alignment.

Flush Right. Type which has been set so that the *right-hand margin* has been vertically aligned and the left-hand margin has an irregular alignment. This practice has its artistic application, but it is often difficult to read. Flushing left or flushing right is accomplished by setting the lines to a near uniform length and aligning the margin which is to be flush. The lines are then squared off by inserting the necessary number of quads at the ragged ends of the lines.

Flush Left and Right. Justified.

Run-around. Composition where a portion of the text has been indented (left or right) to accommodate the insertion of an illustration.

Live Type. Type which has been set (by hand or machine) and is intended to be physically used for letterpress printing.

Standing Type. Type which has been kept intact with the definite intention of reuse. Unless so requested, type is generally disassembled or remelted after a reasonable period of time.

Matrix. A mold with which an individual type is cast.

Hot Type. Type which has been cast by an automatic typesetting machine. Hot type is cast from metal matrices.

Cold Type. Type which has been produced by a phototypesetting machine. Cold type is produced from photographic negative matrices.

HAND-SET (FOUNDRY) COMPOSITION

Hand setting was the original method of setting movable type. It is still used today because of the infinite variety of faces that are available. Foundry type is so-called because it is cast by, and purchased from a type foundry in sets, or *fonts,* rather than being cast by the typographer with an automatic machine. Foundry type is readily made up as it is set, for the spacing and leading materials are close at hand, and alien faces may be easily inserted as the setting progresses.

Definitions

Type Metal. Type metal is an alloy of lead, tin, and antimony. Lead, with its low melting point, is toughened by the tin binder and given hardness by the antimony. This alloy shrinks very little in cooling.

The following terms constitute the nomenclature of a printing type:

Face. The part of the type that makes the impression on the paper—the printing surface.

Serifs. Cross-lines at the ends of the strokes—not present in all faces.

Counter. The hollow part surrounding the face.

Beard. The beveled edge beneath the face.

Shoulder. The blank space on top of the type not covered by the letter, specifically above and below the letter. The side spaces are *side-bearings.*

Kern. The part of the face that extends beyond the body—usually occurring in the letters "f" and "j". Italic and script faces require a larger number of kerned letters than Roman or Gothic faces. Kerned type is easily damaged and must be handled carefully.

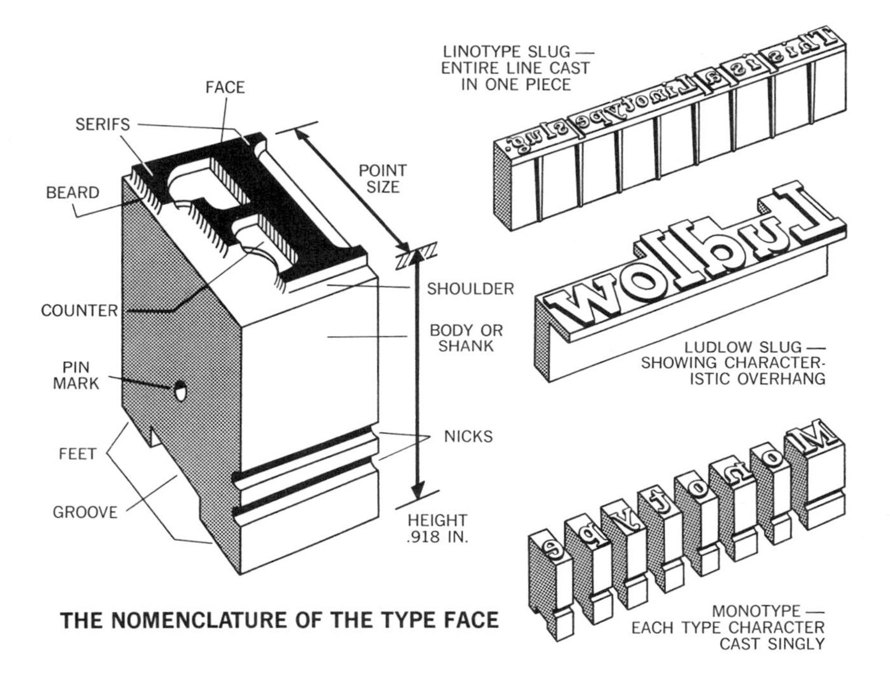

THE NOMENCLATURE OF THE TYPE FACE

Pin Mark. The mark left by the pin which removes the type from the mold, often bearing the mark of the founder.

Nick. A notch on the side of the type, used by the typographer to determine if the types are set in the stick correctly. In perfectly set type, the nicks align. Should a type be backwards, the nick will not appear and the offending type can be easily spotted. The number of nicks varies from one to five, and serves to distinguish one size and face from another.

Feet. The base of the type, upon which it stands.

Groove. The indentation between the feet.

Body or Shank. The entire mass of the type which bears the face.

Type Height. The overall height, from the base of the feet to the printing surface. Type height in the United States is .918 in. It differs abroad.

Composing the type

Hand-set type is composed from sets of individual characters known as *fonts*. A font of type is a complete assortment of one face and size, together with the appropriate spaces and quads. It contains a greater quantity of the letters most often used. Each font is stored in a compartment drawer, called a *case,* from which the desired characters are picked by hand and transferred to the *composing stick.* The stick is a metal frame with a movable part, known as the *knee,* which can be adjusted to the desired measure. The types are placed in position, upside down, and are held in place with the left thumb. Alignment of the nick indicates that the types are positioned properly—an incompatible type can be spotted immediately.

When the type nears the desired measure, it is determined whether the last word will run over or fall short. If the word runs over by only a few characters, the word spacing can be uniformly decreased—by substituting smaller quads—until the line fits. If the word runs considerably over, and cannot be properly hyphenated, it must be dropped, causing the line to fall short. The short line is then spaced out to the desired measure by inserting a larger quad in each space until the line becomes tight.

Some words, because of the nature of their first or last letters, appear

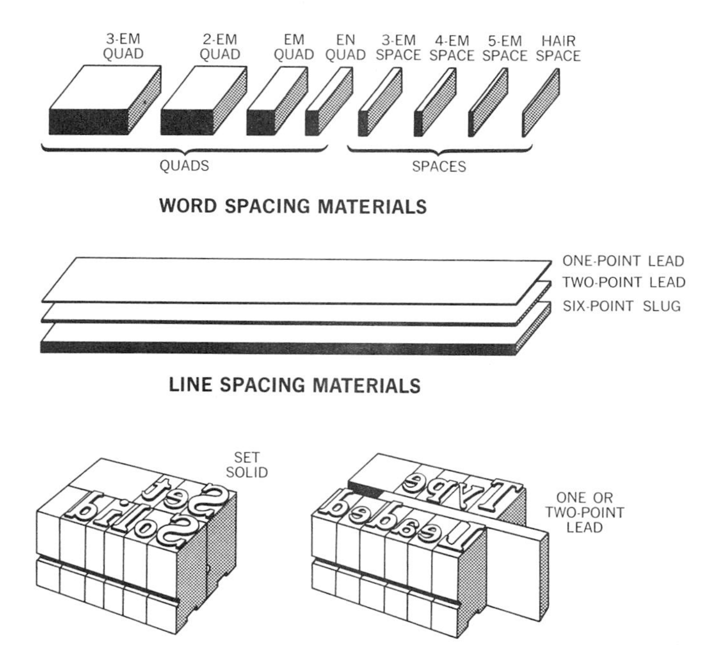

WORD SPACING MATERIALS

LINE SPACING MATERIALS

HOW LINE SPACING IS INSERTED

This block of copy has just been set solid in 9-point News Gothic. The shoulders of the face provide normal spacing between the lines.

This block of copy has just been set in 9-point News Gothic, leaded one point. A one-point lead has been inserted between each line.

This block of copy has just been set in 9-point News Gothic, leaded two points. A two-point lead has been inserted between each line.

These characters have no letterspacing.

T h e s e c h a r a c t e r s h a v e b e e n l e t t e r s p a c e d t w o p o i n t s .

LINE SPACING AND LETTERSPACING

to have more or less word spacing than others, even where identical quads are used. Thin spaces, inserted in such areas, will tighten up a loose line. The space between sentences can be wider than the space between words and still be visually acceptable. This is an ideal place to take up slack.

Letterspacing is not used indiscriminately, as it is intended to affect the visual appearance and readability of the entire composition. Letter-spacing is employed between each of the types, or not at all.

When the end of the paragraph is reached, the line is *quadded out* so that it will be flush with the rest—the largest quads being placed at the end of the line. A line may be centered by placing the same number of quads at each end of the line.

When the type has been set solid, the shoulders provide for the spacing between the lines. Additional line spacing is accomplished by the use of leads, which are stored in specially designed cases. The leads are placed between the lines as they are set in the composing stick.

After the full stick of type has been set, it is transferred to a flat metal tray called a *galley*. Depending on the layout, the type is *squared up* with spacing material, and *tied up* by wrapping string around its perimeter. If it is a more complex shape, it is locked up in a chase, preparatory to *proofing*.

The *proof press* is a small, but precise, printing press, designed to print an impression of type or plates which can be examined for errors or defects (*proofread*). The press is also used to provide type impressions of sufficient quality to be used on the mechanical assembly. The proof press is hand inked and fed, and is not intended for long printing runs.

Correction of hand-set typography may be readily accomplished by the removal and replacement of individual characters. *Corrections* are the rectification of errors made by the typographer, which are done at his expense. *Author's alterations* are changes made by the client after the first proofs have been pulled, and are effected at additional cost to the client.

Type wears during printing; as a result, most typographers do not encourage long press runs with their foundry type, as this necessitates frequent replacement. If a long run is involved, electros or stereos are made from the foundry type, or a photoengraving is made from the repro proof.

After use, type is distributed back into the cases. This process is time consuming, but its cost is considerably less than the cost of new foundry type.

TYPE PROOFS

Type proofs may be classified in three categories: proofs of book or editorial matter, proofs of composition of other matter designed for direct letterpress printing, and proofs for the purposes of photomechanical reproduction.

Book or Editorial Proofs

Galley Proofs. Type for running (page-to-page) text is initially set in long (19″ x 22″) galleys, without regard for page separation. A galley proof is a proof pulled from such type, often on newsprint, which is used for proofreading purposes.

Pink Proofs. Proofs that are pulled on colored paper, which are used for making up a dummy in order to determine how the finished pages will appear. Although known as "pink proofs," they need not necessarily be pink.

Page Proofs. Proofs of the text after it has been arranged into separate pages. Sometimes the illustrations appear on the page proofs. If not, space is provided for them.

Stone Proofs. Proofs of the complete form, ready for the press. The name is derived from the large table where the forms are assembled; the table was originally stone, but is now made of steel. Stone proofs are not often pulled.

Letterpress Proofs

Rough Proofs. Proofs that are pulled without regard for perfection. They show all elements in press position, and are used for the purpose of proofreading and checking positioning.

Proofs for Photomechanical Reproduction

Reproduction Proofs. Clean, perfect proofs are pulled on coated stock, which are used for paste-up on the mechanical art. Four are normally supplied; there is an additional charge for extra copies. These are commonly known as "repros."

Although rough proofs may be obtained for the purpose of proofreading, it is a common practice to proofread the repros; in the event that they are perfect, they may be utilized immediately. Minor corrections are often effected by the paste-up artist in order to save time.

Glassine Proofs. Proofs that are pulled on semi-transparent glassine. These are utilized for placement over the layout in order to check the "fit" of the copy.

Transparent Proofs. Proofs that are pulled on transparent glassine or cellophane. They are used as a substitute for the film positive in the production of deep-etch offset plates for books or other printing which involves a large amount of straight text. These are also known as *bronze proofs* because the wet ink is dusted with bronze powder in order to make it more opaque.

MACHINE COMPOSITION

There are three basic typecasting machines—the Linotype and Intertype, the Monotype, and the Ludlow Typograph. The type produced by these machines is known as "hot" composition, since molten metal is employed.

The Linotype

The Linotype is an automatic typecasting machine, invented by Ottmar Mergenthaler in 1886. As the name implies, it casts (molds) a line of type at a time.

Operation of the machine is from a keyboard similar to that of a typewriter. When a letter key is depressed, a brass matrix, contained in a magazine atop the machine, is dropped to an assembling elevator which delivers it to the matrix line. Words are formed by the matrices. The spaces between the words are occupied by wedge-shaped *space bands* which have been inserted by depressing the space-band key.

The Linotype is self-justifying. The machine is preset by the operator to cast lines to a desired pica measure. When the line is nearly full, the justifying lever is pressed. This forces the space bands in further, expanding them and increasing the spaces equally until the line is tight.

When the line of matrices has been thus justified, molten type metal is forced against the indented characters in the matrices, producing a single line-long slug of relief type. The machine is equipped to cast a slug with a maximum measure of either 30 or 42 picas. Wider lines are made up of several slugs butted end-to-end.

When the metal has cooled, the slug is trimmed and released from the machine. The used matrices are transferred to an elevator bar which lifts them back up to a distributor above the magazine. Each matrix is keyed by a set of notches, so that it will drop into its proper magazine compartment, thus returning it for immediate reuse.

Each magazine contains a single face and size, but most matrices are two-letter matrices—a Roman and an italic, or a Roman and a bold version of the same letter. Small capital letters are placed under characters that have no italic counterpart—punctuation, symbols, etc.

It is possible to cast a Linotype face of a particular size on a body of a larger size. For example, if a 10-point type is to be leaded two points, it can be cast on a 12-point body. This provides the required spacing material on the slug, saving the trouble of inserting leads by hand.

Magazines can be placed on the machine in a few minutes. Modern machines are constructed to hold several magazines at once, making a wide variety of type sizes immediately available without changing magazines.

Linotype composition can be used directly for letterpress printing, as it is expendable and deterioration is therefore no problem. Used Linotype slugs are remelted. If repro proofs are required, the slugs are tied up and proofed from the galley. Linotype and foundry type are compatible; therefore, where make-up is required, both are locked up in a chase preparatory to proofing.

Linotype correction is accomplished by recasting the entire slug.

Typesetting by machine is far cheaper and faster than hand-setting, provided the job is big enough to warrant its use. It is easier to set one or two lines of type by hand than it is to select the Linotype magazine, insert it, warm up the machine, and adjust it for the measure of the line.

METHODS OF TYPE COMPOSITION

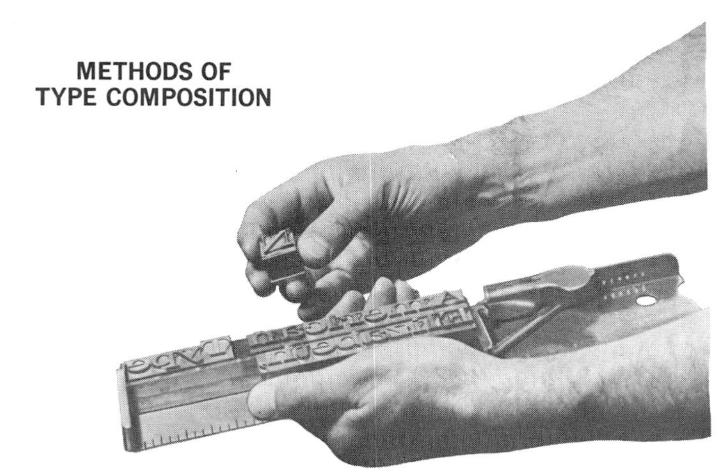

HAND-SETTING FOUNDRY TYPE
IN THE COMPOSING STICK

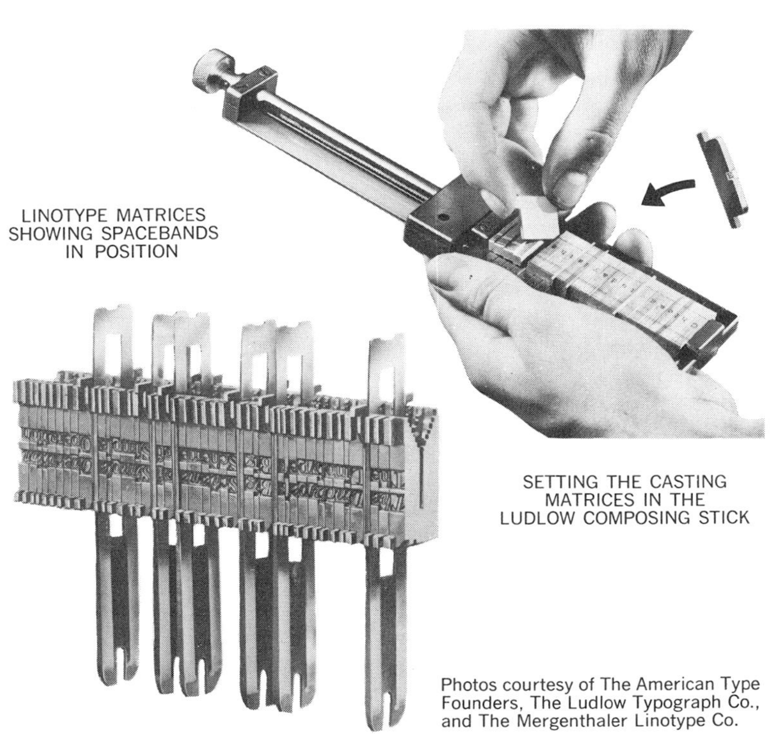

LINOTYPE MATRICES
SHOWING SPACEBANDS
IN POSITION

SETTING THE CASTING
MATRICES IN THE
LUDLOW COMPOSING STICK

Photos courtesy of The American Type Founders, The Ludlow Typograph Co., and The Mergenthaler Linotype Co.

The Intertype

The Intertype is an automatic, keyboard-operated typecasting machine which, from the production standpoint, is essentially similar to the Linotype. Some differences in the design characteristics of certain type faces may be noted by comparing Linotype and Intertype specimens.

The Monotype

The Monotype is a dual-unit, automatic typecasting machine, invented by Tolbert Lanston in 1887. It came into commercial use around 1900. The machine casts single type characters, rather than lines of type.

The "keyboard" unit of the machine is also similar to that of a typewriter. Depression of a letter key punches perforations in a paper strip—the controller ribbon—similar to the roll in a player piano. At the same time, the width of the particular letter is recorded on a justifying scale, located at the top of the keyboard. This enables the machine to measure the actual length of the accumulating characters *before* they have been assembled into casting position. When the line is nearly full, the operator depresses a spacing key which perforates the ribbon to indicate the additional spacing required to fill the line.

The ribbon is then transferred to the "caster" unit. Since it is inserted *backwards* into the caster, the perforations governing the necessary amount of justification are the first instructions the unit receives. Thus the machine is in a position to predetermine not only the word spacing, but also the body width of each letter *before it commences to cast the individual characters.* This produces a justified line in which the characters are slightly *letterspaced* in proportion to their word space, presenting an appearance considerably superior to most machine typography.

The Monotype will cast a justified line up to a 65-pica measure. A 90-pica line may be cast by using a large scale.

The caster unit is operated by compressed air. As the controller ribbon passes over a tracker, compressed air is forced through the perforations, controlling the action of a case containing 225 matrices. The case comes into position over a mold and an individual letter is cast. Justification is accomplished by an automatically shifting wedge, controlled by the spacing perforations on the ribbon. The type is cooled and ejected into a galley, where it is mechanically advanced to make room for the next line. The caster can produce small type at the rate of 150 characters per minute.

It is possible to use a harder metal in a Monotype caster than in a Linotype or Intertype, thus permitting longer wear. Foundry type can be produced by the Monotype—to be distributed in cases and set by hand.

Because of its flexibility in spacing, Monotype is preferred for tabular matter, catalogs, timetables, and other complex typography. It is more economically practical to make up such material with the Monotype than to set it with Linotype and paste it in position on the mechanical.

Monotype correction can be accomplished by the replacement of individual characters, in a manner similar to hand-set type.

The Ludlow Typograph

The Ludlow is a semiautomatic machine which casts slugs of type from hand-composed matrices, ranging in size from 4 to 96 points. Special matrices will cast up to 220-point characters lengthwise on the slug.

Brass Ludlow matrices are stored in compact cases, requiring considerably less room than a comparable selection of foundry type. These matrices are inserted by hand into a specially designed composing stick, and are locked into position with a thumbscrew. Spacing is easily controlled by the compositor. Italic faces are composed in a special stick, using matrices which slant at a 17-degree angle. This stick produces a full-kerned italic letter which is unbreakable.

After the matrices have been assembled, the stick is inserted in a casting machine, which casts all large faces on a 12-point body mold. The resulting T-shaped overhang, found on all sizes larger than 12 points, is a characteristic of the Ludlow slug. In printing, this overhang is blocked up with spacing material. A 6-point mold is available for casting smaller sizes. Ludlow slugs in the larger point sizes must be burnished. This is accomplished with emery cloth or a special power-driven machine. The Ludlow is equipped to cast lines of 21 or 22½ picas—smaller measures must be trimmed. Justified lines, up to 112½ picas, may be assembled in a special stick and cast in sections.

When the casting has been made, the matrices are returned to their cases. Correction must be accomplished by recasting the entire line. An advantage of Ludlow results when the same line must be cast many times. The line is set only once, and the caster will automatically produce the required number of duplicates.

Ludlow matrices and spacing material are easier to handle than foundry type, making the machine ideal for the composition of display lines of 14 points or larger. It is a completely impractical method for the composition of body type in any quantity, although a few lines of type can often be cast in less time than it takes to set up an automatic machine.

Auxiliary machines

There are several varieties of auxiliary casting machines which are used in conjunction with machine typography.

THE ELROD. The Elrod is a machine for casting leads, slugs, rules, and base material, which automatically molds and cuts these items to the desired size. Elrod leads and slugs are used to build up the overhang in the Ludlow slug.

THE MONOTYPE MATERIAL MAKER. The Material Maker is a machine which molds and cuts leads, slugs, and borders so economically that there is no practicality in the retention of this type of material for possible reuse.

THE TYPE AND RULE CASTER. The Type and Rule Caster casts Monotype in sizes from 5 to 36 points for use as foundry type. An extra attachment produces leads, slugs, and rules.

THE GIANT CASTER. The Giant Caster is used for producing Monotype in 14- to 72-point sizes, as well as leads, slugs, spaces, quads, and furniture. Furniture is metal (it can also be wood) pieces designed to fill the blank spaces between pages and around type-forms when locked in a chase.

THE MONOTYPE-THOMPSON CASTER. The Monotype-Thompson Caster is a machine which will produce single types, of from 5 to 48 points, as well as borders, ornaments, special quads, and a variety of other items. It will cast single types from the matrices of any typecasting machine.

PHOTOCOMPOSITION

The phototypesetting machine is basically a device which produces typography on film or photographic paper by the use of master photographic type negatives, rather than casting matrices. The manner in which each negative is brought into position, exposed to the film or paper, and developed, varies from system to system. Typography produced in this manner is known as "cold" type. The principal use of photocomposition is for the production of film negatives and positives for use in offset or gravure platemaking. There are several types of phototypesetting machines:

The Linofilm

The Linofilm, manufactured by the Mergenthaler Linotype Company, is a complete system for photocomposition. It consists of a keyboard, photographic unit, composer, and corrector.

THE KEYBOARD UNIT. The keyboard unit produces a punched tape and a typewritten copy simultaneously. The keyboard is similar to that of an electric typewriter; use of a shift key makes 88 characters available. A dial on the right-hand panel of the console enables the operator to select point size, leading, and any one of 18 different type faces. Each face is available in sizes ranging from 6 to 32 points. The left panel provides five end-of-line functions: flush left, center, flush right, justify, and erase. A buzzer sounds when the line is 4 ems from the end and the justification button is pushed. This operation also returns the typewriter carriage and moves it to the next line. A scale above the typewriter shows the operator his location in the line, making it easy for him to produce run-arounds. Any line may be tried experimentally on the type-

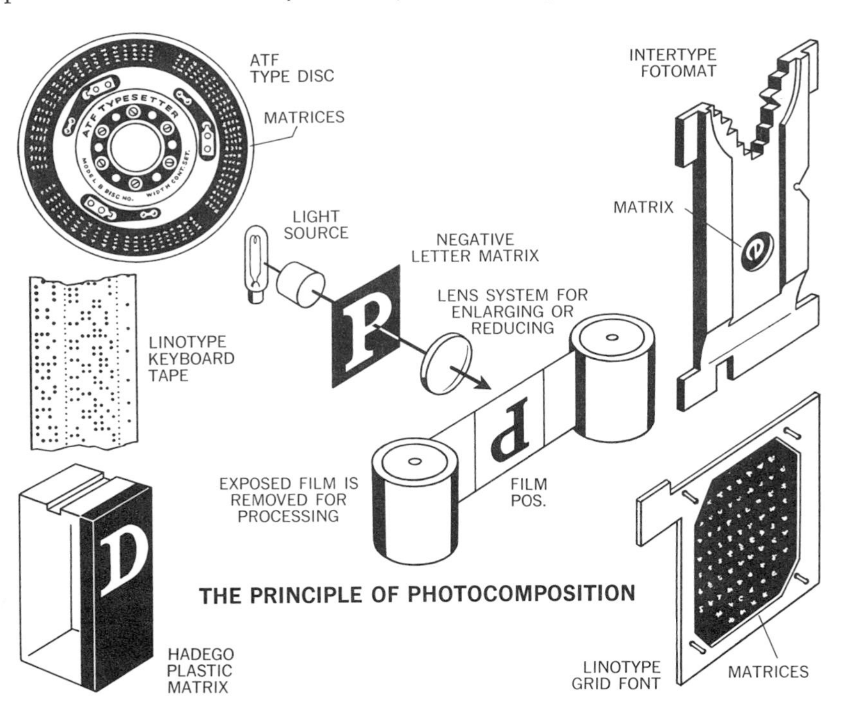

THE PRINCIPLE OF PHOTOCOMPOSITION

writer without punching the tape. The erase key voids the entire line before it is photographed and resets that line immediately. Unlimited mixing of type faces is possible, since any number of faces can be used within a single line. Plus or minus letterspacing is under the operator's control—automatic justification occurs between the words and does not affect the letterspacing. Characters are full-kerned.

THE PHOTOGRAPHIC UNIT. The operator feeds the punched tape into the reading head of the photographic unit, and the machine sets according to the information on the tape. The master negatives of the characters are called grid fonts and are housed, 18 at a time, in a rotating grid turret. The information on the tape brings the proper character on the grid font into position for exposure to film or paper. The unit photographs at a rate of 15 newspaper lines per minute in line lengths up to 42 picas.

After exposure, the film or paper is advanced into a removal container and is taken to a darkroom for processing. The unit produces positive frontwards-reading type on film or photographic paper.

THE COMPOSER. The composer performs all of the functions of make-up. In addition, it has the ability to enlarge or reduce type to *any size* without regard for conventional point-size limitations. The composer rephotographs the galley, line for line, simultaneously projecting each line onto a viewing screen. By convenient dial settings, the operator is able to move the image horizontally or vertically, and enlarge or reduce in a range from 3 to 108 points. This enables the make-up to be accomplished by visual comparison to the layout. The product of the composer is a film or paper positive, up to 96 picas in width and of any desired depth, with all elements of the layout made up in proper size and position.

THE CORRECTOR. The corrector looks somewhat like a photographic film splicer. The necessary corrections are first set on the keyboard; they emerge from the photo unit in galley form. This is placed in the corrector, side by side with the original film in which the correction is to be inserted. The corrector automatically cuts out the error and replaces it with the corrected line, welding the new material onto the original film so smoothly that no opaquing is necessary. Any number of lines can be removed, replaced, or added by this operation.

The Intertype Fotosetter

The Fotosetter is a single-unit, keyboard-operated machine, similar in appearance to the regular hot Intertype. A 117-channel magazine, located atop the machine, contains the photographic negative matrices called *Fotomats.* These are similar in appearance to Intertype matrices, but bear a negative image of the character imbedded in the flat side between transparent covers. Blank Fotomats are used as spaces and quads for the basic spacing between words.

When the operator depresses a letter key, the Fotomat drops from the magazine to a conveyor belt which carries it to the assembling elevator where it is assembled as a composed line. Justification is accomplished without the use of space bands. The mechanism automatically measures a composed line to determine the space that must be distributed throughout the line in order to justify it. During the exposure of the individual characters, this needed space is automatically included. It can be distributed between the characters as well as between the words.

For exposure, the Fotomats are lifted, one at a time, and placed in front of a light beam. This beam is projected through the negative, through a lens, and onto the film or paper held in the film carriage. There are eight lenses in the lens turret (as many as 14 different lenses can be used by the machine) which are capable of producing type from 4 to 54 points from four basic Fotomat sizes. As many as 14 type sizes can be set from one basic font. Up to four Fotomat magazines may be carried on one machine and Fotomats from any two adjacent magazines can be mixed in the same line.

As each matrix is lifted for exposure, the matrix rack moves the thickness of the removed matrix; a rack-and-gear device moves the film carriage accordingly. Line spacing is preselected and automatic, and is controlled by a film-feed dial setting. After exposure, the Fotomats are removed to a distributor bar where they are redistributed in a similar manner as in the hot machine.

Exposed film is removed in a container and developed in a darkroom. Either film or paper can be used. The Fotosetter produces: frontwards-reading film positives, backwards-reading film positives, frontwards-reading film negatives, backwards-reading film negatives, or photographic paper positives.

Correction is easily accomplished on the film. Faulty lines are reset and developed. A line-correcting device aligns the new line over the old, cuts out both, and fastens the new line in position with transparent tape.

The Monophoto

The Monophoto is produced by the Monotype Corporation of England. It is a two-unit system, run on compressed air, which produces exposed photographic film ready for developing. The machine uses the standard Monotype keyboard to perforate a paper controller ribbon. All material is set to a maximum line width of 60 picas.

The paper ribbon is placed in the photographic unit of the machine. Compressed air passes through the perforations and controls the action of the master negative (photo-matrix) case in a way similar to that used in the Monotype caster. This case contains 225 characters. Film is cut to the size needed for the job, placed in a film drum, and positioned on the machine. The ribbon feeds into the machine and brings the master negative into exposing position. A light beam passes through the negative. The beam is then reflected by prisms through another lens which controls the point size. It is then reflected by mirrors onto the film drum where the image is exposed.

After exposure the film is removed and developed, with normal dark-room procedures. Negatives are produced by chemical reversal of the originally exposed film. The machine produces frontwards- or backwards-reading typography on film or paper.

Corrections are accomplished with a device that removes the emulsion from the film and strips in the necessary new material.

Spacing and justification are set after the keyboarding operation, and can be changed at will, even while the machine is in operation.

The ATF Typesetter

The ATF Typesetter is a two-unit system, produced by the American Type Founders Company. The *keyboard unit* resembles an oversized typewriter, and produces a typewritten proof and perforated tape simultaneously. The keyboard is similar to that of a standard electric typewriter, with special keys for justification, line and letter spacing, and line deletion. As in other systems utilizing perforated tape, the tape can be filed, rerun, revised, or even mailed to another installation.

The larger *photographic unit* also contains a keyboard, which is used for the composition of unjustified material and for the insertion of new or corrected material. The photographic type negatives are contained on high-speed type discs. Each disc contains two fonts, which are available in sizes ranging from 5 to 14 points. The unit will set lines up to 7⅜ in. wide.

The tape is inserted into the unit and the desired disc is selected. The perforations on the tape control the action of the disc which rotates into proper position. A beam of condensed light passes through the type negative, exposing the character on the film, which is then automatically advanced to the next position. The exposed film is fed into a receiver for removal for developing. The machine can produce frontwards- or backwards-reading copy on positive or negative film, as well as a positive image on photographic paper.

The Hadego Phototypesetter

Used primarily for display composition, the Hadego Typesetter is manufactured in the Netherlands and distributed in the United States by the American Type Founders Company. The Hadego employs plastic negative-faced matrices, which are set in a composing stick in a similar manner as with the Ludlow. The matrices are either 20- or 48-point and can be supplied with either frontwards- or backwards-reading images. The machine can produce a continuous range of sizes from a single font. With 20-point matrices, sizes from 4 to 34 points can be produced; 48-point matrices will extend the range up to 82 points. Any fractional in-between size is possible.

The composed stick of matrices is inserted in the machine for photographing. Composing sticks are either 90 or 150 picas, and proofs up to 11″ x 15″ can be produced. The end product of the machine is a film positive. Negative prints are made by contact printing or reverse developing. Paper prints can be made by using backwards-image matrices and reverse developing.

A special copy holder is available which will convert the Hadego into a small reproduction camera for copying sketches, trademarks, logotypes, etc. A repeat mechanism, which enables the operator to readily produce frames and borders, is also available.

The Photon

The Photon is a three-unit photocomposing machine, consisting of a *console,* a *relay rack,* and a *photographic unit.* The console contains a typewriter keyboard and push-button controls. The operator sets the line width—up to 42 picas—selects the desired leading, and chooses the type size and style. The machine will produce type ranging from 5 to 36 points, in any one of 16 faces.

The operator composes a line which appears on a typewritten proof as it is simultaneously "stored" by the machine. The entire line must be composed before this information is released to the photographic unit. As each line is typed, a buzzer indicates that the line is almost full. The line will be automatically justified from the point where the operator stops typing and moves to the next line. If the operator attempts to overset, the keyboard will lock. Depressing the carriage-return key actuates the photographic mechanism, which is controlled by the relay rack. The information on the line, which has so far been withheld from the photographic unit, is released for photography while the operator is setting the next line.

Correction is easily accomplished before the line is released to the photographic unit. Back-spacing, from right to left, removes characters; thus, corrections can be made by back-spacing and retyping. There is also an error key which can be used to erase when the typewriter carriage is placed at the point of error. In addition, an entire line can be erased by depressing the "kill-line" key.

The relay rack can be adjusted to accommodate any variety of perforated tape containing character identification codes.

The Photon make-up panel gives the operator full visual control of both horizontal and vertical positioning, so that any layout placed on the page make-up board can be readily duplicated with direct keyboarding. A transparent indicator moves over the layout in exact correspondence to the movement of the film in the machine's magazine.

The product of the Photon is photographic film, ranging from 3 in. to 8 in. wide.

Film type

Film type should not be confused with photocomposition. Photocomposing machines, although equipped to produce a great variety of sizes, are primarily employed to produce lengthy headlines, subheads, and running text in standard type faces. Many systems can be utilized to deliver made-up film composition. Film type, often known as *photo lettering* or *film lettering,* is used for display lines and eye-catching headlines. It is a substitute for hand lettering, rather than for typography.

The film-type machine delivers positive or negative lettering in single strips, usually about 35 mm., which are pasted up on mechanical art. The fonts consist of fancy scripts, brush letters, outline letters, and unique shadow arrangements. Standard type faces are also available.

Since a skilled film-type operator can connect script-letter strokes more accurately than a typographer, film type represents an excellent source of inexpensive script lettering. Some machines enable the operator to distort letter and word shapes in order to obtain unique effects. This is especially useful when it is necessary for lettering to appear in perspective.

Although more than one line can be included on a single strip, film type is best utilized for display headings. The composition of body copy is impractical.

There are several film-type machines on the market.

THE TYPRO. The Typro is a photolettering machine for the composition of display headings in either hand lettering or type styles. Scripts, casual brush styles, novelty lettering, and standard type styles are available in 1,500 varieties, ranging in size from 6 to 144 points. These are available as negative film fonts, which are stored in the machine on a master reel.

An illuminated magnifying viewer locates the characters on the film font. Letterspacing can be controlled as accurately as .001 in. Justification and copy fitting is easily accomplished. More than one line can be composed on a strip, and overprints, drop-shadows, and screened backgrounds can be readily produced.

The machine produces negative or positive lettering on paper or on film. A motorized developer and dryer is available.

THE FILMOTYPE. The Filmotype is a portable unit slightly larger than a typewriter, used for the photocomposition of display headlines. Filmotype offers a wide variety of type and hand-lettering styles, ranging from 12 to 144 points in size. These fonts are supplied as strip-film negatives, which can be stored individually or on a master reel.

A color signal system, rather than a viewfinder, facilitates letterspacing. A guide chart provides a method of justification. Special patterns and screened effects are possible, as well as the intermixing of several type sizes.

The Filmotype produces work on paper or film in both positive and negative.

THE TYPOSITOR. The Typositor is an extremely versatile photolettering machine for the composition of display headlines. The machine has over 500 fonts available in all styles and, additionally, will accept any existing 2-inch negative film reel. Sizes ranging from 9 to 144 points may be set. A modification lens system condenses, expands, backslants, and italicizes—and is capable of bouncing, staggering, and altering proportion. Lettering can be curved, arced, or set in perspective.

The machine is electronically timed and controlled. A viewing system allows the operator to see every letter, space, or distortion; a visible developing chamber develops each letter individually and instantly as it is exposed. The film is developed with concentrated liquids; no darkroom facilities are necessary.

The Typositor produces lettering on paper or on film. Film and paper positives are converted to negatives with a reversal apparatus.

Typewriters

The increased popularity of offset lithography, especially the use of the paper offset plate which can be typed on directly, has resulted in considerable use of typewriter composition for work where economy is an important factor. Although an ordinary manual or electric typewriter may be used, these contain no mechanism for letterspacing or for the justification of lines. Common typewriter faces are somewhat less than distinctive. As a result, typewriters which have letterspacing and justifying devices, as well as unique and often interchangeable type faces, have come into popular usage. Some of these machines are:

The Vari-typer. The Vari-typer is a type-composing machine which is designed for office use. Resembling a typewriter, its removable type bar comes in over 600 varieties of type faces, ranging in size from 6 to 18 points.

The machine is equipped with a differential letterspacing mechanism which spaces out the different characters of the alphabet to their individual widths. Thus, wider characters like "M" and "W" are set in wider spaces than narrow characters such as "i" and "l." An automatic justification mechanism spaces out each line of the copy to a predetermined width. Line leading is accomplished by means of a special point-calibrated scale.

The Friden Justowriter. The Justowriter is an automatic, tape-operated composing machine, consisting of two units: the *recorder* and the *reproducer*. The first unit produces unjustified typewritten copy and a punched tape. The tape is fed into the second unit which justifies the lines automatically from information contained on the tape. The units are similar in appearance, each having an electric-typewriter keyboard.

The reproducer is capable of reproducing justified lines at the rate of 100 lines per minute. The end result may be an opaque justified page, a galley, or a direct-image plate for offset reproduction. Errors can be corrected easily; whole lines may be deleted by pressing the "delete" switch. They may be also corrected by deleting portions of the coded tape.

The Fairchild Lithotype. The Lithotype is a type-composing machine similar to the Vari-typer, except that it is capable of letterspacing to a more critical degree. It, too, has a built-in justifying device.

The IBM Electromatic Typewriter. The Electromatic typewriter has a standard electric typewriter keyboard. It comes equipped with only one face and size of type (although there are several styles to choose from). The machine is capable of proportional letterspacing and will produce justified lines.

In order to justify lines on the IBM typewriter, the operator must first type a rough copy in order to determine how much the lines must be expanded to attain justification. The copy can then be readily justified in the second typing.

Automatic Electric Typewriters. The automatic electric typewriter is used to produce multiple letters for direct-mail purposes when it is desirable to have each letter appear as if it had been individually typed, rather than reproduced. These typewriters operate from a punched master tape; several are used simultaneously. The operator produces the master tape—the body of the letter—on a special machine. A letterhead is inserted in each typewriter and the address and salutation are individually typed by the operator. The tape takes over and each machine automatically types the body of the letter from the information stored on the tape. The operator can stop any machine and insert individual information at any time. This system is practical only when 50 or more copies are required.

There are several such typewriters, including the *Hooven*, the *Flexowriter*, the *Auto-Typist*, and the *Robotyper*.

Paste-up lettering

There are several available devices to enable the mechanical artist to produce display lines and emergency jobs for which there is no time to call the typographer. These devices are economical and can be highly effective in the hands of a competent artist.

Fototype. Fototype is a lettering system for composing headlines and display type by hand, for use on the mechanical art. It provides characters which are printed on cardboard and assembled, face down, in a composing stick. Pressure-sensitive transparent tape is placed on the back of the assembled characters, after which the line can be lifted out and positioned on the mechanical.

Individual characters come in pads of 100, and refills are available. The pads are precision-cut and the letters snap into the stick in perfect alignment with proper letterspacing. Positive or negative paper letters, as well as transparent positive letters, are available. Fototype is available in over 300 type styles.

Transfer Type. Transfer type consists of a transparent font sheet containing letters which, when rubbed with a pencil or a stylus, will transfer to any smooth surface directly beneath the sheet. This is an effective method only if the artist has an eye for letterspacing and alignment, as each letter must be hand positioned and rubbed off one at a time. Transfer type is available in over 300 faces, ranging in size from 10 to 188 points.

Adhesive Type. Adhesive type is furnished in transparent, adhesive-backed fonts. Each letter must be individually cut out, positioned, and burnished in order to make the adhesive adhere. Adhesive type is not as effective as transfer type, since the transparent sheet is still in evidence after the letter has been fixed in place. This type is also available in a wide variety of faces and sizes.

COPY-FITTING

Copy-fitting is the process of determining the exact area that a piece of typewritten copy will fill, or can be made to fill, when set in a specific type face and size.

Copy area must be measured to determine the space it will occupy so that a well-designed layout may be created. After the layout and the copy have been approved for production—often entailing changes from the originally submitted versions—the typography must be specified, in order that the typographer can compose it in accordance with the layout. The neophyte artist may be content to submit an outline of the desired area, instructing the typographer to "fit this," but the professional artist is concerned with accurate measurement and specification which will produce a predictable result.

Copy area is determined by counting the number of characters in the typewritten copy, ascertaining the number of characters of a particular type face and size that will fit in a desired measure, and dividing the total number of characters by this figure in order to determine the required number of lines. Once the characters have been counted, it is a simple matter to refer to a chart showing the number of characters per pica measure of a particular type face. Thus, the method which provides the fastest, most accurate character count is obviously the most efficient.

No typographer stocks all the existing type faces; nor is he generally equipped with all of the various composing machinery. The average commercial typographer seldom has Monotype, nor will he have both Linotype and Intertype. He usually has but a fraction of the foundry faces that are available; therefore, it is often frustrating to attempt type selection from specimens supplied in a textbook. Any typographer who anticipates doing business will gladly supply specimens of the faces he stocks. Such specimens are commonly known as *type books.*

Some specimen books contain *single-line specimens.* These are sample lines, printed in a single convenient size, of each face the typographer stocks. Accompanying these specimens is a listing of the available point sizes, together with an indication of whether the face is foundry, machine, or Ludlow.

Other more elaborate books contain each face printed in a variety of sizes; often, in the case of body type, with various line leadings. Many contain copy-fitting charts showing the number of characters that will fit in a desired pica measure. If not, such charts are readily available from most foundry and machine-type manufacturers. To attempt to fit or specify type accurately without such material at hand is unwise.

Few type specimen books contain complete alphabets. Usually the specimen is composed in some sort of sentence; sometimes a portion of the alphabet is included. This is done because typographers are in business to sell type and wish to discourage the photostatting of alphabets for use in pasting up display lines by hand. A complete alphabet book is an invaluable asset as reference for finished or comprehensive lettering and should be preserved with the utmost care and regard.

In order to determine the size of a printed type, it should be compared with a specimen of known size. Measurement of a printed impression with a point scale does not determine the *actual point size,* since a type face does not occupy the entire area of the body. The face of a 14-point type may measure only 10 points, the rest of the measurement being taken up with shoulder. An 18-point light condensed face can measure more than an 18-point bold of the same family.

The Quikpoint Typesizer is an inexpensive transparent device with which one can identify various type faces quickly and accurately.

The printer's (and the specifier's) ruler is known as the *pica rule.* Inches, picas and nonpareils, agate lines, and often 8- and/or 10-point scales are included.

Fitting display type

The fitting of display type is generally a simple matter, because such copy is seldom so lengthy that an accurate character count cannot be easily made. A comparative count of a specimen of the desired type will determine the space the copy will occupy in that particular face and size.

This measurement can be transferred to or from the layout with a ruler or dividers. (It should be kept in mind that capital letters occupy more space than lower-case letters.)

Body copy is generally indicated on the layout by a series of ruled lines. Headlines, however, are generally lettered out, since it is desirable to give the client an indication of how the headline will actually appear. Therefore, when lettering the headline on the layout, the artist should provide an accurate representation of the particular type face and size that will eventually be ordered. For layout purposes—if the specimen contains most of the alphabet—the desired lettering can be traced. In order to prepare a tight comprehensive layout, either transfer or adhesive lettering may be used. If the layout lettering has been done accurately, it is a simple matter for the type specifier or the mechanical artist to locate the matching face and size in a specimen book, and specify accordingly.

The type specifier and the mechanical artist should become accustomed to checking headline fit in the event that the layout artist has miscalculated.

Headlines are not always set in a single line. A headline may consist of several lines—flush left or right, centered, or justified. When a headline sentence is broken into several lines by the artist, care should be taken that the breakup does not alter the meaning of the sentence in any manner. Headline width is a critical factor, since it may have been designed to fit within a certain limited area, to run the extreme width of an advertisement, or to align with an illustration or accompanying body copy. Therefore, it is often necessary to have the headline attain an *exact* measure. A precise fit may be obtained by any one of the following methods:

1. Select a size that will come to slightly less than the desired measure, and instruct the typographer to space the line(s) to the desired measure. This can be accomplished by letterspacing, word spacing, or both. It should be borne in mind that the typographer can only *increase* the normal length of a line; he cannot *decrease* it.
2. Select a type size that will come to slightly less than the desired measure; cut the proof apart and word space the line(s) on the mechanical art.
3. Set the line in any convenient size and photostatically enlarge or reduce it to fit.

Fitting body type

The Square-Inch Method. Often an approximation of the required type area must be determined from a rough typewritten draft.

Since numerous copy changes are likely to occur, it is impractical to make an accurate computation, especially where several pages are involved. The square-inch method produces a quick estimate of the area such copy will occupy; this method may also be used to determine how much copy can be written for a desired area. The word-count per square inch may be determined by using the chart below.

The total word-count of the copy must be estimated. Count the words in the first three lines of the copy and divide the total by three; this indicates the average number of words per line. Multiply this figure by the total number of lines in the copy; this count indicates the approximate number of words in the copy, and is sufficient for a rough estimate.

Measure the number of square inches in the desired copy area.

Referral to the table will show the approximate number of words that can be set per square inch in a particular type size. This figure has been multiplied by the number of square inches in the desired area, indicating the number of words the area will accommodate:

Desired area × words per sq. in. =
Number of words area will accommodate

The required space for any copy (in square inches), or the word-count per square inch, can be just as easily determined:

NUMBER OF WORDS TO THE SQUARE INCH										
Sq. In.	5-pt. Solid	5-pt.* Leaded	6-pt. Solid	6-pt.* Leaded	8-pt. Solid	8-pt.* Leaded	10-pt. Solid	10-pt.* Leaded	12-pt. Solid	12-pt.* Leaded
1	69	50	47	34	32	23	21	16	14	11
2	138	100	94	68	64	46	42	32	28	22
4	276	200	188	136	128	92	84	64	56	44
6	414	300	282	204	193	138	126	96	84	66
8	552	400	367	272	256	184	168	128	112	88
10	690	500	470	340	320	230	210	160	140	110
12	828	600	564	408	384	275	252	192	168	132
14	966	700	658	486	448	322	294	224	196	154
16	1104	800	752	544	512	368	336	256	224	176
18	1242	900	846	612	576	414	378	288	252	198
20	1380	1000	940	680	640	460	420	320	280	220
22	1518	1100	1034	748	704	506	462	352	308	242
24	1656	1200	1128	816	768	552	504	384	336	264
26	1795	1300	1222	884	832	598	546	416	364	286
28	1932	1400	1346	952	896	644	588	448	392	308
30	2270	1500	1410	1020	960	690	630	480	420	330
32	2308	1600	1504	1088	1024	736	672	512	448	352
34	2346	1700	1598	1156	1088	782	714	544	467	374

*Figures given for a 2-point leading

Courtesy of Edwin H. Stuart, Pittsburgh, Pa.

A CHART FOR COPY-FITTING BY THE SQUARE-INCH METHOD

$$\frac{\text{Words in copy}}{\text{Words per sq. in.}} = \text{Required space in sq. in.}$$

$$\frac{\text{Words in copy}}{\text{Desired area (in sq. in.)}} = \text{Words per sq. in.}$$

The purpose of accurate copy-fitting is to predetermine, as closely as possible, the actual area the copy will occupy, in order to produce a layout or to order typography that will fit the layout. This fit is determined by count and measurement, and by the clarity of instructions that are given to the typographer.

The typographer sets type to a specified size and measure. Once these have been established, the amount of copy will govern the number of lines, and no degree of wishful thinking will cause the lines to shrink. For example; 630 characters, set solid in 8-point Times Roman to a 20-pica measure, will run 10 lines deep or 6.6 picas. They cannot be set in fewer lines nor made to occupy less depth as long as the type size and measure are maintained. By leading 2 points, 18 points can be gained—increasing the total depth to 8.1 picas—but there will be *10 lines of copy.* If the depth must be decreased, a wider measure or a smaller or narrower size must be used. If the depth must be increased beyond the 2-point leading, a narrower measure, or a larger or wider size must be employed. It is the ability to manipulate size, measure, and leading that constitutes good copy-fitting.

THE CHARACTER-COUNT METHOD. The square-inch copy-fitting method is based upon the assumption that there is an average word length. This is an inaccurate approach due to the wide variation in the length of words, especially in technical copy. The character-count method is the most accurate and widely used means of copy-fitting.

Copy to be fitted should always be typewritten, and it is within the province of the copy-fitter to insist that this be done. Each typewriter character occupies the same width.[1] Thus, if the left-hand margin has been kept flush, the total character count of any typed line will be equal to any other line of the same measure. If a vertical pencil rule is drawn through the last character in the shortest line of the copy, all of the lines to the left of the rule will contain an equal character count. The

---

[1] Most American manually operated typewriters employ one of two sizes: Pica (12-point), which has 10 characters to the inch, or Elite (10-point), which has 12 characters to the inch. Character-counting scales are available for these sizes. Electric typewriters and newer imports often have distinctive type which must be measured individually when encountered.

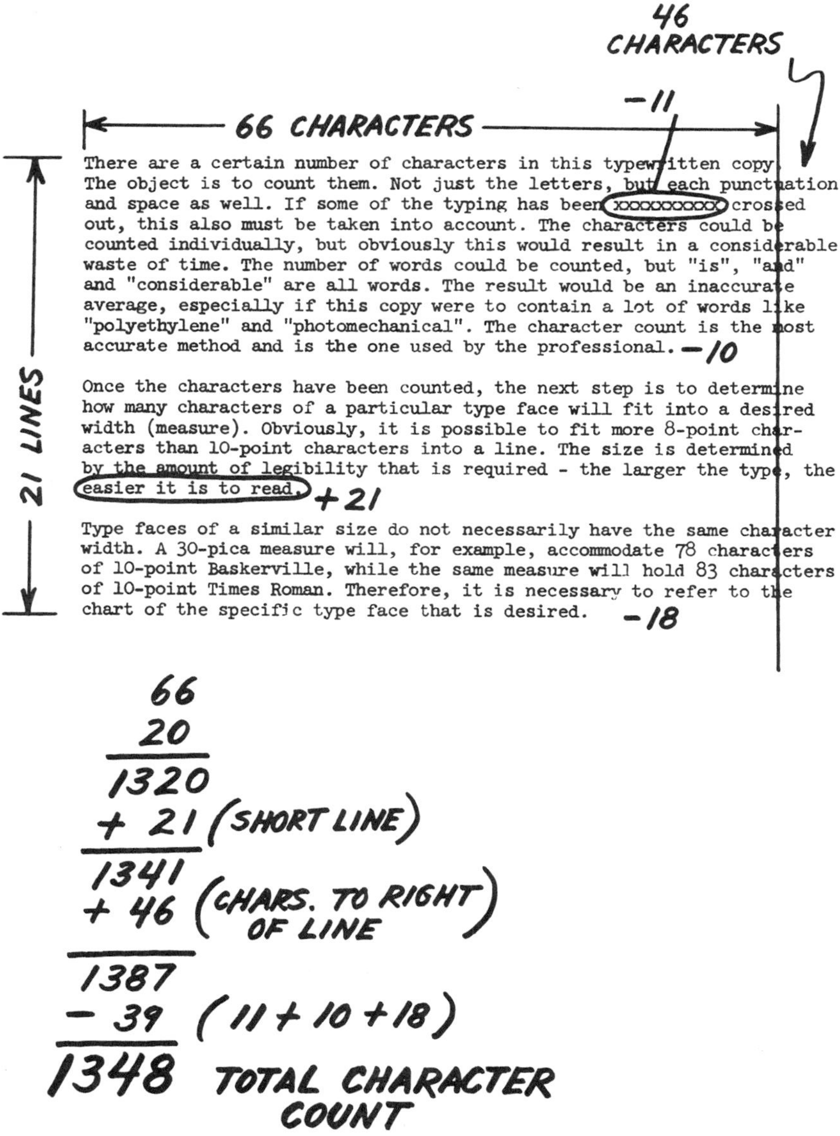

46 CHARACTERS

−11

66 CHARACTERS

21 LINES

There are a certain number of characters in this typewritten copy.
The object is to count them. Not just the letters, but each punctuation
and space as well. If some of the typing has been xxxxxxxxxx crossed
out, this also must be taken into account. The characters could be
counted individually, but obviously this would result in a considerable
waste of time. The number of words could be counted, but "is", "and"
and "considerable" are all words. The result would be an inaccurate
average, especially if this copy were to contain a lot of words like
"polyethylene" and "photomechanical". The character count is the most
accurate method and is the one used by the professional. −10

Once the characters have been counted, the next step is to determine
how many characters of a particular type face will fit into a desired
width (measure). Obviously, it is possible to fit more 8-point characters than 10-point characters into a line. The size is determined
by the amount of legibility that is required - the larger the type, the
easier it is to read. +21

Type faces of a similar size do not necessarily have the same character
width. A 30-pica measure will, for example, accommodate 78 characters
of 10-point Baskerville, while the same measure will hold 83 characters
of 10-point Times Roman. Therefore, it is necessary to refer to the
chart of the specific type face that is desired. −18

66
20
1320
+ 21 (SHORT LINE)
1341
+ 46 (CHARS. TO RIGHT OF LINE)
1387
− 39 (11 + 10 + 18)
1348 TOTAL CHARACTER COUNT

COUNTING CHARACTERS IN TYPEWRITTEN COPY

characters to the right of the line can be easily counted and added to the total of those on the left. The pencil rule should not be drawn through a short line at the end of a paragraph, or any other abnormally short line.

Steps in the character-count method of copy-fitting are:

1. Draw a vertical pencil rule through the shortest line of the typed copy.
2. Count the number of *characters* in the line. A character consists of *every* letter, space, and punctuation mark. Do not forget to include the character that falls on the line.
3. Multiply this count by the total number of lines. Do not include the short, end-of-paragraph lines in this total.
4. Count the characters to the *right* of the pencil rule and in the short lines (if any) at the ends of the paragraphs. *Subtract* any characters that have been crossed out or otherwise deleted.
5. *Add* this figure to the multiplied total. This gives the *total character* count.
6. Select an appropriate type face—Times Roman, for example—and refer to its character-count table in the type specimen book. (See chart on page 191.)
7. Measure the layout width in picas. In this instance, assume that the layout area measures 24 picas.
8. Referring to the chart, locate a point size whose pica width and character count per line most closely matches the figures determined by steps 2 and 7. The chart shows that a 24-pica measure will accommodate 66 characters of *10-point* Times Roman.
9. *Divide* the per-line character count obtained from the chart into the total character count obtained in step 5. This gives the total number of *type lines* required to set the copy in the particular face. Each fraction of a line must be counted as a line.

$$\begin{array}{r|l} & 20.4 \text{ or } \mathit{21\ lines} \\ 66 & 1348.0 \\ & \underline{132} \\ & \quad 280 \\ & \quad \underline{264} \end{array}$$

10. *Multiply* the total number of lines by the *point size* of the type. This gives the depth of the required area in points when the type is set solid.

$$21 \times 10 = \mathit{210\ points}$$

11. *Divide* this figure by 12 in order to determine the *depth in picas.*

```
       17.5  picas
12 ⟌ 210.0
      12
       90
       84
        60
        60
```

12. *If the copy is short of the layout area,* lead out the lines. Add the *point total* that is added between the lines to the total depth. Obviously, if a paragraph is 10 lines deep, and 9 points short of the desired depth, a 1-point lead between each line will cause the type to fill the area. More than 2-point line-leading is seldom desirable in normal body copy. If leading is impractical, try a larger size or an expanded face in order to fill the space.

13. If the copy exceeds the layout area, try a smaller size or a condensed face. In either case, if the depth is a critical factor, a different measure may be tried, provided the width is not critical as well.

TIMES ROMAN WITH BOLD								
Width in Picas	6 pt.	7 pt.	8 pt.	9 pt.	10 pt.	11 pt.	12 pt.	14 pt.
1	3.8	3.4	3.1	3.0	2.7	2.5	2.3	2.1
10	38	34	31	30	27	25	23	21
12	46	41	38	36	33	30	28	25
14	53	48	44	42	38	35	32	30
16	61	55	50	48	44	40	37	34
18	69	62	56	54	49	46	42	38
20	77	69	63	60	55	51	46	43
22	85	76	70	66	60	56	51	47
24	92	83	76	72	66	61	56	52
26	100	90	83	78	72	66	61	56
28	107	97	88	84	77	72	65	60
30	115	104	94	90	83	78	70	64

Courtesy of Mergenthaler Linotype Co.

A TYPICAL COPY-FITTING CHART

14. If all steps prove impractical, and the fitting of the copy into the area becomes a complete impossibility, request the client to cut or add to the copy.

It is often necessary to calculate copy depth when the type size and measure have been predetermined. Suppose it is mandatory to set copy in 10-point Times Roman to an 18-pica measure. Referral to the Times Roman chart shows that an 18-pica measure can accommodate 49 characters. The 49 characters are counted off on a typewritten copy line, and a vertical rule is drawn through this point. The number of *lines* to the left of the rule are counted. The *characters* to the right of the rule can be physically counted or estimated, and converted to lines by dividing by 49. This line count is added to the total. The total number of lines, multiplied by the point size of the type, *plus the point size of the intended leading,* gives the total point depth of the copy, which can be readily converted to picas.

It is often necessary to set copy to a predetermined depth. On such occasions, it is desirable to ascertain the width that the copy will occupy in order to make sure that, when set to this specified depth, the copy will be neither too narrow nor too wide. This is done in the following manner:

1. Count the characters in the copy.

2. Measure the desired copy depth in points, or measure in picas and convert to points.

3. *Divide* the depth (in points) by the point size of the selected type. If the lines are to be leaded, add the line-leading (in points) to the type size before dividing into the depth. The resulting figure gives the number of lines that will fit into the depth.

4. *Divide* the number of lines into the total number of characters. This gives the number of characters *per line.*

5. Locate this figure on the type chart. This will give the pica width of the copy.

6. If the copy is too narrow, try an expanded face or a larger size. Do not expect the typographer to overjustify, as this will produce word spacing that is awkward and difficult to read.

7. If the copy is too wide, try a condensed face or a smaller size.

In determining how much copy *should be written* to fill a desired space, the square-inch method is best for the initial estimate. Once the rough copy has been written to conform to such an estimate, a more accurate space determination can easily be made.

The Haber Rule

The Haber Rule is a patented device which affords easy specification of body copy, without reference to additional copy-fitting charts. The Haber Rule consists of a plastic depth-measuring scale, a complete listing of body-type faces, and a set of spiral-bound scales for the determination of pica width.

The desired face is selected from the listing. Each face has a key number which refers to a particular pica scale. This pica scale, when used to measure the copy width indicated on the layout, will show immediately how many characters of the selected face will fit in the width. The number of characters per measure is then divided into the total character count. This gives the number of lines that will be required to set the copy. The depth of any number of lines in any particular type size can be readily measured with the depth scale. Leaded lines are measured by using a section of the scale that equals the point size plus the leading. For example, if 10-point type is selected, the 10-point section is used; if 1-point leading is desired, the 11-point section is used; and if 2-point leading is desired, the 12-point section is used. The scale also provides a section which can be used for an easy count of typewritten characters, both pica and elite.

The requisites of good typography

Readability. Layout design notwithstanding, the criterion of good typography is readability. Distortion for artistic effect, to the detriment of readability, is poor artistry. If it is *intended* to be read, body text should be easy to read.

Lower-case letters are easier to read than capital letters. This holds true even in headlines. However, this does not mean that the elimination of *all* capitalization increases readability further. The eye is accustomed to perceiving proper capitalization at the beginning of sentences and of individual words, and the elimination of this practice, even though artistically in vogue, makes reading more difficult.

Serif faces are easier to read than sans-serif faces. Although sans-serif faces may be used effectively for display copy, their use in lengthy body text should be approached with caution.

Body type that is too small is difficult to read; type that is too large is cumbersome and wasteful of space and paper. Text is normally set in 10- or 12-point type.

There is a limit to the distance an eye can travel along a line of type before it becomes tired and requires the stimulus of having to jump to the beginning of the next line. This is the reason why typography on wide pages is set in columns. Although there is no fixed rule, a good line-width will contain from 40 to 50 characters of the particular size face. Books in the 6″ x 9″ size range will often employ lines of about 60 characters, since the format is too small to accommodate two columns.

Letterspacing and Word Spacing. The use of letterspacing between lower-case letters is a poor practice. Some letterspacing on lower-case display type of 36 points and larger is occasionally permissible, but it is wise to remember that lower-case type is *designed to fit close* and becomes hard to read when spaced out.

Lines set in capital letters, however, can be often improved by moderate letterspacing, especially when difficult letter combinations such as TY, TA, WA, VA, etc. occur. Straight vertical letters require more letterspacing than curved letters.

It is not necessary to attempt to specify the exact letterspacing that will be required. The typographer will do this when requested, even sawing or mortising the type to insure proper spacing. It should be kept in mind that discriminate letterspacing can be best accomplished with foundry type, and is not practical in most machine composition.

Line and Paragraph Leading. Type that has been set solid is difficult to read, as it represents a tight mass which is hard for the eye to penetrate. Type with a large center body, and short ascenders and descenders, require more line-leading than type with long ascenders and descenders. As previously mentioned, normal body type (10 to 12 points) is seldom leaded more than two points; however, if more leading is desired, a fairly safe rule is to let the line-leading equal the approximate word spacing. Whatever line-leading is utilized, it must be kept consistent between all of the lines.

Paragraph leading varies according to the nature of the copy, but it should be deeper than the line-leading. Since there is no set rule-of-depth, the space between the paragraphs represents an excellent place to locate a few extra points of depth in order to make copy fit. Paragraphs should not be leaded to the extent that they appear unrelated and, once established, the leading should be consistent between each paragraph.

Indention. There are three types of indention: regular, flush, and hanging.

Regular indention means that the first line of the paragraph is indented. The average line is indented one em—a longer line may be indented two ems; there is no set rule.

Flush indention means that there is *no* indention in the first, or in any other line of the paragraph. Flush indention makes smooth, even margins, but it is more difficult to read than regular indention. When flush indention is used, there must be additional paragraph leading in order to serve as a break for the reader.

In the *hanging indention,* the first line is set to the full measure, and all of the subsequent lines of the paragraph are indented. This type of indention does not require leading between paragraphs.

The Widow. Even though the character-count method is an accurate means of copy-fitting, there are always extenuating circumstances which may cause the copy to occupy fewer, or more lines than has been anticipated. This is most often caused by the rules of intersyllabic hyphenation—the fact that a word cannot be arbitrarily hyphenated, even if it will allow the copy to fit and to be spaced better as well. There are times when a word cannot be hyphenated and continued on the next line because the rules do not concur with the space available for the first portion of the word. Thus, the entire word must be moved to the next line, and the original line must be overjustified to compensate for it. This will also cause the copy to take up additional, unanticipated depth. On the other hand, hyphenation may, by chance, fall ideally, and the copy may take up less depth than predicted. Any undue presence of capital, wide, or narrow letters may affect the copy depth.

Artistically speaking, it is desirable to have a block of copy "square up" perfectly. The margins should be justified, and the last line should be as wide as the first. This is an ideal which is not always attained, at least not in the first setting. When the last line occupies more than half the measure, the block of copy will optically appear to be squared up and generally can be left untouched.

When the last line occupies *less than half* of the measure, particularly when only one or two words fall at the left margin of the last line, the visual effect is undesirable. This occurrence is known as a *widow.* A widow is capable of spoiling the appearance of a layout and should be eliminated.

This elimination can often be accomplished by the removal of word space in some of the preceding lines in order to move up the offending widow. This must be calculated by careful character count, and will seldom require the resetting of the entire paragraph. It is often practical

THIS IS AN EXAMPLE OF A TYPICAL "WIDOW"

to delete a word or two from the copy in order to get rid of a widow, but this deletion should be done by the copywriter, *not* the artist.

Initial Capitals. Initial capitals are larger capital letters—often decorative—which are sometimes used at the beginning of an article or a chapter in order to lend interest and break up the monotony of the text.

A *standing initial* is one which aligns with the bottom of the first line and protrudes into the empty space above the line. In order to accomplish this, it is merely necessary to specify the face and size of the initial and the indention of the first line to correspond to the width of the initial. There should be no hole between the initial and the beginning of the line; therefore, such letters as T, W, V, F, and P must be undercut by the typographer in order to make a tight fit.

The *set-in initial* is one which is set into the first few lines of the composition, which have been correspondingly indented. The base of the initial should align with one of the lines of the text, and the line directly beneath it should come to the margin. The top of the letter should preferably line up with the tops of the letters in the first line. If this is not possible, the top of the letter should project *above* the top line; it should never be allowed to fall below it. The first word or phrase of the top line is often set in capital letters to provide an optical transition from the large initial to the body face, and to make sure that the initial is read as part of the first line.

Initial capitals should harmonize with the body type. Careful measurement is necessary for the specification of such initials. This measurement should be made with an actual specimen of the desired initial at hand, since, for example, a 30-point initial is not necessarily as high as three lines of 10-point type. The face and size of the initial, as well as the desired indention, must be specified.

It is possible to order the typography with merely the desired indention and to insert the initial by hand with either transfer or adhesive type. This is hardly worthwhile unless a good many such initials are involved.

The Run-around. It is relatively easy to master the specification technique for a block of body copy. However, when confronted with the run-around, and the necessity of manipulating the text to accommodate illustrative matter, the task may appear to be hopelessly confusing. This need not be so if the copy is broken down into its simple rectangular components.

It is seldom that copy completely encircles an illustration; the copy may be interrupted in order to accommodate the illustration. The illustration occupies the entire column or page width, aligning with both the left and right margins. In this instance, the specifier need only determine the copy depth above and below the illustration which will allow its insertion and still maintain the overall size and format of the column or page.

The illustration may be inserted flush with one margin (right or left) and protrude into the copy to any desired width. The copy, set to the measure of the remaining width, runs alongside the illustration and resumes its normal measure beneath it. An illustration inserted in this manner can be located at any point—top, bottom, or middle—of the page. There may be more than one illustration on a page.

The empty space which is to accommodate the illustration should be considered as a large indention, from either the left or right margin. If the copy is specified as blocks—located above, alongside, and below the illustration—the necessary calculation becomes a simple matter.

Take, for example, a page that carries an overall copy area of 27 x 43 picas. Starting from the top, the copy runs the full 27-pica measure to a depth of 12 picas. At this point, an illustration measuring 13 x 20 picas is to be inserted, flush with the right-hand margin. This size includes the necessary marginal space around the illustration. Beneath the illustration, the copy resumes its normal 27-pica width and continues to the bottom margin of the page.

This gives the specifier three blocks of copy to consider. The first block runs the width of the page and down to the top of the illustration—27 x 12 picas. The block alongside the illustration measures the width of the page, minus the width of the illustration, and runs the depth of the illustration—14 x 20 picas. The remainder of the copy, which returns to the normal measure, will obviously have to be 27 x 11 picas. Thus, the page is composed of three blocks of copy: 27 x 12 picas, 14 x 20 picas, and 27 x 11 picas. Following is the manner in which the copy is fitted:

1. Count the characters in the typewritten copy.
2. Select the type face and size.
3. Refer to the appropriate copy-fitting chart and determine the number of characters that will fit into the 27 x 12 pica rectangle. Note this place on the typewritten copy. Then figure how many lines of the particular type will fit into the area.
4. Determine the number of characters that will fit into the 14 x 20 pica rectangle. Add this figure to the figure obtained in step 3, and

note the place on the typewritten copy. Again, figure how many lines will fit into this area.

5. Determine whether the remainder of the copy will fit into the remaining 27 x 11-pica area. If it fits, the type may be specified as follows:
Set in: ____ point (size), ________________ face. Set: ______ lines 27 picas (step 3); set ____ lines 14 picas, flush left (step 4); set ____ lines 27 picas (step 5).

If the job consists of a single page and the copy does not fit, try a smaller, larger, more condensed, or more expanded face. If the job consists of more than one page, *neither the face, size, nor line-leading can be varied from the preceding or following pages;* nor can the margins generally be violated. However, if the text runs from page to page, and specific copy is not necessarily required to fall on a particular page, the only critical area is the *last page*. It is usually permissible to utilize any portion of the last page. If the copy falling on the last page comes to only a few lines, causing the page to look empty, the needed space can be picked up from the caption page by additional paragraph leading, or by enlarging the illustrations. It may even be possible to add another illustration. If the copy is too tight, illustrations must be reduced or eliminated, or a smaller type face must be selected for the entire job.

The following steps, listed in order of preference, can be taken in order to insure proper fit:

1. Proportionally enlarge, or reduce, or drop the illustrations. This is by far the simplest method. One or two minor size alterations will probably be sufficient.
2. Increase the paragraph leading on the troublesome page, or increase the paragraph leading throughout.
3. Select a new face or a new line-leading for the entire job. This will require complete recalculation.
4. Add additional pages. This is the least desirable method, since pages must be added in multiples of four. It may be difficult in a brochure, for example, to adequately fill four more pages. Also, the extra paper required will add to the cost of the job.

Irregularly Shaped Copy. If the margins of the copy are required to take on a specific shape, either of their own or to conform to the outline of some adjoining design, the typography must be specified line for line. An accurate characters-per-pica figure must be obtained for the face selected. The number of characters that are to be set in each line must be carefully counted and specified. This is done by inserting slash (/) marks in the typewritten copy, indicating the exact number of characters that are to fall in each line. Each line will be set on a slug containing the indicated number of characters.

The slugs must then be aligned by the typographer to conform to the desired shape. The best way to specify such alignment is to make a careful tissue layout of the desired shape, indicating with ruled lines the exact length, alignment, and leading of each slug.

TYPE SPECIFICATION

There are no fixed rules as to the manner in which type is ordered (specified) from the typographer. It is even possible, and oftentimes most practical, to order a few lines of type over the phone. The important thing is that understanding communication be maintained between the specifier and the typographer. The specifier should know what he wants, and should be capable of conveying adequate instructions in order to make certain that he gets what he wants.

The best rule is to leave nothing to chance. Specify everything so that there will be no questions on the part of the typographer. It is better to overspecify than to leave half the job open to guesswork. The typographer should be provided with the following information concerning *each* type face to be set:

1. The type size.
2. The type family and face.
3. Specifications for capital letters, lower-case letters, or both.
4. The pica measure to which the lines are to be set.
5. Line-leading instructions.

Example: 10 pt. Times Roman Ital., caps and l.c.
24 picas wide, 2 pt. lead

Pica width may be indicated by drawing a horizontal arrow above the typed copy, from margin to margin. The necessary information is inserted between the arrowheads. Type which is to be leaded by casting it on a larger body is indicated as a fraction: 10/11, 10/12, etc.

The procedure for marking copy is as follows:

1. All copy should be typewritten and proofread. If excessive handwritten corrections have been made, the copy should be retyped.
2. Number each page in the copy; mark "end" on the last page of the copy.

3. Clearly indicate every different size, type face, and measure. Use a colored pencil.
4. Indicate line-leading in points.
   (a) If measure and leading are indicated, the depth will be automatic and need not be noted. However, it should have been determined by the specifier for fitting purposes.
   (b) If the type face is specified on a larger body, line-leading automatically occurs, and need not be further noted.
5. Indicate paragraph leading in points.
6. Indicate indentions, as they may not have been typed in the manner desired.
   (a) Regular indentions are indicated by square boxes representing ems.
   (b) The copy probably will have been typed with regular indentions. Flush indentions are indicated by drawing an arrow from the first letter to the left edge of the copy.
   (c) Hanging indentions are indicated by drawing an arrow from the first letter beyond the left edge of the copy, and noting the desired overhang in ems.
7. An indication of copy alignment should be made. A vertical pencil line through the left marginal letters indicates that the copy should be flush left. A vertical line through the right end of the longest line indicates flush right. Use of both lines indicates flush left *and* right, meaning that the copy is to be justified. A vertical line through the center of the copy indicates that each line is to be centered over the next line—an equal number of characters to the right and to the left of the center character. In addition to the ruled lines, "flush left," "flush right," "flush left and right," or "center" should be marked next to the copy.
8. Italicized words or sentences should be underscored once.
9. Capitalized letters, words, or sentences should be underscored three times; two underscores mean small capitals.
10. Type to be set in the same size, boldface, may be underscored with a wavy line, but it is preferable to note boldface type in the same manner as any other type face.
11. Note the point size of all rules (ruled lines) that are to be set by the typographer.
12. Mark "don't set" (or d.s.) on anything which appears on the copy sheet that is not to be set by the typographer.

13. Indicate whether the type is to be made up or set in galleys.
14. If extra proofs are desired, indicate how many. Indicate whether or not repro proofs are required.
15. Include your *job number* with each order. This enables easy identification for both art and billing purposes.

PRODUCTION TECHNIQUES

A true feeling for typography requires a certain degree of taste, as well as a sense of design. Typography is one of the most neglected aspects of the graphic arts. If one is incapable of seeing the difference between Varitype and Linotype, or appreciating the subtleties of hand-set composition, there is little point in attempting to *list* the distinctions. Any of the methods are capable of producing type that is readable. The test of the specifier's and the typographer's skill is the ability to produce work which has quality.

Typography is billed on a time basis. This includes the time that is spent setting the copy, in make-up, in puzzling over the specifier's instructions, and struggling through poorly organized copy. Thus, the more the specifier can do in order to decrease the time that must be expended by the typographer, the less the job will cost. For example, suppose the typewritten copy contains body text which is to be set in a machine face, and a large number of paragraph titles which are to be set by hand. The captions are typed in their normal location on the copy. Because of the surrounding text, and the abundance of specifications on the copy sheet, the titles are difficult to spot at a glance. If someone takes ten minutes to retype all the captions on a separate sheet of paper, the main copy can be given to the Linotyper, while the separate sheet can be given to the handsetter. Both can then work on the job at the same time. This means not only that the job can be done more efficiently; it will be finished sooner as well.

The use of a great variety of type faces in a single layout results in needless expense, since there is a minimum charge for each face. It is considered poor taste, as well. A good rule is to limit the type to no more than three different faces per layout. Size, of course, may vary as required.

Typographers work on a union scale which imposes strict charges for overtime. As a result, it is essential to give the typographer sufficient time to do the job so that no overtime work will be necessary. Many typographic shops employ a night shift. Since this is not an extension of the day shift, but a separate eight-hour shift, there is no extra charge for overnight work. Work sent out at 5:00 p.m. will generally be ready at 9:00 a.m. the following day—without overtime charges.

The maxim for efficient production is: "Get the type out first." The type should have been set, proofread, checked for fit, and corrected by the time the mechanical artist is scheduled to begin pasting up the job.

Galley Proofs vs. Make-up. Galley proofs are proofs that are pulled from the type as it comes from the machine or from the hand-setter, without regard for make-up. Complicated make-up by the typographer entails additional expense. The deciding factor between galley and make-up is time. It is cheaper to order galley proofs and paste them up by hand, *provided there is time to do so.* When the job comes in at 5:00 p.m., and is due at 10:00 a.m. the next day, it is better to let the night typographer make up—he has eight hours to do the job—so that, in the morning, the type can be rapidly pasted on the mechanical in a single piece.

Another example is the preparation of tabular matter that is to appear within a ruled form. The artist can rule much cleaner lines than the typographer can set. If time permits, the ideal method is for the artist to rule his lines, boxes, or grids; order the type in galley form; cut it out and paste it in position. Again, time may be limited, and make-up may be required in order to expedite the job. Line ruling may be accomplished in two ways: the typographer may make up the material using no rules, and the artist may rule them on the proof; or the typographer can make up the horizontal rules, and the artist may rule the vertical ones. The typographer can only set vertical lines between the horizontal rules; he cannot set vertical rules.

It is poor economy to order made-up type, if the proof must necessarily be cut apart in order to fit the elements into the mechanical art.

Photostatting Type. Since type is line copy, it is practical to moderately enlarge or reduce type photostatically. Overly enlarged type becomes ragged and necessitates hand retouching, while overly reduced type tends to fill in and become unreadable. However, a glossy photostat, within a reasonable size range, can be as sharp and clean as the typography itself. All type that is to appear in reverse must be negatively photostatted —even if it has been set to size—for positioning on the mechanical. It may also be enlarged or reduced at the same time it is negatively photostatted. Thus, the photostat serves as an effective tool of the copyfitter.

It is well to keep in mind that when type is photostatted, over or underdevelopment may adversely affect the weight of the characters. All photostats should be inspected carefully to make sure that this has not occurred. Photostats of type, especially body copy, should be carefully checked for dirt spots and sharpness of focus.

Some typographers supply photostat service. It is good to use such a typographer, since proofs can be photostatted immediately after they have been pulled. The entire job, type plus photostats, can be received at the same time—there is no further time spent in waiting for photostats. Such service requires careful planning on the part of the production man or artist, since he must determine the exact size of the type in advance in order to be able to specify the photostat sizes before he has seen the type proofs.

Many typographers also have film type machines. When ordering film type, it is more expensive to order the type in an individual size than to accept it in the size produced by the machine (about 35-mm. strips). It proves economical to accept the work in strip size, gang it up, and photostat it to the desired size. This, too, requires accurate advance planning.

Checking Typography. Upon receiving proofs from the typographer, the artist should perform the following functions:

1. Check the glassine proofs against the layout in order to determine if the copy will fit properly.
2. Have the typography proofread. More problems arise from typographical errors than from any other reason. It is safe to assume that there will be at least one or two typographical errors in every sizeable type job. For this reason, the proof should be read promptly in order to allow the typographer time to make the necessary corrections. Every typographer proofreads his work; nevertheless, it should be rechecked by the specifier. If there is sufficient time, a duplicate proof should be submitted to the client for his approval. Ideally, every job should be ordered with a sufficient time allowance for correction, or else the mechanical artist must be prepared to make paste-up corrections himself.
3. Repro proofs are usually still wet when delivered, and smear easily. They should be sprayed immediately with fixative or dusted with talcum powder.
4. Many clients are in the habit of revising copy (author's alterations) after it has been set. Thus, a revised proof may differ considerably in content from the first proof. Typographers have various methods of identifying revised proofs. When revised proofs are received, all previous proofs should be discarded in order to avoid any confusion.

5. Make sure that all type is left standing until the job receives its final approval. On large, complex jobs, this may be a matter of a month or so. Most typographers will leave a job standing for a month without extra charge.

IMPERFECT OR BROKEN CHARACTERS. It is the responsibility of the typographer to discard worn foundry type. Linotype matrices can become nicked or damaged, and the imperfection will appear many times in the composition. These, too, should be replaced. Proofs pulled from badly worn type should not be accepted.

Certain minor imperfections will occur due to inking and proofing. A good typographer will retouch broken characters with pencil. The alert artist should be constantly on the lookout for imperfections and should be capable of retouching them. This is especially true in the case of photostat negative made from type—the thin lines and the serifs have a tendency to fill in. These should also be retouched by hand. Type which has been excessively photostatted will tend to lose its sharpness.

Typographic production hints

The first rule of economical typography is: "Keep it on the machine." Foundry composition is more expensive than machine composition because it is more time-consuming. The cost of Ludlow, since it is part hand and part machine composition, falls somewhere between. Unless there is a specific reason, such as the sole availability of a desired face, or the criticalness of spacing, hand-set type should never be utilized for body copy.

Although machine faces are available in larger sizes, most commercial typographers do not stock them in larger than 14 points. Larger sizes must be hand set. It is often economical to order 14-point machine type and photostatically enlarge it to 18 or 24 points, rather than pay for hand composition.

In Linotype and Intertype, either Roman and italic, or Roman and bold are often contained on the same matrices. Since there is a minimum charge for each magazine used, this results in a two-for-one economy. There is a separate magazine for each type face and size, making it wasteful to use machine type to set only one or two words. This should be borne in mind when selecting type faces.

If an identical line of copy—a slogan, an address, a line of mandatory copy, etc.—is to appear on the mechanical in *several sizes,* it should be set once and photostatted to the desired sizes.

If an identical line of copy is to appear several times in the *same size,* it should be set once and additional proofs should be ordered. If a line of copy is to appear many times, it should be set in Ludlow. The line need only be set once; the machine will automatically duplicate as many slugs as are needed.

Any copy that is liable to appear from job to job should be negatively photostatted and kept on file. It should be positively photostatted, rather than reset, for each succeeding job.

No area of body text should be photostatted to fit—unless it is to stand by itself—since photostatting reduces or enlarges the point size and makes it incompatible with the rest of the text. If the entire text must be enlarged or reduced, it should be done *photographically;* this provides a more accurate size control and there is less tendency toward paper shrinkage.

In a complex job, if it is possible to typewrite all of the type that is to be set in each face on an individual page, it will expedite the typographer's job and result in considerably less expense.

Remember, a typographic bill is a charge for typographic services rendered *to your order and to your specifications.*

13 THE PREPARATION OF MECHANICAL ART

INDICATION OF SIZE

Definitions

Size. Sizes are stated as width by depth; 9″ x 12″ is 9 inches wide by 12 inches deep.

More production difficulties are encountered as a result of improper sizing of the mechanical art than for any other reason. It is imperative that before the mechanical is begun, the *exact* size should be determined.

Trim Size. The actual extremities of a piece of printed matter. In the case of an advertisement not occupying a full page, it is the total area—including margins—that the advertisement will occupy. In the case of a full-page advertisement (which will be trimmed after the publication is bound) or of a printed sheet, folder, brochure, etc., it is the final size to which the paper will be trimmed (cut). Trim size is indicated on the mechanical with *crop marks;* often with both blue outlines *and* crop marks.

Crop Marks. Crop marks are ruled *black* lines, placed at the four corners of the mechanical to indicate the actual finished size. These are retained on the printing plate and serve as guides for sawing the plate when positioning in a press form, or for aligning the cutting knives when the printed piece is to be trimmed. Crop marks should be ruled as *thinly and accurately* as possible. They should be placed no less than 3/16 in. from the corners (so as not to interfere with bleed lines), and should be no more than 1/2 in. long. Excessively long crop marks increase the size of the plate, adding unnecessarily to its cost. It takes eight separate crop marks—four vertical and four horizontal—to properly size a mechanical.

Bleed. An excess portion of the plate that extends *beyond* the trimmed edges of the sheet or page. It is utilized when a printed area is to appear to extend off the edge(s) of the page, and is designed to eliminate white spaces between the printing and the trimmed edge caused by improper alignment of the trimming knife. It is not necessary to bleed on all four sides of the piece. Where one side of a printed piece is to be bound or folded, bleed on this side is impossible.

Bleed Size. Normal bleed size is 1/8 in. This means an additional 1/8 in. on *each* side that is to bleed; thus, the bleed size of a 7" x 10" piece that bleeds four sides is: 7 2/8" x 10 2/8", or 7 1/4" x 10 1/4". If a 7" x 10" ad bleeds top, right, and bottom—leaving the left side for binding—the bleed size is: 7 1/8" x 10 2/8", or 7 1/8" x 10 1/4". Bleed extremity is indicated by a *red* line ruled *outside* the trim line.

Plate Size. The over-all size of the printing plate, including bleed—if any.

Black Line. Any line on the mechanical which is intended to print. Thus, black lines become an integral part of the mechanical which require no further attention from the platemaker.

Light Blue Lines. Guide lines for trim sizes and shapes, as well as the indication of irregular trim (die-cut), folds, perforations, etc. These lines are for the convenience of the artist and for the alignment of the folding or the cutting machinery. They will not appear on the negative, as light blue does not photograph on normal film.

Red Lines. Lines that are used to indicate the size, shape, and position of all halftone, tint (Ben Day), and color areas. These lines should be strong, clean, and accurate. Red lines indicate to the platemaker that work, such as stripping or opaquing, is to be done. Red lines will appear on the negative, but will be removed after they have served their purpose and will not appear as lines on the plate.

Fold Marks. Dashed black lines that are used to indicate the extremities of a fold. Placed *outside* the trim line, they are kept at approximately the same distance as crop marks and are the same length. These, also, will be retained on the plate, as a guide to the folder. The actual fold line is indicated within the mechanical as a thin, dashed blue line. Such an indication is not always necessary, but sometimes serves as a guide for positioning copy so that it will not fall across a fold.

Perforation Lines. Short-dashed blue lines that are placed inside the mechanical, and are used to show the exact location and alignment of perforations. The length of the individual dash need not be precise, as the perforation die is a manufactured item and is not made photomechanically from the lines on the mechanical.

Die-cut. Any irregular shape or design which requires cutting with a specially made die; a shape that cannot be cut with a straight blade.

Die-cut Line. A solid blue line on the mechanical art indicating the shape in which the job is to be die-cut. The cutting die is handmade to conform to this line.

Gutter. The inside margin between the printed matter and the fold or the binding.

Double Spread. Two facing pages in a publication.

Live Matter. The printed message of a piece, which should be kept sufficiently within the trim to preclude any possibility of being cut off. Live matter should not extend into the gutter.

Agate. A unit of measurement: $\frac{1}{14}$ of an inch—5½ points. The agate is used in the measurement of the depth of newspaper advertisements. Every mechanical artist should have an agate ruler as part of his equipment.

The determination of correct size

The initial step in the execution of a mechanical is "laying it out" —delineating its size with the proper trim and bleed lines. It is ruled with T-square and triangle in order to define precisely the areas in which the illustrations and copy will be pasted.

The mechanical artist should always check the proper authority to make certain of the correct size. This should be indicated on the layout; if it is not, it is the responsibility of the mechanical artist to find out the correct size. Measurement of the layout is not sufficient—the layout may be off a fraction of an inch, or the paper may have shrunk or stretched.

Information is available for determining the proper size for every magazine and newspaper published in the United States or Canada.

Magazine size requirements

Specifications for sizes of advertisements in individual magazines are listed in guides published by the *Standard Rate and Data Service.* Sizes are given for double spreads, full pages, and fractions of pages, depending upon the mechanical requirements of the publication. Both bleed (or plate) and trim sizes are given, as well as gutter allowances. Some publications list the maximum allowable area of nonbleeding live matter.

A double spread, which cannot be printed on the same sheet unless it is the center spread, is prepared as a single, double-width mechanical. The plate is cut when it is received by the publication. Double gutter allowances, one on each side of the center line, should be made, but no bleed should be inserted *between the pages*. Lateral bleed should be at the extreme left and right only.

Unless front, inside front, inside back, back, or center-spread insertions are purchased (at additional cost), it is impossible to predetermine the exact location of one's advertisement. As a result, mechanical requirements (trim and bleed) are specified to compensate for any possible location. In a thick, staple-bound publication, the pages nearer the front and back must be wider in order to accommodate the wrap around the back edge, or spine. To compensate for this extra width, extra bleed (left and right) is specified. Gutter allowances should be carefully observed, lest the live matter become jammed too close to the binding for readability.

Since it is impossible to predetermine whether a single-page advertisement will appear on the left or on the right, bleed should be furnished on *both sides*. The gutter bleed will be trimmed off the plate by the publication. Gutter allowances should be observed on *both* sides of the advertisement.

Rescale mechanicals

Often, an advertisement will be scheduled to appear as a full-page in one publication, and as a half-page in another. All of the material included in the larger advertisement must also appear in the second. If there is no proportional relationship between them which will permit camera reduction, a separate layout and an individual mechanical must be prepared for each.

It is often practical to utilize a single mechanical for the production of plates for several, various-sized publications. Suppose, for example, an advertisement is to appear, full-page, in four different publications. The plate sizes required are: 4″ x 5″, 8″ x 10″, 8½″ x 10½″, and 7¾″ x 9¾″. All four plates may be produced from a single mechanical, if proper allowances are made:

1. A basic mechanical, 8″ x 10″ is prepared.
2. The 8″ x 10″ plate may be made from a same-size negative.
3. The 4″ x 5″ plate may be made by camera-reducing the negative 50 per cent, since this is a proportional reduction.
4. In order to accommodate the 8½″ x 10½″ plate, the margins or bleed of the original mechanical are extended ¼ in. on each side. The live matter remains the same size as in the 8″ x 10″ advertisement; it merely "floats" in the larger size. A separate set of crop marks,

preferably in a different color for easy identification, is added to the original mechanical to indicate the extra enlargement. A same-size plate is made, which is then cut to the size indicated by the second set of crop marks.

5. Provided the live matter pasted on the original mechanical is kept within a 7¾" x 9¾" area, a third same-size plate may be made and cut down to the reduced size. A third set of crop marks should be added to indicate this size. The live matter may be tight, but this is often tolerated if it eliminates the need for an extra mechanical.

   If the presence of three sets of separate crop marks becomes confusing, the same effect may be accomplished by cutting a paper mask to each desired plate size and hinging it in position over the mechanical.

   Care should be taken so that there is no confusion between plate size and trim size—both should be clearly indicated. Appropriate bleeds should be calculated for each size variation.

Newspaper size requirements

Newspaper size requirements are specified in a separate volume published by the *Standard Rate and Data Service.*

Newspaper advertisement widths are measured in *columns,* and depths are measured in *agates.* An *agate line* is one column wide and one agate deep. Publisher's rates are quoted at so much *per agate line.* In former days, most newspaper columns were two inches wide, eight columns to the page, but with modern formats and tabloid sizes, column widths vary considerably. The column width for every newspaper in the United States and Canada, both daily and weekly, is specified in *SRDS.* Sizes are specified for full and half pages, as well.

If the column width for a certain newspaper is specified to be 1¹¹⁄₁₆ in. wide, two columns are 3⅜ in. wide, etc.

Newspaper advertisements are referred to by their total linage—the width (in number of columns) multiplied by the depth (in agates). An advertisement that is 1 column wide by 100 agates deep is a *100-line ad* (1 x 100); one that is 2 columns wide by 100 agates deep is a *200-line ad* (2 x 100), etc.

However, an advertisement that is 1 column by 200 lines (1 x 200) is also a 200-line ad. So is one that is 4 columns by 50 lines. Although the charges for these variously-shaped 200-line ads would be the same, it is well to know the proportions the client favors.

IMPOSITION, BINDING, AND DIE-CUTTING

Imposition

After pages are printed, they must be cut, folded, and bound. The bound copy may take a great variety of forms. In order to print both sides, cut, fold, and bind with the highest degree of efficiency—both in the saving of time and the elimination of waste—the printer must arrange his page forms on the press so that these operations may be best accomplished. This arrangement of the page forms is known as imposition.

Imposition is the responsibility of the printer; he will impose his pages properly, regardless of the order of their mechanical preparation. However, the artist can expedite matters considerably if he is familiar with the practices of imposition and has learned to work in close operation with the printer.

The simplest type of printed form is the 4-page folder. This is printed on both sides of a single sheet, which is then folded vertically in the middle. Pages 2 and 3 will print side by side, with page 2 on the left. On the back of the sheet, pages 1 and 4 will be printed, with page 4 impressed so that it will print on the reverse side of, or "back up," page 3. The mechanical flats are prepared in the following manner:

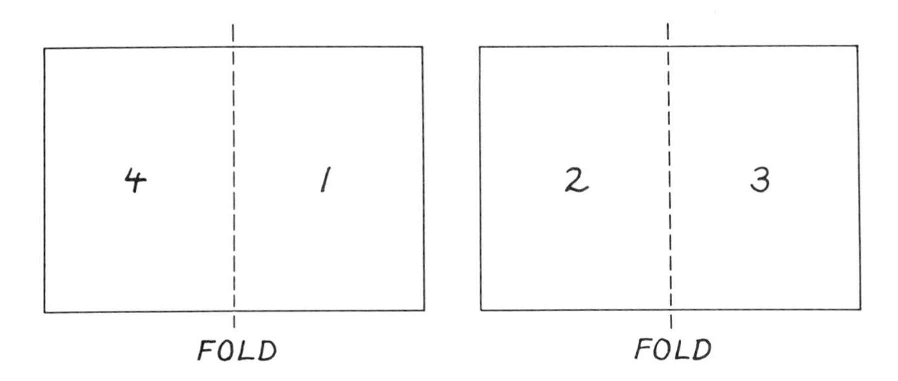

The 4-page folder requires no binding. An 8-page folder, however, requires two sheets which must be bound—usually with staples—along the fold. The mechanical flats for an 8-page folder are prepared in this manner:

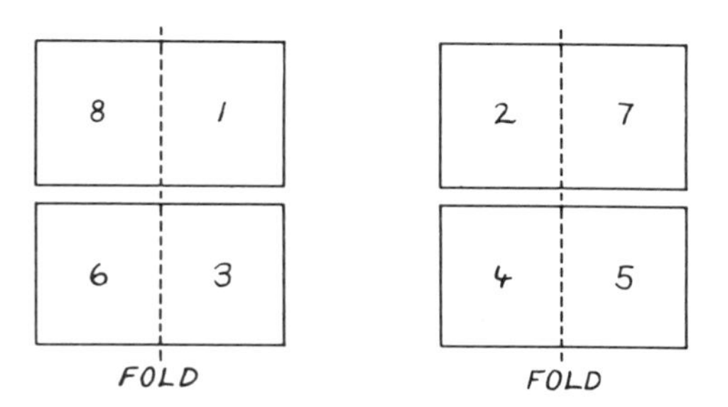

These flats are known as *engraver's flats*. This type of preparation is preferred by the platemaker because he can shoot a negative of each 2-page flat; there is no need for further repositioning of the pages.

It can readily be seen that booklet pages occur in multiples of four. Thus, booklets must contain 4, 8, 12, 16, 20, etc. pages. It is not necessary to print on every page, but there can be no such thing as a booklet containing, for example, 5, or 11, or 18 pages.

When preparing engraver's flats for more than eight pages, it is best to make up a paper dummy containing the desired number of pages. Each page is then numbered. When the dummy is taken apart, it will show the exact combinations in which the pages occur.

It is not always practical, from the standpoint of the artist, to prepare the flats in this manner. The layout may feature a complex design which runs across the entire spread. If this is the case, it is more convenient to prepare the art in facing pages. This may also prove easier for the client to visualize and evaluate than would engraver's flats.

An 8-page folder is laid out *in spreads* in the following manner:

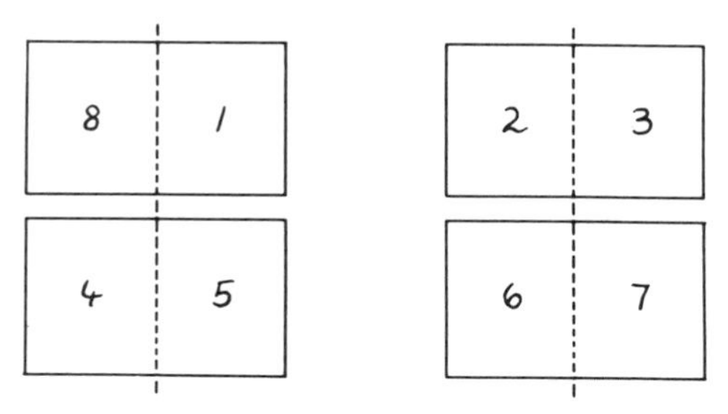

Since neither the front nor the back cover (pages 1 and 8) can be treated as part of a spread, they are laid out as they will appear on the plate. The platemaker shoots negatives of the spread, and cuts them apart so that they can be imposed according to the requirements of the job.

The choice of the preferred mechanical format should be made after consultation with both printer and client. If the artist has prepared his flats in accordance with the printer's specifications, he is not directly concerned with the manner in which the printer imposes his pages; however, it is still pertinent for him to understand the manner in which it is done.

There are three basic types of imposition: (1) sheetwise, (2) work-and-turn, and (3) work-and-tumble. The type of imposition employed depends upon the length of the run and the nature of the job. The purpose of imposition is the adaptation of the press set-up and the paper size to the proportions of the job, so that a minimum of paper is wasted—to produce the job at the lowest possible cost on available equipment.

SHEETWISE IMPOSITION. Sheetwise imposition utilizes two sets of plates; one set for each side of the job. Half of the pages are imposed on one set; the remainder on the other. The paper is printed on one side, allowed to dry, and then run a second time in order to print the back of the sheet. It takes 2,000 impressions to print 1,000 copies. The plates are imposed in the same manner as shown in the preceding diagram illustrating the preparation of the engraver's flat.

WORK-AND-TURN IMPOSITION. The object of work-and-turn printing is to allow the printer to print both sides of a given number of copies—1,000 for instance—with only 1,000 impressions. This is accomplished with paper cut to twice the desired size. All of the pages are imposed on a single plate. In order to print a 4-page folder, they are imposed in the following manner: [1]

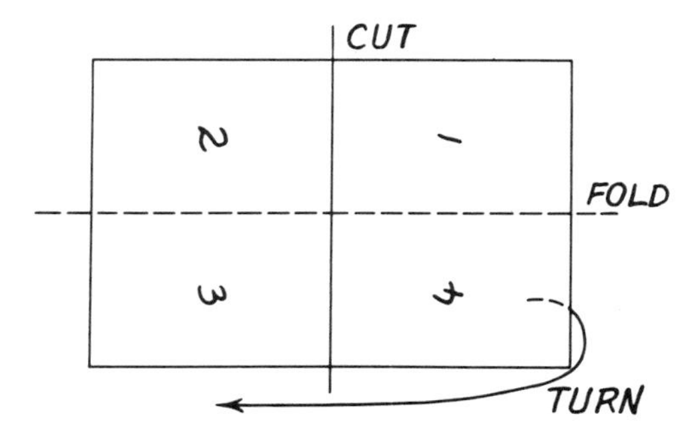

[1] The diagram indicates the page positions as they will appear on the proof sheet. Many sources indicate the positions as they appear on the plate. It should be remembered that letterpress plates are imposed backwards-reading, and litho plates are imposed frontwards-reading.

A total of 500 sheets is run through the press. The entire pile is then turned over, laterally, and rerun through the press. In the second impression, pages 1 and 4 will print on the back of 2 and 3; pages 2 and 3 will print on the back of 1 and 4. When the 500 sheets are cut vertically across, and the other dimension of the paper is folded horizontally, 1,000 4-page folders will result.

WORK-AND-TUMBLE IMPOSITION. Work-and-tumble printing would also be utilized to print 1,000 copies with 1,000 impressions. It differs from work-and-turn in that it is applicable for jobs which are horizontal in format. Work-and-tumble is imposed in the following manner:

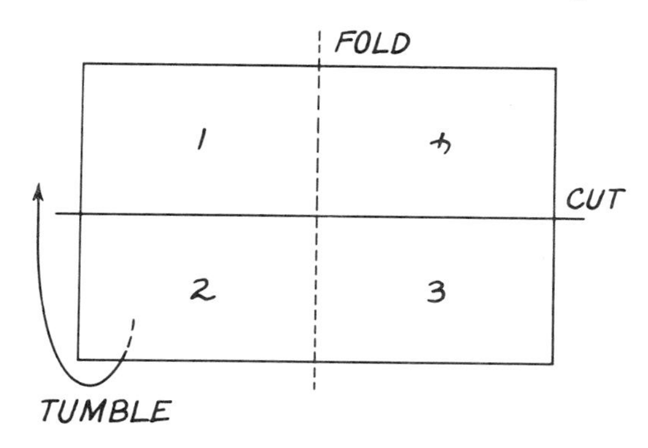

The pile of paper is turned over from bottom to top, instead of laterally. This again causes the proper pages to print on the backs of each other. The paper is cut horizontally across its long dimension, and is folded vertically.

It is possible to impose an 80-page book on a single sheet. This represents a considerable exercise in printing production, which no mechanical artist will ever be called upon to do. The mechanical artist prepares his flats as facing spreads or engraver's flats. Occasionally, he will be called upon to prepare his flats in imposition for a small booklet. Broadsides and other mailing pieces may fold in some complex manner, but they are basically single sheets, printed on two sides. As such, they offer no problem of proper page imposition.

The 6-page folder represents a unique problem for the mechanical artist. A 6-page folder is not bound; the extreme right page is folded between the other two, as is a letter, when it is inserted in an envelope. The *mechanical art* for a 6-page folder is laid out in the following manner:

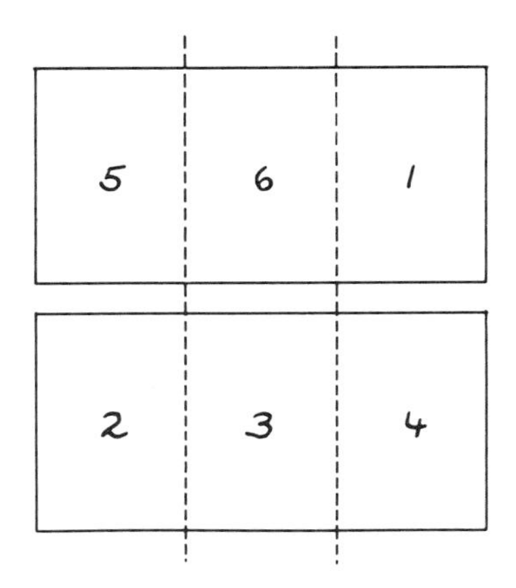

Page 4 is folded inward, covering page 3 and lining up with the right edge of page 2. If page 4 is not laid out *slightly narrower* than pages 2 and 3, the folder will bulge when it is folded. Obviously, page 5 must also be made slightly narrower. If this is not done, the printer will automatically trim the inward-folding side of his sheet at least 1/8 in. to compensate for this tendency. If the artist is not aware of this necessity, vital material may be trimmed off.

Binding

After the sheets are printed, they are shipped, still flat, to the bindery. The binder cuts, folds, binds, and trims the sheets into the desired format. The sheets are cut so that they may be folded, by machine, into signatures. The signatures are bound together; the trimming is done *after* the binding. In trimming, the cutting knives are aligned on the crop marks. This is the reason for bleed; there is 1/8 in. leeway to compensate for faulty binding or alignment of the knives.

The mechanical artist may be concerned with the manner in which the work is to be bound. It may be necessary for him to allow adequate margins on the binding edge, or to allow sufficient gutter clearance for the type of binding that will be used. There are no set rules; the printer will know the binding requirements, and his instructions should be followed explicitly. There are several types of binding in common use.

COVERS. *The self-cover booklet* is one of relatively few pages whose cover is of the same paper as the inner pages; the cover offers no added protection for the contents. The *covered book* or *booklet* has covers made of a material that is more durable than the inner pages. The covering may range in quality from a slightly heavier paper to the finest leather.

SADDLE-WIRE STITCHING. Saddle stitching consists of wires or staples, inserted through the fold, or saddle of the pages. It allows the booklet to be opened fully, but is impractical for the binding of a thick volume. Normal gutter allowances on the mechanical art will generally prove sufficient.

SIDE-WIRE STITCHING. Side-wire stitching consists of wires or staples punched from the front page through to the back page. These wires are inserted close to the fold, and are clinched at the back. Since the pages of a side-wire stitched book cannot be opened flat, extra gutter allowance should be provided.

MECHANICAL BINDING. Mechanical binding requires the punching of holes in the paper so that metal or plastic wire or strips may be threaded through them. A typical variety of mechanical binding is the well-known "spiral" binding. Mechanical binding allows the pages to lie perfectly flat, but adequate gutter clearance must be left for the holes. As there is a great variety of mechanical binding devices, the required hole clearance should be carefully checked.

LOOSELEAF BINDING. Pages that are bound together with removable rings or posts are called looseleaf. Ring binding may be opened flat; post binding may not. Since holes must be punched for either operation, proper clearance dimensions should be obtained.

THE SEWED BOOK. Better books are assembled in signatures which are then sewed together with strong thread. The thickness of the signatures forms a wide spine to which the cover is glued. This method provides considerable strength and flexibility; the pages can be opened flat. The mechanical artist is seldom concerned with the preparation of a book which will be bound in this manner.

Die-cutting

Any irregular shape or design which cannot be cut with a straight cutting knife must be cut with a specially made die. Since there is no standard format for the die-cut piece, each die is custom-made to conform to the requirements of the job.

The die consists of a steel cutting edge, conforming to the outline shape of the job. The die is mounted on a plywood dieboard, cutting edge up, in a manner similar to a cookie cutter. Die-cutting presses are similar to printing presses; the platen printing press is often employed for die-cutting small work.

The die for a simple display or promotional piece is made to conform to the blue die-cut line on the mechanical art. The die-cutting of complex displays and folding boxes requires greater precision than can be accomplished by the average mechanical artist. In the case of such work, the folding shape—together with its required die—is usually designed and approved before the surface decoration is designed; at least before the mechanical art is begun. If this is the case, the mechanical artist will be provided with a *strike sheet*. This is a heavy cardboard sheet which has been struck by the die, but not cut through. This strike sheet serves as a precise guide to the artist for the positioning of his mechanical art.

The printed sheet which is destined for die-cutting will also be imposed in a manner to eliminate waste. In order to do this, several unrelated jobs may be run together. Since most die-cut jobs are not uniform in shape, it is not unusual for the mechanical artist to be requested to alter a size slightly, so that it can be more readily accommodated on the sheet.

SCALING AND POSITIONING OF ILLUSTRATIVE MATTER

Scaling illustrative matter

Illustrations or photographs are seldom submitted in the same size that they will appear on the mechanical. Such art, which cannot be pasted in position on the mechanical, is known as *separate art*. It is necessary for the cameraman to enlarge or reduce this separate art to the required size, and strip it—in negative form—into the master flat. The area into which each piece of separate art is to be stripped must be carefully indicated on the mechanical; each piece of art must be keyed so that there is no mistaking its proper location.

Before its position is indicated, the art should be scaled to the mechanical size in order to determine its proportional adherence to the requirements of the layout. Width and depth enlarge or reduce in direct ratio to each other:

$$\frac{\text{Width}}{\text{Desired Width}} = \frac{\text{Depth}}{\text{Desired Depth}}$$

Example:

$$\frac{12}{6} = \frac{8}{4}$$

Obviously, to alter this ratio photographically would result in distortion. Therefore, it is the manner in which the picture is to be framed or "cropped" that is of concern to the mechanical artist. If an illustration is in silhouette or vignette form, it has no frame; it can be enlarged or reduced at will to fit within the desired area. A square halftone has definite edges which are often subject to alignment with other elements of the layout. If the proportions of the original are not conducive to such alignment, they must be altered so that they will be. The determination of the proportions that will result from a predetermined enlargement or reduction is known as *scaling*. Since any alteration of proportion is normally dictated by the nature of the art, a visual method of scaling has been found to be the most practical.

Visual scaling is based upon the principle that any new rectangle whose diagonal coincides (in angle, not length) with the diagonal of the original—whether in enlarged or reduced form—*is in proportion to the original.* This type of scaling will enable the artist to visualize the area the art will occupy when enlarged or reduced.

Visual scaling, using transparent tracing tissue, is accomplished in the following manner:

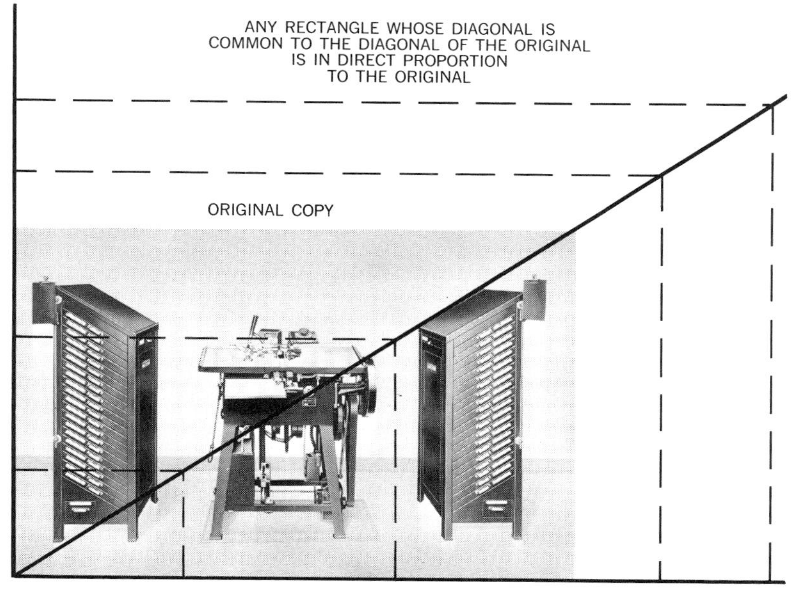

SCALING WITH THE DIAGONAL

The Ludlow Typograph —
Photo courtesy of
The Ludlow Typograph Co.

1. Place a piece of tracing tissue over the original; with T-square and triangle, rule a pencil line along the bottom horizontal edge and the left-hand vertical edge. If the original is an irregular silhouette or vignette shape, draw a rectangle about its extremities.
2. Rule a diagonal through the original rectangle—from lower left to upper right corner.
3. Determine the dimension that is more critical to the layout of the mechanical—depth or width—and mark the desired measurement on the corresponding ruled line on the tissue. With a 90-degree line, project this point to the diagonal. With another 90-degree line, project the point on the diagonal to the adjacent edge—the other ruled line. The resulting rectangle will be in proportion to the original.
4. If the rectangle determined by this process is adequate for the purpose of the layout, it means that the original—enlarged or reduced to the critical dimension—will fit without alteration of its natural edges. Crop marks are then placed at the corners of the original, and the size to which the original is to be enlarged or reduced is clearly indicated between them with a blue-pencilled arrow.

If, when scaled to the critical dimension, the proportions are found unsuitable, the shape of the original must be altered—either by trimming or by adding extra area—to conform to the desired proportions of the layout. For example, suppose a photograph which must occupy the entire width of the layout, when scaled to the desired width, is found to be so deep that it will infringe upon the copy area. It is made to fit within the desired space in the following manner:

1. Take the scaled rectangle (on the tissue), position it over the mechanical, and reduce its depth by ruling a horizontal line at the point where the bottom edge of the photograph should ideally occur.
2. Rule a *new* diagonal from the upper right-hand corner to the point where the new horizontal intersects the left-hand edge.
3. Replace the tissue over the original so that this newly established lower left-hand corner coincides with the lower left-hand corner of the original.
4. By projecting the *right-hand vertical edge* of the original to the newly established diagonal, and then projecting this point of intersection horizontally to the left-hand edge, a new rectangle—*showing the portion of the original which is in proportion to the desired size*—will have been established.

5. If depth is the critical factor, and the width of the original must be cropped to maintain it, the desired width is ruled on the scaled rectangle. A new diagonal is drawn and the new width is scaled back to the original.

6. The advantage of working on tissue paper is that once the cropped dimensions have been determined, the tissue may be shifted over the original in order to ascertain which border(s) can be most practically trimmed off. Obviously, it is desirable to crop edges where the subject matter is of least importance.

7. Since it is seldom desirable to destroy a photograph or illustration by physically cutting away portions, crop marks are placed outside the edges. When sized between the crop marks, and reduced or enlarged accordingly, the cropped area of the original should occupy the desired area on the mechanical. If the photograph or illustration must be cropped with no margin for error, it can be masked by cutting an opaque paper frame to the desired size and hinging it in position over the original.

8. Artistic judgment should be utilized when deciding which portions of a photograph or illustration can be sacrificed by cropping. The portions of a photograph which are to be cropped should be its most meaningless areas. Care should be taken not to trim off vital detail, tops of heads, hands, etc.

9. It is often necessary to *add* to a photograph in order to obtain the desired proportions. This is accomplished by reprinting the photo—in its original size—on larger paper. This provides a much wider margin around the photograph; therefore, an extra area may be added without encountering a paper edge. The retoucher is employed to add the additional area. The scaling should be planned so that the retoucher's job can be accomplished in the least complex area; it is simpler to airbrush a tone representing sky than to try to extend a detailed foreground. The job should be planned so that it is necessary only to add to one side; the cost would be double if he were required to add to *both* sides.

10. An illustrator should be fully aware of the size and proportions in which his work will appear, and should be capable of keeping his drawing within the required proportions.

11. If art is to bleed, *the bleed area should be taken into consideration when scaling.* If, due to the nature of the art, all of it must remain within the trim area, a satisfactory bleed area can often be accomplished by adding a compatible gray tone to the edge(s) in question.

Positioning illustrative matter

Once the illustration or photograph has been scaled and properly cropped or masked, its position must be clearly indicated on the mechanical art. This indication aids the platemaker in stripping the separate art into its proper location on the flat. It may be done by any of the following methods:

PHOTOSTATS IN POSITION. Photostats of the illustrative matter, reduced or enlarged to the desired size, may be pasted directly on the mechanical art. This method provides foolproof identification of each piece of separate art, and clearly indicates where any cropping will occur. It also enables the client to visualize the appearance of the finished result. When photostats are pasted up in this manner, bleed should be included. If, for any reason, it is necessary to include a ruled edge for the convenience of the stripper, the photostat is brought almost to the ruled line and deliberately cut with a ragged edge. This leaves the ruled line standing clear. The ragged edge indicates that the stripped-in illustration will terminate at the ruled line. In order to prevent any possibility of the photostats being mistaken for art-in-position, *"Not for Repro"* should be clearly marked on each photostat.

RED KEYLINE WITH BLUE-LINE IDENTIFICATION. A red keyline is drawn on the mechanical, indicating the extremities of the area into which the illustration is to be stripped. If the area is irregular, or a silhouette shape, its proper outline should be determined by enlarging or reducing it to the mechanical size with a camera lucida. The resulting shape is then traced onto the mechanical and indicated with a red line. The stripper uses this red line as a guide, removing it from the negative after the illustration has been stripped into position.

The location of each strip-in illustration is indicated with a blue-line drawing of its essential elements, which will readily identify it. To do this, the image is brought to the desired size with the camera lucida. The essential elements are roughly traced and transferred, in blue line, onto the mechanical art. This method gives positive identification of every strip-in. The blue identifying lines do not appear on the film negative.

RED KEYLINE WITH LETTER IDENTIFICATION. A red keyline is drawn on the mechanical art. A letter or number, written in blue pencil on the border of the separate art, and within the keyline on the mechanical, identifies the proper piece to be stripped into each area. This method affords the greatest possibility for stripping errors, and provides no visual predetermination of the finished result. It is, however, the most economical method; there is no expenditure for photostats, nor is there any time spent in making blue-line facsimiles of the illustrations.

Sizing illustrative matter

Each illustration or photograph should be marked with the size of the negative which must be made in order to strip it into the flat. This saves considerable calculation for the cameraman. One size indication, either width or depth, is sufficient. The words "Reduce to" or "Enlarge to" should accompany the size indication. If the illustration is to bleed, the bleed should be taken into consideration when sizing. Many illustrations have been photographed to an indicated size only to be found lacking sufficient bleed area.

Specifying the screen size

The screen size should be marked on each piece of separate halftone art that is submitted to the platemaker. The screen size must be kept consistent throughout a job; screen sizes do not vary from illustration to illustration, nor from page to page.

The artist should consult the printer in order to determine which screen size is most suitable for the paper on which the job will be printed. The general rule is: The rougher the texture of the paper, the coarser the screen that must be employed. Offset lithography can print a finer screen on a rough-textured paper than can letterpress.

Indications of both size of art and size of screen should be made in blue pencil on the margin of each piece of separate art. If the job is to reproduce in line, it should be so specified.

THE SCREEN PRINT OR "VELOX"

A screen print is a photographic contact print made from a screened halftone negative. Since most screen prints are printed on "Velox"—a Kodak photographic printing paper—the name "Velox" has become a generic term for the screen print.

The screen print is used to provide art that can be pasted in position on the mechanical, art which, since the image has already been screened, can be photographed by the platemaker as line art.

The negative for the screen print is made from a continuous-tone photograph or wash drawing in the same manner as the halftone negative, by placing a conventional halftone screen in front of the camera lens. The resulting screened negative is contact-printed onto photographic paper, rather than onto a sensitized printing plate. The result is a *photographic print* in which the image has been reduced to the appropriate dot patterns.

The screen print, which is ordered to the actual size it is to appear on the printed result, is pasted in position on the mechanical. When the mechanical, with all Velox art in position, is submitted to the platemaker, *a line shot is made.* There is no need for the platemaker to use his halftone screen; *the dot pattern has already been established.* The platemaker makes a line negative of the copy submitted to him. Since the screen prints are positioned on the mechanical, no stripping is required. The line negative makes a perfect copy of the existing dot patterns, which may then be produced on the appropriate printing plate.

When the screen-print negative is first made, it compares in quality with the flat-etched halftone. The entire area, even the white background, bears a slight screen pattern. The highlights are not pure white, nor are the blacks solid. The Velox negative, normally produced, has not been dropped-out. It may be dropped-out by the following methods:

Hand Retouching. The screen print is returned to the mechanical artist, who, upon positioning it on the mechanical art, silhouettes it with white paint, restores the drop-out highlight areas with white paint, and fills in the solid areas with black paint. It takes considerable skill for this operation, especially in the restoration of edges and thin black areas. Any slipshod work on the part of the artist will be incompatible with the precise nature of the dot structure and readily noticeable.

The artist has no means to alter the dot patterns in the middle-value areas. Any attempt to do so will result in objectionable irregularities of the screen pattern.

Automatic Drop-out. This is effected by the photographer. Two negatives are shot—a screened negative and a contrasting line negative in which the white areas appear as solid blacks. A contact print is made by superimposing the two negatives. The line negative serves as a mask for the silhouette and drop-out areas, eliminating the screen pattern in these areas of the print. There is an additional charge for a drop-out screen print.

The Fluorescent Processes. Any continuous-tone art prepared with fluorescent media, or any photographs which have been silhouetted and highlighted with fluorescent paint, will produce a drop-out negative. A contact print of this negative will result in a drop-out screen print.

Screen prints are generally ordered from a photoprinter or a lithographic negative supplier who owns halftone screens; photostatters seldom provide this service. When ordering screen prints, both the size of print and the size (lines per inch) of screen must be clearly specified, as well as the number of prints required. Normally, two prints are supplied.

The screen print must be ordered, and the mechanical prepared to the actual size it will appear on the printed result. Any enlargement or reduction of the screen print will affect the dot size as well. If a 110-line screen print is pasted on mechanical art which is to be reduced 50 per cent, the resulting image will print 165 lines per inch, too fine for normal reproduction. If the art is enlarged 50 per cent, the resulting image will have 55 lines per inch, too coarse for anything but a newspaper advertisement.

The advantage of a screen print is the resulting economy. Although the printed result resembles a flat-etched halftone, it has, nevertheless, been *reproduced as line art.* Line plates are considerably cheaper than halftone plates. Its disadvantage is that, since there is no means of dot alteration, the screen print lacks the quality that can be attained in a good halftone. The drop-out highlights tend to appear coarse and artificial, and there is little subtlety in the tonal areas. As a result, screen prints are most often employed for 55-65 line newspaper reproduction, where halftone quality is not such a critical factor. Photographs destined for screen-print reproduction should be heavily retouched in order to provide sufficient contrast.

When a screen print is being mounted on the mechanical, it should never be *cut* to the desired silhouette shape. The photographic emulsion tends to chip off along a cut edge, forming a ragged dot pattern. The print should be silhouetted with at least a half-inch margin of white paint, and the print cut out around the outer edges of the white. This will serve as protection for the actual edges of the image. A square print should be handled in a similar manner. It is difficult to produce a good vignette effect with a screen print.

REVERSE COPY

All areas where type or art appears in reverse—white copy on a black background—are preferably prepared as such on the mechanical art. The first step in the production of a reverse-copy area of the layout is the ordering of a glossy negative photostat of the copy. If it is of type, it should be carefully inspected to make certain that none of the lines have filled in. If the type has delicate serifs, or an illustration has particularly delicate lines, the photostatter should be instructed to expose the photostat a little less in order to produce a stronger reverse image. Extremely small type should not be printed in reverse.

A reverse area must assume some sort of shape; this shape should be drawn or ruled in black outline by the artist and filled in with black ink. The negative photostat is then cut out and pasted in proper position within the black shape. The cut edges of the photostat should be blackened so that they will not appear on the platemaker's negative. All rubber cement should be carefully cleaned off.

Often, a reverse panel or area will bleed. When this occurs, it is necessary to indicate the location of the trim line. If the panel involved is rectangular, and merely bleeds off one or more of the square edges of the job, crop marks, located outside the extreme corners of the mechanical, will be sufficient to indicate the trim line. If the trim is an irregular die-cut, and the reverse area bleeds off its edge, the exact die-cut line must be indicated. This is done by means of a *trap-line.*

The trap-line is a *blue* line used to indicate a die-cut edge, a fold line, or a perforation guide line *falling within a reverse panel or area.* The blue line, whatever its purpose, is ruled or drawn in the normal manner. The outline of the panel is drawn in its proper position, overlapping the blue line. When the reverse area is filled in, the solid black is painted *almost* up to either side of the blue line. Thus, the blue line is "trapped" in a white area within the reverse panel. The edges of the black panel adjacent to the blue line are deliberately made ragged. This ragged edge is a signal to the stripper that the area must be opaqued-out on the film positive.

In this manner, the blue line is retained on the mechanical to serve as a guide for the correct alignment of the trimming knives, the folding mechanism, or the cutting die. The blue line does not appear on either the film negative or the positive which will be made from the negative for opaquing purposes. All that appears on the positive is a wide, clear, ragged line, which can be readily obliterated by the opaquer. Once obliterated, the area will appear as the desired solid on the printing plate. Since use of the trap-line requires the production of both an extra film positive and a negative—the positive for opaquing and the negative for stripping into the flat—it should be avoided, unless it is imperative that the blue line appear on the art as a guide for some cutting or folding operation.

Often the occasion arises where there is no time to order negative photostats. In this instance, the type or art is pasted on the mechanical in positive form—to be reversed by the cameraman. Where camera reversal is required, a tissue overlay—clearly indicating the desired result—should be included with the job. If an area is to be camera-reversed, it should not be filled in, but should be delineated by the artist with a thin red outline, or *keyline*. The cameraman makes a film positive; the red keyline appears on the positive as a black line. The opaquer paints *up to this line from the outside*. The resulting black-silhouetted positive art is stripped onto the negative flat. In reverse to the negative flat, it will appear as a reverse area when printed.

Some mechanical artists will paste a negative photostat within a red keyline, leaving the cut edges of the photostat deliberately ragged in order to indicate that the opaquer is to fill in the space between the edges of the photostat and the keyline. This method involves the most work on the part of the opaquer/stripper; he must make a positive which he can opaque. He cannot strip this positive directly onto his flat, he must convert it to negative form so that the values will be in reverse from the rest of the flat. Thus, art produced in this manner requires, as does trap-line art, the production of an extra negative.

The platemaker can produce reverse areas regardless of the manner in which the mechanical art has been prepared. His charges will be based upon the amount of work he must perform in order to do so. Keyline art, with copy pasted up in either positive or negative form, requires opaquing; it also requires extra positives, negatives, or both. This is indicated in the following chart:

Manner of Preparation	Work Required of Platemaker
Negative photostat of copy pasted on solid black area.	Makes single negative and produces plate from it.
Positive copy pasted within red keyline.	Makes negative. Shoots positive from negative. Opaques *around* keyline on positive. Strips positive onto negative flat. Makes plate from negative flat.
Negative copy pasted within red keyline.	Makes negative. Shoots positive from negative. Opaques *within* keyline on positive. Shoots negative from positive and strips negative onto negative flat. Makes plate from negative flat.
Negative copy pasted on solid black area. Blue guide line trapped within black area.	Same procedure as above.

Unless there is a specific reason for doing otherwise, reverse art should be prepared with photostatically reversed copy, with all solid areas painted in by the artist. This requires the least work on the part of the platemaker. If it is prepared in any other manner, the artist should be capable of visualizing the extra work required of the platemaker, and the effect it will have on platemaking costs.

SCREEN TINTS

Ben Day

"Ben Day" has become a generic term used to denote a screen tint of a color produced by reducing an area, or "block" of solid color, to a uniform pattern of tiny dots. The tonality is regulated by the size and proximity of the dots.

Screen tints are used to provide emphasis to certain portions of the layout. The background may be screened; the copy may be screened; solid copy in positive or reverse may be either surprinted or dropped-out of a screen background. The screen tint differs from the halftone screen in that there is no tonal variation within an area. Screen tints are generally produced by the platemaker to the artist's specifications, but they can also be applied directly on the mechanical with Craftint or Zip-A-Tone.

The original Ben Day is a mechanical shading process, developed by Benjamin Day in 1881. It is a line medium used for introducing tonal patterns into a line illustration, to reduce the tonal value of type or the lines of an illustration, or as a background tint panel or shape. Ben Day antedates shading film, and is available in a wide variety of patterns—dots, lines, cross-hatches, stipples, etc.—but the uniform dot pattern is the one most generally used. Unless otherwise specified, the term Ben Day implies a dot pattern.

Screen tints are described in percentiles of 100, in multiples of ten, with 0 per cent representing white and 100 per cent representing solid black. They may also be designated as A, B, C, D, and E tints (multiples of twenty), with "A" representing the lightest tone. Screen tint charts are readily available.

In the original Ben Day method, the shading pattern is applied directly to the letterpress plate, using equipment leased from the parent firm. The pattern is applied in the following manner:

1. The letterpress plate is clamped to a board, over which is a hinged metal frame holding the Ben Day master pattern sheet.

2. The area to be screened is silhouetted with a gum gamboge solution.
3. The pattern sheet—a gelatin composition bearing a slightly raised design—is inked with a special grade of etching ink.
4. The inked pattern sheet is lowered onto the plate, and transferred by the pressure of a stylus or a rubber roller.
5. When the plate has been inked, the gum is washed off. The pattern is treated with topping powder and burned in. This causes it to become acid-resistant and, as such, ready for etching.
6. Ben Day film can be cleaned and is reusable.

In current usage, particularly in offset lithography, master negative pattern sheets are purchased by the platemaker. These are reproduced as thin film positives and are stripped into position on the flat.

There are four possible screen-tint combinations:

1. Tint background—black copy surprinted. Produced from positive art.
2. Tint background—white (reverse) copy dropped-out. Produced from negative art.
3. Tint copy—white background. Produced from positive art.
4. Tint copy—black background. Produced from negative art.

When solid copy—art, type, or a reverse panel—is screened, the printed result is found to contain a *white dot pattern* superimposed over the original copy. When a background area—delineated on the mechanical with a red outline—is screened, the printed result will consist of a pattern of *black dots*. The artist should fully understand this in order to properly prepare the mechanical art.

The platemaker (or stripper) always works with positive film in which the dots are black. If he strips positive dot film onto a film positive of the mechanical art, the background will bear a positive dot pattern surprinted by the copy. Although a negative must be made for platemaking, the printed result will appear as it does in the film positive.

If positive dot film is stripped onto a film negative, the transparent areas will receive the dot pattern. In the resulting proof, the copy will be screened with white dots. Since the negative is in reverse from the proof, the stripper must work in *reverse percentages*. If the desired tint is to proof 80 per cent, a 20 per cent positive film must be stripped. If the desired tint is 20 per cent, an 80 per cent positive pattern is stripped onto the negative.

When the copy is to surprint on a background of black dots, a *red line* is used on the mechanical to delineate the screened area. The screen positive (black dots) is stripped onto a film positive of the art, within

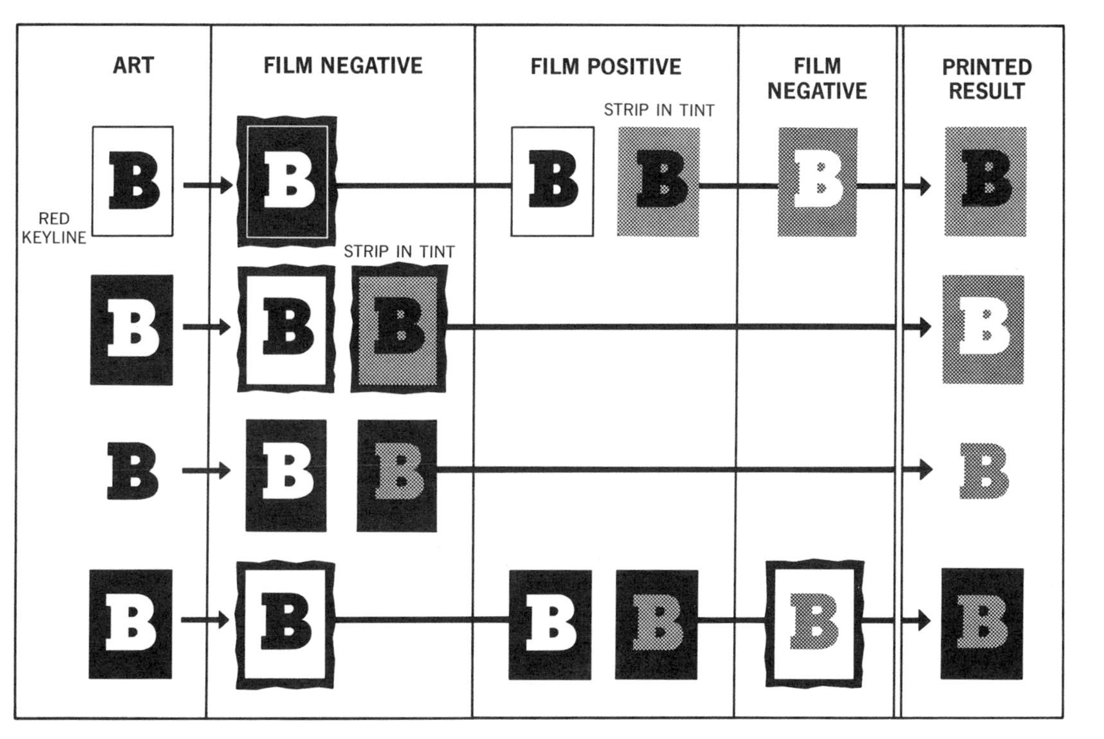

CHART SHOWING THE FOUR POSSIBLE SCREEN TINT COMBINATIONS, THE PREPARATION OF THE ARTWORK AND THE MANNER IN WHICH THE TINT PATTERN IS STRIPPED ONTO THE FILM.

the delineating lines. A negative is made for platemaking, and the lines are removed by opaquing.

When the copy is to drop out of a screened background, it is prepared as a reverse panel. This produces a transparent area, or "window," on the negative onto which positive dot film is stripped. The resultant proof will be a background with a white dot pattern, bearing dropped-out copy.

When the copy itself is to be screened, positive art is provided. This also produces transparent areas on the film negative onto which positive dot film is stripped. In the resultant proof, the copy will appear with a white dot pattern.

When screened copy is to appear on a black background, a reverse panel is provided. The positive dot film is stripped onto a film positive of the reverse panel. Thus, in the printed result, only the copy will bear the screen, while the background remains solid.

When Ben Day is to be applied to a drawing by the platemaker, blue wash areas are painted on the actual drawing to indicate the location of the Ben Day areas.

Each area of the mechanical that is to receive Ben Day should be carefully marked with percentage of tint and color of ink. This should be done in blue pencil on a tissue overlay or, if practical, on the art itself.

There are several precautions that should be taken in the utilization of screen tints:

1. If positive copy is utilized, background tints should be light enough to keep the copy legible. Screen tint charts generally show the effects of copy surprinted on various screen percentages.
2. If reverse copy is utilized, the background tint should be dark enough to carry the copy.
3. Screen tints have a tendency to print 5 to 10 per cent *darker* than specified. This tendency should be taken into consideration when the specification is made.
4. It is not advisable to run a tint behind type that is less than eight points in size; the dots will tend to obliterate the letter structure of type that is extremely small.
5. Screen areas cannot be effectively butted together, since the variation in angle will produce a ragged edge. Adjacent screen patterns should be separated with a black holding line.
6. One screen superimposed on top of another produces a moiré pattern—a wavering pattern that lacks tonal uniformity.

Shading media

Craftint Board is a drawing paper resembling Bristol board, in which tonal patterns may be produced by the application of a chemical developed. Craftint is available in a wide variety of Singletone (one) or Doubletone (two on the same board) patterns. It is used for the toning of line illustrations and is especially applicable for comics or technical drawings.

Shading Film is a transparent, adhesive sheet, bearing a printed pattern which may be applied over artwork and removed from the undesired areas. Removal is accomplished by scraping off the dots with a stylus, or by cutting them away with a razor blade.

The preparation of artwork with shading film

Shading film may be fixed to the mechanical itself in order to produce a screen tint area. This results in the elimination of Ben Day charges. The film is placed on the art, cut to the desired shape, and attached by burnishing with a triangle or the back of a comb. If air bubbles should result, they can be released by pricking them with a divider point. Shading film is most practically applied to line illustrations. This keeps the process directly under the control of the artist, and enables the artwork to be presented for approval in the exact form in which it will appear when printed.

The following procedures should be followed when attaching shading film to the mechanical art:

1. Check to make sure there are no imperfections in the printed film.
2. White dot patterns are impractical for application over reverse areas, or on top of line copy. Although they may appear opaque upon initial examination, they are seldom opaque enough after they have been burnished. The result is a gray dot that is unsuitable for sharp reproduction.
3. Make certain that if there is to be any reduction in the printed size of the art the pattern will accommodate this reduction without filling in. Most manufacturers provide charts showing the various patterns in reduced size.
4. Make sure there are no pencil lines or dirt under the film. The wax backing of the film attracts dirt readily.
5. Do not attempt to attach film over cut edges. When burnished, these edges will distort the pattern and will be picked up by the camera.

This possibility may be eliminated by fastening the film, in registered position, on a transparent overlay; however, a stripping charge will result.

6. Except in an attempt to produce a cross-hatched effect with single-line patterns, films cannot be effectively applied on top of each other; a moiré pattern will generally occur.

MECHANICAL ASSEMBLY

Mechanical assembly, or "paste-up," is the preparation of the elements of the layout for the platemaker's camera; the "final assembly" of the art. The mechanical may be prepared as camera-ready art—with all elements pasted in position; or it may be submitted as a mechanical plus separate art—with the position of all strip-ins indicated on the mechanical with red keylines.

The elements of the layout are pasted on a sheet of illustration board known as the *flat*. This may or may not have overlays, depending on the nature of the job.

Three colors are used in the execution of the mechanical; each has a definite purpose:

Black. Anything which is to appear on the printed piece is prepared in black on the mechanical.

Red. Thin red lines are used to indicate the size, shape, and position of halftone and Ben Day areas. Red lines are used to indicate the outlines of reverse panels which have not been filled in. These lines will be used by the platemaker to strip in separate art, or as a guide for opaquing. After their use, they will be removed by the platemaker; they will not appear on the printed result.

Light Blue. Instructions for sizing, Ben Day percentages, screen size, stripping instructions, etc. are written on the mechanical (or on a tissue overlay) in light blue pencil. Light blue lines are used to indicate shapes and positioning for the convenience of the artist in assembling the mechanical. They will not appear on the platemaker's negative. Die-cut lines are indicated in blue, since the die is not made photomechanically. Light blue shading is often used to indicate Ben Day areas; this may be done directly on the flat or on a tissue overlay.

The principal steps in the assembly of mechanical art are as follows:

1. The mechanical should not be commenced until the layout has been approved by an authorized person.
2. Mechanical art should not be commenced without knowledge of the *exact* size.

3. The job is "laid out" on the flat, either in actual size or in a logical multiple of the actual size. Actual size is always preferable. The job should be laid out with generous margins on the flat in order to provide adequate room for registration marks, instructions, etc. The outline size is first ruled with T-square and triangle, using a well-sharpened hard pencil. The size should be exact; a thirty-secondth of an inch is a critical factor in mechanical art, especially where accurate registration is required.

4. Thin black crop marks are ruled at the corners of the job. Fold marks, consisting of thin black dashed lines, are appropriately located. After these have been ruled, the pencil lines may be erased or reruled as light blue lines to serve as a guide for the artist.

5. Bleed is added. This is indicated with thin red lines. Normal bleed is 1/8 in., but it is always well to check. If the mechanical is being prepared in a larger size, the bleed must be increased proportionately.

6. The mechanical artist is responsible for the execution of any irregular shapes—balloons, cartouches, bursts, borders, underlines, dashed rules, etc.—which appear on the layout. These should be done cleanly and precisely. If the shape is complex, it may be drawn on thin Bristol and pasted in position. This prevents spoiling the flat if a mistake is made. Dashed lines are usually drawn by ruling a solid line and breaking it evenly with white paint. If a complex border design is required, a short portion may be drawn separately, and additional portions duplicated with photostats. The photostats are then pieced together.

7. All type proofs, lettering, line art or photostats of line art, logotypes, trade marks, photostats used to indicate position, and any other material photostatted to size, are pasted on the mechanical. All material should be "square"—in perfect alignment with the top and bottom edges of the flat.

Paste-up is accomplished with *thin* rubber cement; a mixture of one part cement to four parts thinner works best; it permits easy removal if changes are necessary. It is true that a carelessly executed mechanical can still be reproduced, but many firms are judged by the appearance of their mechanical art. An untidy mechanical is an invitation to check thoroughly for further discrepancies. In order to improve the appearance of mechanical art, all material to be pasted-up should be cut square with a straightedge rather than cut haphazardly with scissors.

In paste-up, rubber cement is applied to both surfaces and they are allowed to dry before they are joined. Material cemented while still wet has a tendency to shift and may eventually become stained, since the trapped cement does not always dry properly. A good practice is to cement the entire back of the type proof. When dry, the proof is placed, face up, on a sheet of cardboard (the back of a pad or a spoiled piece of illustration board). The blocks of type are cut out with a razor blade and a T-square. The dried rubber cement will hold them in position on the cardboard until they are ready to be transferred to the mechanical. This practice keeps small type from being lost and serves as a check to make certain that all of the type has been transferred to the mechanical. The glassine type proof is used to predetermine the proper fit of the type.

The type or photostat is aligned on the mechanical by placing the T-square along the base of the bottom line, and maneuvering the piece into position by holding an upper corner. Tweezers are indispensable for this purpose. A large block of copy may be slip-sheeted (a tissue placed underneath the upper portions to prevent adhesion) until it has been lined up. If, for any reason, the material must be removed after it has been attached, thinner should be used to loosen the cement. The area should be liberally flooded with thinner; a small oil can is ideal for this purpose. If a cemented piece is pulled up without the use of thinner, bumps of cement will form, making smooth replacement difficult.

8. Type proofs should be sprayed with Krylon, Spray-Fix, or some other fixatif before paste-up. Proofs remain wet for some time, and are easily smudged if not sprayed.

It should not be taken for granted that all type has been set square. If it has not been tied up properly, the lines may not be precisely parallel. This should be checked and, if necessary, the offending lines cut apart to make certain of their accurate alignment.

The mechanical artist is responsible for the checking and repair of smudged or broken type characters. Excessive cases should be returned to the typographer. It may be assumed that the copy has been proofread; nevertheless, the artist should be on the alert for typographical errors.

9. All excess rubber cement, pencil lines, dirt, eraser residue, etc. should be thoroughly removed. It is easy to spot unremoved rubber cement if the flat is held at an angle to the light. There is no excuse for mechanical art which has not been properly cleaned up.

10. When the type and photostats have been pasted in position and all of the rubber cement has been cleaned off, the keylines for the halftones are ruled. Photostats may be used to indicate the position of the halftones. These may be cut to size and pasted in position. They may also be mounted within a red keyline area, with their edges cut ragged, just short of the line. This provides a precise, ruled line to serve as a guide for the stripper, while still providing visual identification of the halftone. Some artists paste transparent red film on top of the position photostats. The transparent film does not obliterate the photostat image, but will produce a transparent "window" on the platemaker's negative. The negative made from the separate halftone art is stripped into the window; no opaquing is required. All photostats used to indicate position should be marked "For Position Only," or defaced in some manner to indicate to the platemaker that they are not in-position halftone art.

11. All separate art not indicated by photostats on the mechanical should be keyed for positive identification.
12. The printing size should be clearly marked on the mechanical. Both bleed and trim sizes should be indicated.
13. All Ben Day areas should be indicated on a tissue overlay, together with the desired tint percentage.
14. There should be a blank tissue sheet hinged over each mechanical flat and over each piece of separate art. These are provided for marking corrections so that there is no temptation for anyone to mark on the actual art.
15. Both mechanicals and separate art should be further protected with a paper flap. Brown wrapping paper is often used for this purpose.
16. Mechanicals and separate art should bear the name of the source and the number which has been assigned to the job.

OVERLAYS

The overlay is a transparent or translucent sheet which is positioned over the mechanical flat. It is used either to position material which cannot be conveniently pasted on the flat, or to position elements of the design which are to print in an additional color.

The overlay must be registered. Registration consists of providing markings which will enable the overlay to be replaced exactly in its original location, or will enable a plate, made from the overlay, to be printed precisely over the underlying impression.

Registration marks are thin, 90-degree cross-lines, drawn with a ruling pen. They are first drawn on the flat on at least three sides of the artwork. They should not be too far from the edges of the mechanical; nor should they be close enough to extend into the bleed area. They should be no longer than ¾ in. After the overlay has been securely taped in position—hinged across the top edge with a single strip of tape—the registration marks are drawn on the overlay exactly on top of those on the flat. The registration marks on each overlay should be slightly shorter than the ones on the flat, or overlay beneath. This enables the artist to make certain that his marks are directly on top of each other. The thinner the marks, and the more accurate their superimposition, the more exact the registration will be. Registration marks preprinted on transparent tape are available; however, a much thinner, more accurate line can be drawn with the ruling pen. Platemakers have various types of printed multiple marks which are used to provide accurate registration for multicolor work. The fact that they will be used by the platemaker does not excuse the artist from providing precise registration marks; it may be necessary to remove and replace the overlay before it reaches the platemaker.

The material used for the overlay depends on the work which is to be done on it. Transparent acetate affords the most accurate registration, but it is a difficult surface on which to rule lines. Frosted acetate constitutes a better surface for ruling lines, but it is more difficult to see through, especially when several overlays are required. Heavy tracing vellum is ideal for pen work, but affords even less visibility. It is possible to buy treated clear acetate which will readily accept pen lines, but it is extremely expensive.

It is difficult to produce large solid black areas on any of the three surfaces; large areas of black paint or ink will chip from either clear or frosted acetate, and will cause vellum to wrinkle. As a result, *red film*—Contak, Bourges, or Zip-A-Tone—is used to produce large solid areas on the overlay. Such film is self-adhering and is easily cut to the desired shape. The red film will photograph on the negative as black, but because it is *transparent* red, it can be seen through. This is a useful asset for the accurate registration of the overlay.

Overlays are used for the following purposes:

1. The positioning of art or type which is to be either surprinted or dropped out of a halftone background.
2. The preparation of line and halftone combination drawings.
3. The delineation of Ben Day areas when the nature of the paste-up makes it difficult to rule keylines or paint solid areas on the flat. These areas may be indicated on the overlay with either red keylines or solid areas of red film.
4. The location of alternate copy. For example, a brochure may be printed in which the name of the dealer changes in each area of distribution. The copy for each of these changes is registered in position on a separate overlay. In instances where, for certain reasons, prices or other information may vary, alternate copy is positioned on an overlay.

5. The preparation of preseparated color art, in which a separate overlay is made for each color that is to be printed.

COLOR PRESEPARATION

Color preseparation consists of the preparation of artwork with a separate, accurately registered overlay for each color that is to be printed. The platemaker makes a negative of the flat and of each overlay; there is no need for him to become involved with filter separation and opaquing.

Good color preseparation is completely dependent upon the skill and accuracy of the artist; there is no prepared medium which will insure foolproof results. Preseparation is undertaken in an attempt to eliminate the cost of camera separation and to allow the artist to maintain a closer control of the job. It allows him to execute and thus be paid for work that might otherwise be done by the platemaker. Preseparation and camera separation require a similar expenditure of time for their execution. Camera separation is more expensive because of the photomechanical equipment involved; preseparation requires no special equipment. Most printers prefer to have art submitted in preseparation form. Printers realize their profit from the use of their presses, not from their camera-art department.

Poorly executed preseparation may cause registration problems which will prove difficult to repair. This could result in more expensive complications than if the job had been originally camera-separated. The preseparation of mechanical and illustrative art should be entrusted to an artist who has a reputation for craftsmanship.

The preseparation of mechanical art

Color separation of mechanical art involves line separation of two or more colors, plus whatever additional effects may be obtained by the addition and/or superimposition of screen tint areas. There are two types of registration involved: *loose register* and *hairline register*. A job is in loose register when the component colors never print less than 1/16 in. from each other. Hairline register occurs when two color areas meet, with neither overlap nor white space between. If the second color is considerably darker, it is possible to have a hairline of overlap for safety's sake.

The simplest variety of line separation involves a typographic layout which is to print in two colors. The caption and the logotype will print in red, while the body copy prints in black. Since no type area touches any other type area, there is no problem of hairline registration. It is a simple matter to paste all of the black-plate type on the flat, and all of the red-plate type in registered position on an overlay. Negatives of both the flat and the overlay will be made, and a plate will be produced from each negative. Should the plates print slightly off-register, it will be scarcely noticeable.

The inclusion of a red panel or some other design shape will not complicate the job unless it must print in hairline register with some element of the black plate. When this occurs, the overlay must be carefully registered, and the edge of the area on the overlay must coincide *exactly* with the edge of the adjoining area on the flat underneath. A ruling-pen line which is too thick provides sufficient latitude to throw the job off-register.

Any solid or Ben Day area is indicated on an overlay in the same manner as it would be indicated on a one-color mechanical—with either a solid area or a red keyline. Most hairline registration of solid-color areas is accomplished with red film. It is possible to cut a more precise edge than can be ruled or drawn with a pen. If a panel or shape is cut slightly off-register, it can be readily picked up and shifted into position. Film can be easily trimmed or patched to produce a more accurate registration. Some red film, such as Bourges, is manufactured so that the color may be deliberately scraped off. This may be used to great advantage in complex line separation, but when using such film, care should be taken that the pigment is not accidentally scratched.

Every overlay which is to print in a color should bear a color swatch—a sample of the color in which the plate is to print. The swatch should be at least 1″ x 2″; sizeable enough so that it may be easily matched by the printer. It is not necessary to provide a swatch for a Ben Day tint, as long as one is provided for the solid color. Color swatches may be hand painted, cut from colored paper, or cut from the samples provided for this purpose in an ink sample book. It is the responsibility of the printer to match the color accurately. However, if a sample of *printed color* is submitted, care should be taken that it is a flat *solid* color. A process color or a varnished color may be difficult to match.

The preseparation of illustrations

Line drawings are separated in the same manner as mechanical art. Each additional color is drawn on an overlay, in either loose or hairline register. As in the preseparated mechanical, accuracy of registration is a critical factor.

Various additional color combinations may be obtained by the superimposition of screen tints. In the separated line drawing, solid areas are prepared as such; tint areas are prepared with red keylines and are stripped in by the platemaker. The use of shading film on a separated line drawing is impractical; the dot pattern is too coarse and a moiré effect will invariably result.

FAKE PROCESS. The purpose of fake process is the creation of a full-color effect through the use of superimposed screen tints, rather than with halftone process plates. Since the plate that utilizes screen tints is a line plate, it is considerably less expensive than a true process plate.

Fake process jobs are preseparated by the artist. The artist who prepares fake process art should have a set of color charts at his disposal. These charts, published by various sources, contain small swatches which are printed in almost every conceivable hue and value. Each color is arranged on the chart so that its component percentages of the process hues can be readily determined. The artist selects a particular color area which is to appear on the printed result, noting the component percentages. For example, the color he selects may contain 80 per cent yellow, 40 per cent cyan, and 20 per cent magenta. He must then produce, either by drawing or by cutting film, an identical, accurately registered area on each overlay. Each area must then be marked, in blue pencil, with the percentage of the screen which will be stripped into the area. The resulting surprint of the three screened areas will produce the color that was originally selected.

The screened areas of fake process produce flat tones; there is no modeling. In an attempt to produce some degree of tonal variation, the black plate is often drawn and printed in halftone. Fake process art may be prepared in either of the following techniques:

1. A black line drawing is made. Three overlays are registered over the line drawing: one each for magenta, yellow, and cyan. The screen percentages of each desired color must be determined, and a solid or keyline area must be produced, in register, on every applicable overlay. Each area must be marked with the correct screen percentage found on the color chart.
2. A black halftone drawing is made, rather than a line drawing. This will afford some degree of modeling when the flat color areas are printed over it. The black drawing should be kept light in value so that there will be a minimal discoloration of the surprinting hues.

HALFTONE PRESEPARATION. Some artists produce preseparated halftone art with a set of accurately premixed gray paints; one for each tone percentage. The artist first makes a thin-keyline drawing in black. A line plate is made from the drawing and several proofs are pulled, in *blue ink,* on illustration board. Since all proofs are pulled from the same plate, they are identical, and thus, in perfect registration. The artist then designates a proof for each process color and paints in the appropriate areas with the proper percentage of gray. Provided he paints accurately within the blue lines, and his percentage calculations are correct, the result will be superior to a fake process job. Since the separations must be reproduced in halftone, the artist has the opportunity to introduce modeling into any desired area.

Preseparated halftone art may be prepared with Bourges sheets. Transparent Bourges sheets are available in the process hues, and in various percentages of the process hues. The sheets are printed as continuous tints, rather than as screen tints. As a result, any multicolor illustration, preseparated with Bourges, must be reproduced in halftone.

Since the sheets are printed in color, they provide a visual method of preparing preseparated art. The color may be scraped from any desired area with a plastic stylus, or may be darkened with special water-soluble colors or modeling pencils. Bourges separations are prepared in the following manner:

1. A key wash drawing is prepared in black.
2. Bourges sheets—either solid color or a percentage of the solid color—are registered over the key drawing. If a great variety of tint percentages are required, it may take more than three overlays to produce the job.
3. The desired color combination is effected by either scraping off, darkening, or leaving untouched the appropriate area of each overlay. As the artist can see through any or all of his overlays, he has constant visual control over his work. The color that appears through the combined overlays is the color that will appear on the printed result.

14 PRODUCTION FOR THE PRINTING PROCESSES

Much has been written about the best methods of producing art for the various printing processes. In actuality, properly prepared art should present few difficulties for any of the processes. Many artists feel that the printing will somehow minimize their mistakes. No printing process can perform miracles if the art is poorly executed, or if poor plates are supplied. If slipshod work, clearly evident on the mechanical art, is no longer present in the printed result, it is because *someone*—usually the stripper or the opaquer—has repaired it. Such additional work is, of course, billed accordingly. It is reasonable to assume that there is no excuse for imperfections in professionally prepared art.

The following is a list of criteria for well-prepared art, regardless of the printing process to be employed:

1. All copy should be proofread.
2. Sizes should be *exact*.
3. The art should be *clean*. Rubber cement, dirt, fingerprints, and pencil lines should be carefully removed. All art should be protected with a paper flap.
4. Line copy should be prepared in black, regardless of the color of ink that will be used to print the job. The black should be *black,* not gray. Line art should be clean and sharp. Lines should be heavy enough to stand up during the press run, and spaced far enough apart to avoid fill-in. Bleeding lines, resulting from the use of soft paper, should be avoided.
5. Halftone copy should have well-defined tonal areas. Tonal areas should be cleanly rendered; scrubbed or muddy tone does not reproduce well. Photographs should not be over-retouched.
6. Broken type should be repaired. Smudged type should be replaced.
7. All elements of the mechanical art should be "squared up" with T-square and triangle. No printing process can realign copy which has been carelessly pasted in position.
8. All overlay material should be accurately registered. No printing process is capable of registering inaccurate preseparation. Material for the drop-out, the mortise, or the surprint should be submitted in

the manner that will require the least amount of photography on the part of the platemaker.

9. All separate art should be keyed for positive identification. Its position on the mechanical art should be delineated with either photostats or precisely ruled lines. The required enlargement or reduction of every piece of separate art should be clearly indicated.
10. No instructions should be left to guesswork. Instructions for every desired operation should be clearly written on the art in a pertinent location. It is better, whenever possible, to write instructions on the base art rather than on an overlay. Overlays are torn off during photography and may become lost. All instructions should be written in *blue pencil.*
11. Every screen-tint area should be carefully marked with the tint percentage and the color of ink desired. A swatch of the desired color(s) should be attached to the mechanical art. A tissue overlay, showing the color and location of all screened and solid-color areas, should be provided.

The best-printed results are obtained when the artist makes an effort to learn the manner of preparation preferred by each individual printer for whom he is liable to prepare art. The following preferences of the printer should be ascertained in order to prepare the art in the most efficient manner:

1. Whether the printer (or the platemaker) prefers "in position" or separate art.
2. Whether photostats or keylines should be used to indicate the position of separate art.
3. Whether color and tint areas should be indicated by solid areas or with keylines.
4. How line/halftone combination art should be prepared.
5. Whether the art should be camera-separated or preseparated; whether the artist or the platemaker should be paid for the separations.
6. Whether the pages should be prepared in spreads (facing pages in numerical sequence) or as engraver's flats (the sequence in which they are imposed on the press sheet for cutting and folding).
7. When the press run is scheduled. Missed deadlines mean idle presses —an expensive occurrence for all concerned.

Additionally, the artist should ascertain, either from the printer or the client, the following information concerning the job:

1. The exact finished size.

2. The number of colors in which the job will be printed.
3. The process which will be used to print the job.
4. The size and type of press the printer intends to use.
5. The type of paper on which the job is to be printed.
6. The quantity desired.
7. The screen size that will be used for the halftones.
8. The manner in which the printer intends to impose his plates.
9. The manner in which the job is to be cut. If it is to be die-cut, whether or not the die already exists, and if so, whether there are strike-sheets available.
10. The manner in which the job is to be folded, bound, stitched, or mounted.

PRODUCTION FOR LETTERPRESS PRINTING

Advantages of the process

Letterpress is an excellent medium for the reproduction of line, halftone, and color art. Printing plates are extremely durable and readily withstand long press runs. Proofs of letterpress plates can be readily supplied.

Existing letterpress plates can be cut apart and rearranged for further use. Printing may be accomplished from metal type without recourse to the reproduction proof. Letterpress plates may be converted for lithography; letterpress material is often designed with this further purpose in mind.

Disadvantages of the process

Except in the case of newspaper art, which utilizes a coarse screen, letterpress halftones must be printed on quality paper.

There is an additional charge for all halftone work. Continuous-tone art must be supplied for halftone printing. An exception is the screened Velox print—which is etched as a line plate rather than a halftone. Screen prints are used extensively in newspaper advertising, but are seldom employed for quality, fine-screen printing.

The letterpress plate is expensive. Any error requiring the production of a new plate is a costly one. Ease of correction is often mentioned as an advantage of the letterpress process; this is only true when actual type, which is easily replaced, is used for printing. Correction of a letterpress *plate* is a difficult and expensive operation.

The preparation of art for letterpress

Mechanical Art. Most letterpress-printed advertising material is produced from mechanical art. Since halftones are often engraved separately, it is not necessary to paste halftone art in position on the mechanical. Line art is either drawn or photostatted to size, and pasted in position.

Small advertisers, with limited art facilities, will often provide the newspaper with illustrative matter, but request that the newspaper set the type. In this instance, no mechanical art is required; a layout is sufficient.

If metal type and separate engravings are used for letterpress printing, actual mechanical art need not be produced. A paste-up—using galley proofs and keylines to indicate the position of the illustrations—may be supplied as a guide for page makeup.

The engraver should be consulted in order to ascertain whether art for the surprint, drop-out, or mortise should be overlayed on the separate art or on the mechanical.

Photographs and Wash Drawings. The fine-screen letterpress halftone can be produced with remarkable fidelity to the original art. Other than the normal requirements for good halftone reproduction, there are no special procedures for the preparation of photographs and wash drawings for letterpress printing.

There is, however, a considerable difference between the preparation of art for magazine (110-line screen) and for newspaper (55 to 65-line screen) reproduction. Newspaper reproduction requires better-defined contrast—preferably employing no more than four tonal values. Retouching for the 110-line screen is kept subtle; retouching for newspaper screen should be strong. However, excessive retouching will not save a poor-quality photograph.

Line Copy. No special preparation is required for letterpress line work. Excessive reduction should be avoided, although fine-line detail is easily held in letterpress.

If metal type is used for printing, a proof of the composition should be carefully examined in order to make certain that there are no broken characters.

Newspapers are reluctant to print large areas of solid black—especially reverse backgrounds. The printing of such areas requires excessive ink which will oversaturate the newsprint and retard drying. Most newspapers will arbitrarily screen any solid black areas that are considered too large.

PRODUCTION FOR LITHOGRAPHY

Advantages of the process

Offset lithography is the most economical method of printing in quantity. This does not mean, however, that lithography is never expensive; that it is always less expensive than *any* form of letterpress printing; that it is an inferior medium. In lithography, there can be a wider range of quality than in any other printing process. There are lithographers whose specialty is cheap one-color handbills. There are lithographers who print four-color process on coated stock. There is poor letterpress and poor gravure, but it never looks quite as bad as poor lithography. Good lithography rivals the best efforts of the other processes.

Some of the factors that affect both the quality and the price of lithography are:

1. The artistic integrity of the lithographer.
2. The type of plate employed.
3. The type of press used to print the job.
4. The amount of effort expended in color correction.
5. The kind of paper used. Lithography can print halftones well on a cheaper grade of paper than can letterpress, but lithography does not *require* the use of a cheaper grade of paper.

The lithographic plate is inexpensive, but there is considerable difference between the cost of a presensitized paper plate and a deep-etch plate. Plates, duplicate plates, and multiple-image plates take less time to produce than do plates for the other processes.

It is possible to print previously screened material with lithography. This practice should be approached with caution, as there is a noticeable loss in halftone quality. If high-quality work is preferred, it is just as desirable to submit continuous-tone art for offset lithography as it is for any other process.

Lithography is especially adaptable for large-sized work such as posters and displays. The plate lays down an ink film of even thickness on large work—work which would pose a serious make-ready problem in letterpress printing.

Disadvantages of the process

Offset litho plates are not easily corrected. This disadvantage is overcome by the inexpensive nature of the plate. Should the plate be found in error, the correction is made on the negative; the old plate is discarded and a new one is made. The expense of a new plate is small, compared to a letterpress or a gravure plate.

Mechanical art must be prepared. Nonillustrated book printing is now an exception; film negatives and positives which can be used directly for making litho plates are produced by phototypesetting machines.

Not all lithographers have proofing facilities. In lieu of this, blueprints or Van Dykes are submitted for client approval, prior to the press run. Some clients find the interpretation of these blueprints difficult. The Minnesota Mining and Manufacturing Company has marketed a transparent proofing film which can be dyed in some semblance of the desired color. In multicolor work, a separate, appropriately dyed proof is made from each of the separations. This is of great advantage for submission to the client who might become confused by the blueprint, but it does not provide an adequate means for checking the quality of process color.

The preparation of art for lithography

Mechanical Art. Mechanical art for lithography and mechanical art for the letterpress *plate* are prepared in a similar manner. The lithographer would prefer to have all of his halftone art pasted in position. This is seldom practical; the original continuous-tone art is generally too large for the mechanical. Line art is pasted in position, as it is for letterpress.

Material for both the litho plate and the letterpress plate is assembled in film-negative form, with the exception of deep-etch plates which require positives. Mechanical art which has been prepared for expeditious negative assembly is suitable for either process. As in letterpress, it is best to know the preferences of the platemaker.

When a halftone proof is utilized for litho art, it should be pasted on the mechanical, to be reproduced same-size. Reduction will cause the dot pattern to fill in; enlargement will make the pattern too obvious.

Photographs and Wash Drawings. Some artists, especially retouchers, feel that the softness of the offset blanket impression warrants overemphasis of the tonal areas of continuous-tone art. Modern lithographic techniques have rendered this practice unnecessary.

Line Copy. Line copy is prepared in exactly the same manner as for letterpress. Line copy for lithography should be particularly clean. If any undesirable material appears on the negative and goes unnoticed by the opaquer, there is no means of routing it off the litho plate.

Since lithographic plates cannot incorporate letterpress type, reproduction proofs must be utilized on the mechanical art. These should be carefully checked for broken characters, smudges, etc.

PRODUCTION FOR GRAVURE

Advantages of the process

Gravure is an excellent medium for the reproduction of properly prepared halftone art, both in monotone and in color.

The paper utilized (newsprint) is comparatively inexpensive. Gravure plates are costly, but this cost is balanced by the saving in paper cost which is realized over a long press run.

Disadvantages of the process

Since the entire gravure plate carries a screen, line work—especially type with thin lines and serifs—has a tendency to look hairy.

Elements of the design, once etched, cannot be altered or shifted. Due to the speed of the rotogravure press, hairline register is difficult to maintain.

The paper stock used for gravure cannot be relied upon to produce any artistic effects.

It is impractical to utilize materials (negatives, plates, halftone proofs, etc.) from other printing processes.

The preparation of art for gravure

MECHANICAL ART. More special precautions should be taken in the preparation of art for gravure than for either letterpress or lithography. In gravure, there is no counterpart of the line and halftone combination plate—all of the gravure plate is halftone. Thus, anything submitted as line on the mechanical art must be prepared with the knowledge that it will bear a screen on the printed result. Line work is, in effect, silhouette halftone. The center of the line fills in, but the dot pattern is evident at the edges. *Any* line elements of the mechanical art which are too thin are in danger of becoming ragged in appearance.

Once a gravure cylinder has been etched, it is impossible to shift units or make major changes. As a result, all type, lettering, line art, logotypes, etc. should be submitted as a single mechanical.

If drawings or photographs are to be submitted as separate art, an accurate indication of position should be included on the mechanical.

Guide lines for tint areas should be indicated with red keylines, with instructions to delete the lines from the negatives. Neither Ben Day nor shading film is applicable to the gravure process. Second colors should be painted in red or black on acetate overlays, or applied with transparent sheets of red film.

The paste-up should be neat and accurate. Carelessly cut and pasted edges will cause additional retouching costs.

Photographs and Wash Drawings. Gravure is essentially a tone medium. It is used most advantageously as a medium for the reproduction of the color photograph.

Many publications which are printed in gravure also contain signatures (sections) which are printed in one- or two-color letterpress. This enables an advertiser to insert an advertisement in the publication, using duplicate plates of a letterpress advertisement which may have been used elsewhere. A one-color line advertisement is best run in this section.

If the advertiser wishes to advertise full color in a gravure publication, he must purchase gravure plates for the purpose. The quality of the printed result may justify the additional cost of a set of gravure plates.

Photographs submitted for gravure should be printed on smooth paper. Extra flat or extra contrasting prints should be avoided; the middle tones should be rich and sparkling. If several photographs are to appear, they should not be of varying contrasts. Excessive enlargement or reduction should be avoided.

Wash drawings should be held to the same tonal range as photographs. The lightest printable tone should be a good value step away from the white of the paper. Gravure stock has a certain grayness; this should be allowed for in the drawing. Wash drawings which contain two types of black pigment—for example, a drawing rendered with both lampblack and drawing ink—should be avoided.

Line Copy. Fine line copy should be checked with extreme care in order to make certain it will accept the gravure screen.

Excessive reductions should be avoided. If they are necessary, they should be photographically reduced and retouched. Actual-size drawings are ideal for the process.

Delicate line work should be restricted to one color. It is difficult to maintain hairline register on the rotogravure press; the slightest off-register will cause thin lines to blur if they are overprinted in two colors. Off-register on reverse backgrounds will cause the edges of the background to bleed into the lines.

The use of type faces with delicate thin lines and serifs should be approached cautiously. There should be no imperfections in the type proofs utilized for the mechanical. Body type should be no smaller than 8-point; reverse type should be heavy enough to insure that it will not fill in.

Special attention should be given to type surprinting over a panel or a background. The background should be light and contrasting in color. Type should be printed in one color only. Type to be surprinted or dropped out should not be overlayed on the artwork, but should be placed *in position on the mechanical.*

PRODUCTION FOR SILK SCREEN

Advantages of the process

The silk-screen stencil is inexpensive to produce. A hand-operated process requiring no expensive printing equipment, silk screen is an ideal medium for an extremely short run. It is practical to use silk screen to print as few as fifty copies. Automatic equipment is available for quantity printing.

Silk screen will print on virtually any surface. Special inks and paints can be used, many of which would provide difficulties for any other printing process.

Disadvantages of the process

There are certain artistic limitations to the process because it is essentially a medium for printing line. Halftone silk-screen printing has made considerable progress, but there is no comparison with the capabilities of the other processes.

Although silk screen is a most versatile medium, the equipment has neither the speed nor the stamina for book, magazine, newspaper, or other comparable types of printing.

The preparation of art for silk screen

MECHANICAL ART. Mechanical art should be supplied to the silk-screen printer, but it is seldom as complex as that submitted for the other printing processes. Since halftones are to be avoided if possible, there is no problem of stripping; there is no counterpart of the combination plate. The use of screen tints is a questionable practice. It is more practical to print a second color, if any color variation is desired.

A one-piece line mechanical, to size, with all elements pasted in position, will generally prove sufficient.

CONTINUOUS-TONE ART. As previously mentioned, the printing of halftones should be avoided, unless there is no other method of solving the problem. If a silk-screen printer is located who can provide evidence of his ability to print halftones, his advice, and his alone, should be followed for the preparation of the artwork.

LINE ART. Silk screen is an excellent line medium. The artist should ascertain whether the printer plans to use photographic or hand-cut stencils. If he plans to use a photographic stencil, the line art is prepared in the normal manner. It need not be drawn to size; it can be reduced when the film positive is made.

If the screener plans to use a hand-cut stencil, the art should be made actual size. It may save time for the artist if he realizes that *only outlines need be provided.* There is nothing to be gained by filling in lettering, designs, etc.; the screen cutter needs only the outline to serve as a guide for cutting. It is even possible to submit art which has been outline-drawn in pencil.

When producing line art in color, it is necessary to provide pre-separated art only if photographic screens are to be used.

The screen cutter is something of an artist in his own right. He is able to make accurate hand-cut separations of any color art which is submitted to him. The good screen cutter is capable of converting a photograph or a continuous-tone color rendering to the flat color technique of the process, making the appropriate separations. His judgment may be superior to that of the artist who is accustomed to working in tonal values.

15 PAPER

The first practicable, easily handled writing material was developed by the Egyptians in the era of 2500–2000 B.C. It was produced from the split stalks of the papyrus plant, which were cross-laid and pounded together with a stone, and the name of this material provided the derivation of the English word "paper."

The immediate predecessor of modern paper was developed by the Chinese in the first century. Pulp fibers, reduced from the inner bark of the mulberry tree, were formed into sheets by floating them in water and allowing them to settle and dry. It has been since demonstrated that almost any fibrous plant can be made into paper of one quality or another.

The Chinese process was a closely guarded secret for nearly 600 years. The Arab conquest of Samarkand in A.D. 704 introduced paper-making into the Western world; it soon spread to the remainder of Europe. The first American paper mill was built near Philadelphia in 1690.

During the seventeenth century, all paper was made by hand, generally from the reduced fibers of hemp, linen, and cotton rags. The rags were reduced to pulp by the action of a water-driven stamping mill. The pulp was then floated in a vat of water and seined onto the surface of a wire screen. Shaking of the screen by hand felted (matted) the pulp as the water drained off through the mesh of the screen. Sheets of the matted fibers were removed and sandwiched between pieces of felt, where excess water was removed by pressure. The individual sheets of paper were then hung over rods to dry. This process was, naturally, expensive and limited in production.

In 1798 a Frenchman, Nicholas Louis Robert, conceived the principle of making paper with a moving endless wire screen. Robert took his patents to England, where they were sold to Henry and Sealy Fourdrinier. The Fourdriniers developed the first practical papermaking machine in 1804. Present-day papermaking machinery still bears their name.

Rags were the source of fibers for the Fourdrinier process until 1840, when Gottfried Keller, a German, invented a method for reducing wood to pulp by mechanically grinding it with a revolving stone. In 1867 Benjamin Tilghman, of Philadelphia, furthered the technology of pulp reduction by the introduction of an acid process for separating the fibers. It took many years to overcome the imperfections of this process, but by the end of the nineteenth century, chemical wood pulp was becoming commercially practicable. This is the process by which the bulk of modern paper is manufactured.

THE PAPERMAKING PROCESS

The raw materials

Paper is a matted web of cellulose fibers. Almost any organic matter with a suitable fibrous structure can be manufactured into paper. The nature of fibers from different sources makes it difficult to categorize minor differences, but the following classification should prove adequate.

Rag Pulp. Rag pulp is made from new, unlaundered, and undyed cotton rags. This pulp yields almost pure cellulose which produces a strong, durable paper.

Vegetable Fibers. Esparto (Spanish and Algerian grasses), straw, and bamboo (which may be considered a gigantic straw) are chemically reduced to pulp. The chemical treatment of bamboo, a more complex fiber, is necessarily the most severe. Cardboard is made from straw, plus wood fibers.

Jute. Jute (plant fibers), in the form of old bagging, is chemically reduced for use in the manufacture of strong, cheap papers, where whiteness is not a requisite.

Reclaimed Pulp. Used paper is reclaimed by submitting it to an alkali solution to dissolve the ink. It is then chemically reduced to pulp form.

Mechanical Wood Pulp. Mechanical pulp is ground, rather than treated chemically. Logs are ground into tiny particles resembling fine sawdust. These are mixed with water and floated onto the screen of the papermaking machine. Spruce, balsam, and hemlock are the principal sources. Mechanical pulp is used for newspaper stock.

Chemical Wood Pulp. Chemical pulp is wood treated chemically for the purpose of removing gums, resins, and other undesired substances. The result is pure cellulose fiber. The type of chemical reduction process utilized is determined by the nature of the wood fiber. Long-fibered pulps are needed to provide paper with strength and durability. Varying mixtures of long and short fibers produce degrees of bulk, opacity, and smoothness. Short fibers produce the best formation, matting closely with a minimum of pores, but paper made exclusively from short fibers will not hold together for prolonged use. The following are the principal processes for the chemical reduction of wood fiber:

The Sulphate Process. The reducing agent (or "cooking liquor") in this process is a modified form of caustic soda which provides a pulp suitable for bags or wrapping paper (kraft paper). Pitch-bearing woods, such as pine, are generally utilized; they provide the longest and strongest of the pulp fibers.

The Sulphite Process. In this process, calcium bisulphite is the reducing agent. Long-fibered coniferous (evergreen) woods are used. The resultant pulp responds well to bleaching. Sulphite pulp is used for writing papers.

The Soda Process. In this process, fibers are reduced with caustic soda (sodium hydroxide). Short-fibered deciduous (seasonal, such as poplar) woods are utilized. Pulp manufactured by this process is used extensively for book papers.

Alpha Pulp. This pulp is an extremely white, purified fiber which is utilized as a substitute for rag stock. Alpha pulp is considerably superior to ordinary wood pulps.

The logs are ground into small, uniform chips, and are screened free of dust. The chips are placed in acid-resistant, brick-lined tanks called *digesters.* The cooking liquor is pumped in under controlled temperature (steam). The process separates the pure cellulose fibers from their incrusting impurities; the cellulose is subjected to repeated cleanings until all such impurities have been eliminated. When thoroughly cleaned, the fibers are bleached white with chloride of lime.

Papermaking machinery

In order for fibers to form into paper, small clusters must be broken into individual fibers, the walls and ends of the fibers must be frayed, and they must be conditioned with various nonfibrous ingredients.

The fibers are beaten in water in order to fray them so that they will mesh together (or "felt") more strongly in the paper. The *beater* is an oval-shaped vat in which the pulp is circulated and beaten with blunt bars. These bars are mounted on a revolving drum and rotate against a bed plate of similar, but adjustable bars. The bars in the bed plate may be set for the type of treatment required for the character of the paper which is to be made from it.

Various nonfibrous materials are added to the pulp while it is being processed in the beater. Some of these materials are:

Sizing. This reduces moisture penetration and acts as a binding agent which prevents fuzzing from the pull of sticky ink or erasure. It gives the paper a greater hardness. Rosin, starch, wax, animal glue, and silicate of soda are prominently used. Different amounts of sizing are used for different purposes.

Blotting paper is unsized.

Mimeo, newsprint, and gravure stock are slack-sized for fast ink penetration.

Uncoated book stock is medium-sized—enough to prevent moisture-absorption wrinkling, but not enough to retard ink drying.

Writing, litho, and offset stock are hard-sized, in order to bind the fibers and prevent absorption.

Fillers. These are fine particles of clay, calcium carbonate, talc, calcium sulphate, and titanium or zinc pigments that are used to fill up the spaces between the fibers—increasing density, opacity, and smoothness. Titanium imparts additional whiteness; clay accepts polishing readily.

Dyes. Pigments and aniline dyes, necessary for the manufacture of colored paper, are introduced at this point in the processing of the pulp.

Alum. A weak acidifying agent used to hold the sizing and fix the dye on the fibers.

The pulp, with its additives, proceeds from the beater into the *Jordan engine,* or "Jordan." The Jordan consists of a conical, horizontal shell, with a plug that revolves within it at high speed. Protruding bars exert an action similar to that of the beating process, which reduces the fibers to a more uniform length.

Recently, beaters have been replaced with faster, more efficient machinery and are now used only for mixing purposes. However, the basic function of the new equipment remains the same.

The fibers are now ready to pass through storage vats and into the papermaking machine.

The *"wet end"* of the papermaking machine, the end into which the treated pulp or "stock"—now about 1 per cent pulp and 99 per cent water—is pumped, is known as the *Fourdrinier section.* The stock is forced through microscopic straining slots onto the finely woven wire mesh of the moving, endless Fourdrinier screen. This screen vibrates constantly, causing the fibers to become interwoven and matted together. The fibers tend to flow lengthwise in the direction of the screen travel, but the shaking somewhat disrupts this tendency, dispersing the fibers

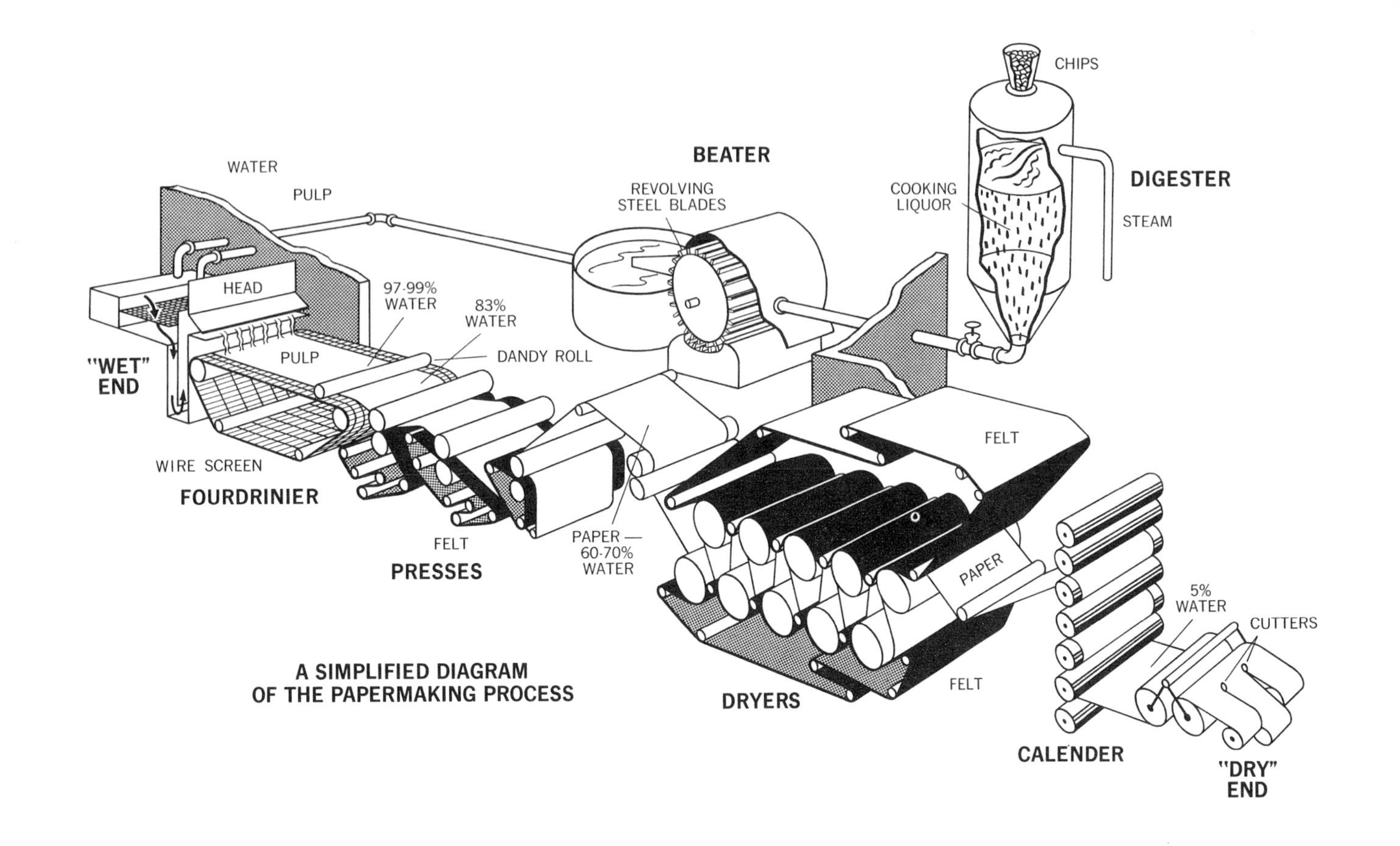

A SIMPLIFIED DIAGRAM
OF THE PAPERMAKING PROCESS

Book Stock. The basis size of book stock is 25″ x 38″. Basis weights range from 45 to 120 lbs.

Writing Stock. The basis size of writing (business) stock is 17″ x 22″. Basis weights of bond papers range from 9 to 24 lbs.; ledger papers range from 24 to 40 lbs.; and manifold (onionskin) is made in a 9-lb. weight.

Cover Stock. Cover stock has a basis size of 20″ x 26″, and generally comes in 50- to 80-lb. weights. Heavier cover stock is measured in caliper thickness (thousandths of an inch—.010 in., .012 in., .014 in., etc.).

Book stock

Book stock possesses desirable qualities for book and fine magazine work. It may be roughly classified in the following categories:

ANTIQUE FINISH. Antique finish is similar to the paper of early printing days. Paper in the antique category is machine finished—produced in the papermaking machine and not requiring additional finishing. Rough in comparison to other book papers, due to the minimum of smoothing pressure, it is usually sized to a moderate degree. Its absorbency depends upon the amount of sizing mixed with the pulp. Antique is used for books, programs, and some forms of advertising. There are several subcategories of antique stock:

Eggshell Antique. A rough paper with a surface texture resembling an eggshell. It is produced on wet presses, using special felts.

Text. A high-grade antique, smoother than eggshell, used for quality books, booklets, and brochures. It is often watermarked and deckle-edged (feathered and untrimmed). Wove and laid stock is most often found in antique and text papers.

Vellum Finish. Classic vellum is paper of finer quality than parchment, made from the skins of calves. Vellum finish is the smoothest grade of the antique category, finished to resemble genuine vellum. It is available in the following grades:

- **Paper Vellum.** An imitation of classic vellum, made from high-quality rags; it is used for fine book editions and documents.
- **Japan Paper.** This is made from the bark of the paper mulberry in imitation of clasic vellum.

OFFSET STOCK. Related to the antique group, offset is a smooth, uncoated book stock, generally with a text or vellum finish. It is ideal for fine-screen offset lithography, and will accept letterpress line work without difficulty. Offset stock is sized on both sides to prevent curling from the moisture inherent in the lithographic process.

English Finish (E.F.). Having a nonglare, slightly roughened surface, English finish is a further development of machine finishing. It is so universally preferred for advertising and sales-promotion printing that many paper houses stock no other finish in the book stock category. English finish has a high clay content; its fibers are short, allowing the papermaking machine to impart extra smoothness. E.F. produces good results with 120-line letterpress halftones, and is especially manufactured for lithography and gravure.

English finish is *calendered.* A stack of five to nine heavy iron calender rollers is incorporated into the dry end of the papermaking machine for the purpose of ironing and smoothing the fibers. The paper may be threaded through all or some of these rollers, depending on the degree of smoothness desired. The rollers are driven by friction, and the resulting slippage adds to the gloss of the finish. The paper passes through the machine calender rolls only once.

Supercalendered Stock. Supercalendered stock has a smooth finish, with less bulk and opacity than English finish, and is known colloquially as "Super." Used for magazines and booklets, it will accept letterpress halftones of 120- to 133-line screens.

Super stock is finished by a stack of calender rollers *independent* of those in the papermaking machine. In the supercalender, steel rollers alternate with cotton or paper-surfaced rollers. The paper is dampened by steam and is polished by the friction of the steel rollers against the softer-surfaced ones. Super stock is sent through the calenders twice—once for each side—and may be sent through four times for an exceptionally high finish.

Coated Stock. Coated stock has a smooth, shiny finish, ideally suited for the printing of 133- to 150-line halftones. The finest coated stock will accept halftone screens of up to 200 lines.

Coated stock is finished by a supplementary operation which also takes place outside the papermaking machine. The coating emulsion adheres to, rather than is incorporated in, the structure of the paper. The coating—a white, milky substance—is a mixture of white China clay (kaolin), calcium sulphate, and aluminum oxide together with whitening agents, such as barium sulphate, titanium oxide, or zinc sulphide. The adhesive agent is casein glue, a skim-milk derivative.

The web of paper passes through a vat containing the coating substances, after which it is dried by hot air and rewound. The coating does not dry glossy; high- and medium-gloss finishes are produced by supercalendering. Coated stock ranges from enamel (super glossy) to dull (smooth, but without gloss).

Litho stock, coated on only one side, is common; recently, two-sided coated litho stock has come into use.

Writing stock

Writing stock is exactly what the name implies—paper used mainly for written (or typewritten) communications and for the keeping of written records. Writing stock is hard-sized to prevent absorption, since it is apt to be written on with a fountain pen. Writing stock is divided into the following categories:

Flat Stock. Flat stocks are calendered writing papers, ranging from cheap memo paper to fine stationery.

Bond Stock. Bond stock has a rough, nonglare surface which accepts both printing and writing ink. It is used for stationery, office forms, catalogs, and booklets. The finest bonds are made from rag stock and have a snap or "rattle" when shaken briskly. High-grade bonds, with their nonabsorbent qualities, accept letterpress printing with difficulty, but good results may be obtained with steel engraving or offset lithography.

Top-grade bonds are generally watermarked, and are available in a wide variety of colors. Bond finishes include regular, laid and wove, glazed, dull, cold pressed, cockle, and ripple.

Ledger Stock. Ledger stock is used for account books, office forms, and quality letterhead printing. It is made from longer-fibered pulp than bond in order to withstand folding. Glare-free, smooth-finished for writing and ruling, and sized for maximum erasure resistance, it has a high rag content which makes it both strong and durable. Ledger is not suitable for fine-screen halftones, unless they are printed by offset lithography.

Manifold Stock (Onionskin). Thin, but strong, manifold is used for second sheets (carbon copies), sales books, and records where less bulk is a requisite. It is also used for lightweight airmail sheets.

Cover stock

Cover stocks are heavier, stronger, easier-folding stocks which are available in a wider variety of colors than any other type of printing paper. Able to withstand rough handling, they are used for announcements, booklets, catalogs, mailing pieces, and pamphlet covers. Unsuitable for letterpress work in halftone, cover stocks accept line letterpress and offset (both line and halftone) readily.

Cover stock is available in a great number of finishes, ranging from antique to imitation leather and cloth. More common finishes include:

Antique. Unfinished, with a rough surface.

Coated. Surface-coated with a smooth, glossy finish.

Crash. A finish similar to coarse linen.

Embossed. An over-all, textured design pressed into the paper.

Laid or Wove. Impressed with the pattern of the wire and/or the dandy roll.

Pebble. Pressed between steel rollers which impart a surface pattern.

Plate. A fine, smooth, hard finish obtained by rolling between plates of zinc or copper.

Ripple. Pressed between sheets of sulphite pulp or embossed rollers which produce an irregular texture suggesting ripples. The finish is glossy, but rough.

Additional varieties of stock

News Stock. Commonly referred to as "newsprint," news stock is 70 to 80 per cent mechanical pulp, which causes it to lack permanence and strength. News stock is slack-sized and, therefore, highly absorbent—a quality which assists the drying of the ink. It will not accept halftone screens of over 65 lines.

The resins and gums which remain in the ground wood cause news stock to be chemically affected by light and air. As a result, newspapers intended to be preserved in libraries, etc., are printed on rag content paper.

Roto Paper. Roto paper is newsprint made specifically for the gravure process. Soft and absorbent, it is capable of handling the fluidity of gravure ink. The cheapest variety is unsized. Normally slack sized, it will accept line and the 150-line gravure screen.

Bristol Board. Bristol board is a heavy, stiff printing paper used for announcements, postcards, index cards, display cards, menus, etc. It has an excellent surface for letterpress printing; it is used as a cover stock for letterpress booklets and brochures. Bristol is manufactured in several varieties:

PLAIN BRISTOL. A surface similar to English finish, but stiffer and heavier in weight.

INDEX BRISTOL. A plain, stiff paper used for index cards or file dividers.

COATED BRISTOL. A stiff paper coated for halftone letterpress printing.

CARDBOARD. Cardboard is a heavy durable board used for box manufacture. Faced with a thin sheet of calendered or coated stock, it is used for boxes, posters, and counter cards. Made from a cheap pulp filler, sometimes reinforced with straw fibers, its thickness is developed by pasting plys (layers) together with a multicylindered machine. Faced cardboard will accept letterpress, lithography, or silk screen—depending on the quality of the facing sheet.

PARCHMENT (GENUINE). Genuine parchment is extremely expensive and is made from the skin of sheep or goats. It is used for documents, diplomas ("sheepskins"), certificates, etc.

PARCHMENT (PAPER). Paper parchment is an imitation of genuine parchment made from a waterproofed, extremely high grade of bond paper.

INDIA (OR BIBLE) PAPER. India paper is a quality paper, similar to English finish, but very light in weight. It is used in fine books, Bibles, dictionaries, and encyclopedias—in instances where compactness is a desirable factor. It is frequently used for letterpress printing.

SAFETY PAPER. Safety paper is paper designed to show up any attempt at erasure or alteration. Used for checks, money orders, or other items of negotiable value, it is chemically treated or printed in a surface design which is readily affected by water, bleach, chemicals, or erasure.

KRAFT (WRAPPING) PAPER. Kraft paper is a strong, unbleached, brown paper made from long sulphate fibers. It will not accept halftones, but may be printed in line—particularly with rubber plates.

Art papers

There are several types of paper which find general use in the production of advertising art. The illustrator may employ a wide variety of paper in an attempt to produce unique textural effects, but the following are the papers normally used by the art department:

TRACING PAPER. Tracing paper is a thin, transparent paper, used for making preliminary drawings, laying out lettering, scaling drawings and photographs, etc. The transparent nature of the paper allows the artist to readily retrace, and thus refine his work. Tracing paper is not suitable for ink drawing; the ink will cause it to wrinkle. A drawing made on tracing paper is transferred to drawing paper or board by blackening the back with a soft pencil. The surplus graphite is rubbed down with a rag or paper towel. Retracing the lines with a hard pencil transfers an image of the drawing onto the desired surface.

TRACING VELLUM. Tracing vellum is heavier in weight and somewhat less transparent than tracing paper. It is available in several weights. Ink will not wrinkle vellum unless it is applied in large areas; its transparency permits tracing from an original layout or sketch in order to render finished line art. It is used for line drawings, lettering, and separation overlays.

BRISTOL BOARD. Bristol boards are high-rag-content boards used for illustration and lettering. Bristol comes in 1-, 2-, and 3-ply thicknesses, laminated for extra strength and permanence. *Plate-finish Bristol* is extremely smooth and is used for precise line work. *Kid-finish Bristol* has a medium finish, which is suitable for halftone drawings and loose brush-and-ink lettering or illustration.

BOND PAPER. Bond paper has a medium finish that is neither kid nor plate; it is ideal for layout purposes. Three grades of bond are used by the artist: layout, medium, and heavy bond. Layout bond is transparent enough to allow the artist to trace and revise previous work. It accepts pastel or charcoal readily, and is used for rough layouts. Medium bond is a heavier, opaque paper, used for comprehensive layouts and simple line illustration. Heavy bond is used for line illustration, lettering, finished layouts, and masks for photographs and illustrations.

ILLUSTRATION BOARD. Illustration board consists of quality, high-rag-content paper, mounted on stiff cardboard for greater durability and ease of handling. The paper surface may range from a smooth Bristol to rough water-color paper. *Hot pressed* board is a smooth surface, ideal for delicate line work and precise mechanical art. *Cold pressed* board has a slightly coarser surface that is suitable for line drawing, opaque renderings, and the normal variety of mechanical art. *Rough* board is generally mounted water-color paper and should be used for the wash drawing. The cardboard mounting is either single thick (1/16 in.) or double thick (1/8 in.). The facing paper may be stripped from the backing in order to facilitate the pasting-up of the illustration.

WATER-COLOR PAPER. The best water-color paper is produced with a 100-per-cent rag content, making it capable of absorbing the excess moisture required for the execution of the wash drawing. Water-color paper is manufactured in sheets, in blocks (pads) bound on four sides, and mounted in the form of illustration board. It is available in a number of surface textures.

NEWSPRINT. Newsprint, bound in pad form, is economical to use when large quantities of paper are expended for rough sketches or quick layouts. Newsprint is best used with pencil, crayon, or charcoal; it will not accept ink or water color.

MAT BOARD. Mat board is cardboard, either single or double thick, used for matting and sometimes mounting illustrations and photographs. Although it is available in a wide variety of colors and textures, the most popular mat board has an "eggshell" surface texture, and is gray on one side and white or cream on the other.

MOUNT BOARD. Mount board is similar in appearance to illustration board, but is surfaced with a cheaper grade of paper. It may be surfaced on one or both sides, and does not bear the manufacturer's imprint. Mount board is inexpensive, and is used for quantity mounting of photographs or for the construction of dummy boxes and displays.

CHIPBOARD. Chipboard is gray, unsurfaced cardboard used when a cheap mounting board or a stiffener is required. Easel devices for counter cards and other displays are usually die-cut from chipboard.

Criteria for selecting paper

Paper may be purchased through the printer or ordered directly from a paper house. The paper house is not a manufacturer; it is a mercantile establishment that may stock the products of several manufacturers. Most paper houses employ salesmen who willingly supply samples and cost estimates for their clients.

Paper should be selected carefully; the cost of paper has a pronounced effect on the total cost of the printed job. When ordering paper, the following factors should be considered:

PROPOSED USE. The paper selected should be compatible with the printing process and the kind of ink that will be used. It should be physically adaptable to the intended purpose of the job. Factors such as strength, durability, foldability, permanence, and any physical situations to which it may be exposed should be considered. Opacity may be an extremely important qualification. In the selection of paper, the most essential requirement becomes the deciding factor, as no paper possesses all these attributes in the exact degree desired.

QUALITY. The quality of the paper should also be compatible with its intended use. It is as foolish to purchase excessive quality as it is to purchase inferior quality.

WEIGHT. The weight of both paper and cover stock should be appropriate. The paper should be heavy enough to stand up to the requirements of the job, but not so heavy as to become cumbersome or difficult to handle. Paper that is heavier than necessary will cause excessive shipping or mailing costs.

SURFACE AND FINISH. The nature of the paper surface should be considered in terms of both the printing process—remembering that halftones are best printed on smooth paper—and the desired aesthetic appearance of the finished result.

SIZE. Paper may be purchased in a wide variety of sizes. The size-capacity of the press employed, the manner of imposition, and the paper size should all be carefully matched for utmost efficiency of press time and a minimum of waste.

COLOR. Paper is manufactured in a multitude of colors. So-called "white" paper is available in a variety of shades, many of which will alter the printing characteristics of a halftone. The color selected should be compatible with the aesthetic requirements of the job; the paper is just as important to the job's appearance as any design element. A well-planned job may incorporate the color of the paper as an integral part of its design.

GRAIN. All machine-made paper has a grain which is caused by the directional movement of the Fourdrinier screen. Paper tears and folds most easily *with* the grain. Paper may be ordered with the grain running in either direction; grain direction may affect folding, binding, and color registration. If the paper is to be ordered through a source other than the printer, he should be consulted about the required grain direction.

BIBLIOGRAPHY

Joachim, Leo H., ed. *Production Yearbook* (eighth edition). New York: Colton Press, 1948.

Kleppner, Otto. *Advertising Procedure*. Englewood Cliffs, N.J.: Prentice-Hall, Inc., 1950.

Melcher, Daniel, and Larrick, Nancy. *Printing and Promotion Handbook*. New York: McGraw-Hill Book Company, 1949.

Neblette, C. B. *Photography, Its Materials and Processes*. Princeton, N.J.: D. Van Nostrand Inc., 1952.

Stanley, Thomas Blaine. *The Technique of Advertising Production*. Englewood Cliffs, N.J.: Prentice-Hall, Inc., 1954.

Strauss, Victor, ed. *The Lithographer's Manual* (2 vols). New York: Waltwin Publishing Company, 1958.

Wirsig, Woodrow, ed. *Principles of Advertising*. New York, Pitman Publishing Corp., 1963.

INDEX

* *Reference in italic is to an illustration.*

S0-AWE-079

THE GHOUL NEXT DOOR

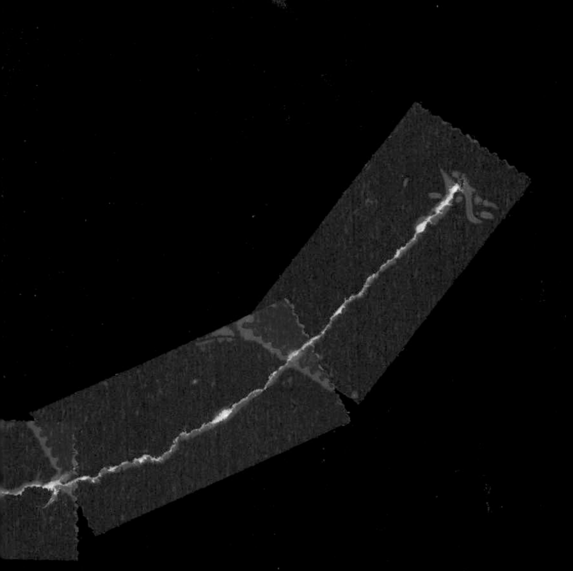

HarperAlley is an imprint of HarperCollins Publishers.

The Ghoul Next Door
Text copyright © 2021 by Cullen Bunn
Illustrations copyright © 2021 by Cat Farris
All rights reserved. Printed in Spain.
No part of this book may be used or reproduced in any manner whatsoever without written permission except in the case of brief quotations embodied in critical articles and reviews. For information address HarperCollins Children's Books, a division of HarperCollins Publishers, 195 Broadway, New York, NY 10007.
www.harperalley.com

Library of Congress Control Number: 2020949436
ISBN 978-0-06-289610-0 — ISBN 978-0-06-289609-4 (pbk.)

The artist used Clip Studio Paint, ink, watercolor, and mixed media paper to create the illustrations for this book.
Typography by Rick Farley
21 22 23 24 25 EP 10 9 8 7 6 5 4 3 2 1

First Edition

THE GHOUL NEXT DOOR

CULLEN BUNN & CAT FARRIS

LETTERING BY
ADITYA BIDIKAR

An Imprint of HarperCollinsPublishers

To Cindy and Jackson, the best family—ghoul, human, or otherwise—a guy could hope for.

—C.B.

For Grandma Mayo, my biggest fan.

—C.F.

"HEY! CHECK IT OUT!"
ANDER'S LANDING
EST. 1692
A PLACE TO GET AWAY

A PENNY!
E PLURIBUS
ONE CENT
UNITED STATES OF AMERICA

UH...SO WHAT?
IT'S A **PENNY,** GREY.
NO BIG DEAL.

BESIDES, IT'S **TAILS UP.**
THAT'S **BAD LUCK.**
E PLURIBUS
ONE CENT
UNITED STATES

COME ON, MARSHALL.
YOU'RE NOT **THAT** SUPERSTITIOUS.
YOU DON'T BELIEVE THAT, DO YOU?
I DON'T BELIEVE IN **CHANCING FATE.**
NOT FOR A **PENNY,** ANYHOW.

PICK IT UP FOR ME, WILL YA?

FOR REAL?
IT'S **JUST** A PENNY.
AND-- I ALREADY TOLD YOU--IT'S **BAD LUCK.**

FINE. WHATEVER.
JUST HOLD THIS FOR A SECOND, OKAY?
WHA--?
IF YOU NEED MONEY THAT BAD, GREY, I'LL **GIVE** YOU A PENNY.

IT'S REALLY OLD.
SOME OF THESE OLD COINS ARE WORTH A **LOT** OF MONEY.
YEAH...LIKE A WHOLE CENT.

IT'S FROM **1919.**
CAN YOU BELIEVE IT?
AND IT'S JUST SITTING HERE ON THE SIDEWALK.

I'LL DO A LITTLE RESEARCH WHEN I GET HOME.
MAYBE IT'S **RARE.**
DON'T WORRY, MARSHALL. IF IT'S WORTH, LIKE, A THOUSAND DOLLARS, I'LL CUT YOU IN ON THE PROFITS.

THANKS.

YOU REALLY WENT ABOVE AND BEYOND ON YOUR HISTORY PROJECT.
A SCALE MODEL OF **ARMITAGE CEMETERY?**
MRS. BEAMAN IS PICKING **THAT** FOR THE LIBRARY EXHIBIT FOR SURE.

IT'S NOT REALLY TO SCALE.
I FOCUSED ON SOME OF THE OLDER GRAVES.
BUT IT DID TAKE ALMOST THE WHOLE WEEKEND TO FINISH.

WHAT DID YOU DO?
FEAST YOUR EYES ON **THIS!**

I MADE A WANTED POSTER FOR **SALLY-BEA HURST.**
SHE WAS ONE OF THE WITCHES THAT FLED HERE FROM SALEM IN THE 1600S.
SHE LOOKS... **MEAN.**
WAS SHE?
WANTED
SALLY-BEA HURST FOR WITCHERY

I DUNNO.
MAYBE.
PROBABLY.
SALLY-BEA HURST WAS LIKE A **REAL** WITCH.

SHE CONSORTED WITH... **YOU KNOW.**

ELVES?
ALIENS?
BUNNY RABBITS?

DON'T BE DUMB.
WHY ARE YOU ALWAYS TELLING ME NOT TO BE DUMB?
BECAUSE YOU'RE **DUMB.**
FAIR ENOUGH.

HEY--LET'S TAKE THE **SHORTCUT.**
UH.
I DON'T KNOW, GREY.

WHAT'S NOT TO KNOW?
THE SCHOOL'S JUST ON THE OTHER SIDE OF THE CEMETERY.
WE CUT THROUGH OR WE WALK ALL THE WAY AROUND.
THIS MODEL IS A LITTLE AWKWARD TO CARRY.
ARMITAGE EAST GATE

BUT THE CEMETERY'S FULL OF...
...Y'KNOW...
...DEAD PEOPLE.
ARMITAGE EAST GATE

THAT'S THE RUMOR.
COME ON.
THERE'S NOTHING TO BE AFRAID OF.
ARMITAGE EAST GATE

NO, THANKS.
YOU PICKED UP AN **UNLUCKY PENNY...** AND NOW YOU WANT TO TRAIPSE ON **GRAVES.**
THAT'S **YOUR** FUNERAL, NOT **MINE.**

ALL RIGHT... WELL...
SEE YOU AT SCHOOL!
WHATEVER YOU SAY, GREY.

"SOUNDS LIKE **FAMOUS LAST WORDS** TO ME!"
LT. COL. DAVID A. MAYO
HE LIVED TO SERVE
IN LOVING MEMORY

"TO MY FATHER'S ARMS SHALL YOU BEAR ME."
DOLORES MYER
IN PERPETUITY

"FULL OF DEAD PEOPLE."
WHAT A GOOF.

PERFECTO!

HERE LI
RUTHUR
BELOV
BRO

R.I.P.
ELENE

OOF!

AAH--
FWUMP!
NNNF!

OW.

WHAT THE HECK?

WHO JUST DIGS A **HOLE** IN THE MIDDLE OF--

--A **GRAVEYARD?**

IT'S...
...NOT A GRAVE...
TOO SMALL...
...BUT...

OMIGOSH!
GRAVE ROBBERS!
I SHOULD GET OUTTA HERE!
I SHOULD TELL SOMEONE!

WHERE'S MY--

AW, NO.

YOU'RE **KIDDING** ME, RIGHT?

OKAY, GREY.
DON'T FREAK OUT.
YOU CAN HANDLE THIS.

NNN--

Hhhhh

Hhhhh

MAYBE...

...IF I CAN JUST HOOK IT, I MIGHT--

THERE WE GO.
THAT'S IT.
EASY DOES IT... EASY--

HsssSSSsss

UH--

SKKKKK

FFFP!

WAIT--

HSSSSSS

YAAAAGH!

...UH...
...UH...
...UH...

WHAT...
...WAS...
...THAT?

AND WHAT ABOUT MY MODEL?

"WHATEVER IT WAS...IT WAS SOME SORT OF **MONSTER!**"

"IT WAS CRAWLING AROUND BENEATH THE CEMETERY...
"...LIKE **BURROWING** OR SOMETHING..."

...AND IT...
...IT...
...IT **STOLE** MY HISTORY PROJECT!
RAVE
RAVENS

NO...GUYS... I'M BEING **SERIOUS** HERE.
I DUNNO WHAT HAPPENED TO YOUR MODEL, GREY.
BUT WHATEVER YOU DO...
...**DON'T** TELL MRS. BEAMAN THAT STORY.

YOU DON'T... BELIEVE ME?
I'M YOUR PAL.
YOU SAY YOU SAW A MONSTER? IT'S MY JOB TO MAKE FUN OF YOU WHETHER I BELIEVE YOU OR NOT.
AND, UNFORTUNATELY FOR YOU, IT DOESN'T MATTER **WHAT** I BELIEVE.
IT MATTERS WHAT THE **TEACHER** BELIEVES.

WHATEVER HAPPENED...HOWEVER **EMBARRASSING** IT IS...
...I **WARNED** YOU...
THAT PENNY YOU PICKED UP IS **BAD LUCK.**

BUT YOU **REALLY** NEED A BETTER EXCUSE.

SO...WHAT YOU'RE SAYING IS...

"...THE TRUTH'S GONNA GET ME AN F."
CELEBRATING OUR RICH HISTORY
PIRATES!?!

EDGAR ALLEN POE SLEPT HERE

FIGHT!
GO FIGHTING RAVENS
SOFT
ART
HARD FACTS!
DID YOU KNOW?
GEOLOGICAL
WHY ANDER'S LANDI
ROCKS
WHAT'S
COOKING
RAVENS
HEY, GREY.
YOU ALL RIGHT?
YOU LOOK SORTA... DOWN.
I'M FINE.
JUST MARCHING ALONG TO MY **IMMINENT DOOM.**
THE MISSING COLONISTS! WHERE DID THEY GO?

GREY BRIGHTON

SIGH
PERFECTO.

TON

GREY?

HI, MRS. BEAMAN.
GOOD MORNING.
WHAT'S GOING ON HERE?
WHERE'S YOUR HISTORY PROJECT?

I...UH... I HAD IT...
I REALLY DID...
I WORKED ON IT ALL WEEKEND...
ON

I SEE.
WELL, THEN.
WHY ISN'T IT **HERE?**
Y'SEE...
...I WAS...

I...

WANTED
WANTED

I TOTALLY SPACED, I GUESS.
I FORGOT IT AT HOME.
I DON'T KNOW WHAT I WAS THINKING.

I MUST ADMIT, I'M VERY DISAPPOINTED.

THIS ISN'T LIKE YOU, GREY.
ALL YOUR CLASSMATES HAVE WORKED VERY HARD ON THEIR PROJECTS. THEY ALL MANAGED TO HAVE THEM HERE FOR THE EVENT.
FAMILY LIFE
WHAT AM I SUPPOSED TO DO WITH YOU?

I DUNNO.

YOU KNOW, THIS PROJECT ACCOUNTS FOR A SIGNIFICANT PART OF YOUR GRADE IN HISTORY.
I'D HATE TO SEE YOU **FAIL** THE CLASS BECAUSE OF THIS.
IF YOU BRING THE PROJECT IN TOMORROW, I'LL GIVE YOU AT LEAST **PARTIAL** CREDIT FOR IT.

THANKS, MRS. BEAMAN.

BUT--LISTEN-- I'M DOCKING YOU **AT LEAST** A LETTER GRADE...

"...SO YOUR WORK BETTER BE **TOP-NOTCH!**"

I DON'T WANT TO SAY I TOLD YOU SO...
THEN **DON'T.**
...BUT I TOLD YOU TO COME UP WITH A BETTER EXCUSE.

I'VE GOT A SECOND CHANCE WITH THE PROJECT, BUT IT'LL TAKE **ALL NIGHT** TO REBUILD.
YOU NEED SOME HELP WITH IT?
NAH. IT'S MY PROBLEM, NOT YOURS.
I MEAN... I WONDER IF I MIGHT FIND IT IF I GO BACK THROUGH THE--

ARMITAGE
WEST
GATE

C'MON, GREY.
I KNOW, I KNOW.

"DON'T BE DUMB."

Hhhhh

HEY, GREY!
HOW WAS SCHOOL?
HOW'D YOUR TEACHER LIKE YOUR MODEL?

WELLLLLLL.
THE MODEL KIND OF GOT...

...MESSED UP.
OH NO.
WHAT HAPPENED?

IT'S NO BIG DEAL, MOM, REALLY.
MRS. BEAMAN'S GIVING ME A CHANCE TO FIX IT.
BUT I BETTER GET STARTED RIGHT AWAY.

"IT MIGHT TAKE ME A WHILE!"

LIZARD KING
GALAXY BATTLE
PLANTS vs ZOMBIES
AND NOW... THE FINAL PIECE.

STEADY.
STEAAAAAAAAADY.

PERFECTO!
GREY, MY BOY, YOU HAVE OUTDONE YOURSELF!
THIS IS EVEN **BETTER** THAN THE ORIGINAL!

#YAWN#

OH, MAN.
WHAT TIME IS IT, ANYHOW?

KLICK

1:15

1:20

SKRTCH
SKRK
SKRTCH

SPACE
GALAXY BATTLE

UH--

SKRAK-
SKRTCH-
SKRK

TAK
SKRIK
T-TAK

FWWWSH

IT CAME FROM THE GRAVE

MARS
TREKKER
6
2
6

MARS
TREKKER
6
2
6

MARS
TREKKER
6
2
6

MARS
TREKKER
6
2
6

MARS
TREKKER
6
2
6

MOM?
DAD?
WHERE IS EVERYONE?

Love, Mom

...EARLY DAY AT WORK...
...CARPOOLING WITH DAD...
...I SET CEREAL AND MILK OUT FOR BREAKFAST...
...DON'T FORGET YOUR **HOMEWORK** THIS MORNING...

GREEEEEEAT.
CRUNCH-
CRNCH-
CRNCH-

WHOA!

THUMP

UH--

WHERE DID **THIS** COME FROM?
LOOK AT IT!
WHO COULD'VE **MADE** THIS?
IT'S SO--

--PERFECTO!

HELLO?
M-MONSTER?
ARE YOU... ARE YOU OUT THERE?
DID YOU MAKE THIS?

WELL...WHATEVER YOU ARE...
...I MEAN **WHO**EVER YOU ARE...
...I'M GONNA ASSUME YOU LEFT THIS FOR ME SINCE YOU RUINED MY MODEL...
SO THERE'S NO REAL HARM IN TAKING THIS ONE TO SCHOOL.

I MEAN...YOU OBVIOUSLY DON'T WANT ME TO GET A FAILING GRADE...

...RIGHT?

RIGHT.

Hsssssssss

KRUNCH!

FTTFFH!
BLLEGH!
SPPFT!
TH THUMP!
THUMP!

"WELL...I MUST ADMIT, GREY..."

...I'M **IMPRESSED.**

THE **DETAIL** YOU'VE MANAGED TO CAPTURE...
...THE **ACCURACY...**
...IT'S REALLY **SOMETHING SPECIAL.**

IF YOU HAD TURNED IT IN ON TIME...
...IT WOULD HAVE BEEN DESERVING OF A **PERFECT** SCORE.
YEAH.
SORRY ABOUT THAT.

HEY! LOOK AT THIS!
THE LITTLE DOORS OPEN AND EVERYTHING!

THEY DO?
I MEAN-- **THEY DO!**

THERE'S SOMETHING **INSIDE!**

IT LOOKS LIKE--

IS THAT A **BONE?!**
GROSS!
TAK

THAT'S PART OF A SKELETON!
IT LOOKS OLD!
IT'S WEARING A RING!
IT'S A **FINGER!**

UH?

CHILDREN-- **CHILDREN!**
PLEASE, IF YOU WOULD JUST TAKE YOUR SEATS.
I'M SURE THAT, WHATEVER THIS IS, IT IS NOT A REAL--

DUNGEON MASTER

WHAT **ELSE** IS IN THERE?
I...UH... I HAVE NO IDEA.

GREY?
WHOSE TOOTH IS THAT?
I...UH... I DUNNO.
BUT, MARSHALL?

"I THINK MAYBE I'M IN **TROUBLE.**"

I'M TELLING YOU, SOME SORT OF...
...**CREATURE...**
...MADE THAT MODEL FOR ME!
IT LEFT IT ON MY DOORSTEP!
IT MUST HAVE LEFT THAT...**STUFF** INSIDE!
GREY
CHEEZ

AND YOU SAW IT? THE MONSTER?
WHAT DID IT LOOK LIKE?

YOU **BELIEVE** ME?
IF YOU SAY A MONSTER DID YOUR HOMEWORK FOR YOU, THEN I STAND BY YOU.
I BELIEVE THAT **YOU** BELIEVE SOMETHING REALLY STRANGE IS GOING ON.

BUT WE NEED TO FIGURE IT OUT-- **FAST.**
I DON'T KNOW IF YOU'VE NOTICED OR NOT, BUT THE OTHER KIDS ARE STARTING TO **TALK.**
GREY

FIGHT
GULP

GO RAVENS!!

OH, BOY.

Hsssssssssss

"WHAT'S **WRONG,** GREY?"

WHY AREN'T YOU EATING?
IS SOMETHING THE MATTER WITH YOUR FOOD?
ARE YOU JUST NOT HUNGRY?

GREY?
EARTH TO GREY.
HUH?
YOUR MOTHER IS TALKING TO YOU.

I'M SORRY.
I GUESS I JUST...
...I JUST HAVE A LOT ON MY MIND.

GREY--YOUR FATHER AND I RECEIVED A CALL FROM YOUR TEACHER TODAY.
SOME OF THE THINGS SHE TOLD US...
WELL, WE'RE A LITTLE **WORRIED.**

OH.

YOU'RE JUST NOT ACTING LIKE YOURSELF.
MRS. BEAMAN SEEMS CONCERNED.
AND WE THOUGHT MAYBE YOU COULD HELP US UNDERSTAND WHAT'S GOING ON.

NOT MUCH TO TELL, REALLY.
I FORGOT MY HOMEWORK.
THAT'S ALL.

GREY.
HAVE YOU BEEN...
MRS. BEAMAN THOUGHT MAYBE...

HAVE YOU BEEN SPENDING A LOT OF TIME IN **ARMITAGE CEMETERY?**

TH-THE **CEMETERY?**
NO, NOT REALLY.
I MEAN, YEAH, I WAS HANGING OUT THERE TO DO RESEARCH ON MY HISTORY PROJECT.
AND SOMETIMES I USE IT AS A **SHORTCUT** ON THE WAY TO SCHOOL.
BUT THAT'S IT.

I SEE.

GREY, HONEY, YOUR TEACHER THINKS...
...AND YOUR FATHER AND I AGREE...
...THAT MAYBE IT'S A GOOD IDEA IF YOU, Y'KNOW, **AVOID** THE CEMETERY FOR A WHILE.

MAYBE YOU COULD JUST SKIP THE SHORTCUT FOR A WHILE?
IF YOU NEED TO LEAVE EARLIER MORNING, A GOOD IDEA.
OR A CARPOOL NEIGHBORS?
ANYTHING MAKE THINGS EASIER
FATHER

"...THIS **FASCINATION** WITH GRAVEYARDS MIGHT NOT BE **HEALTHY.**"

GRAVEYAR
MONSTERS

GHOSTS.
GUARDIAN SPIRITS.
ZOMBIES.
VAMPIRES.

PLEASE.
NOT **VAMPIRES.**
TAK- TAKITY- TAK-TAK

YAWN

THE LAST
DIPLOMAT

SKKRRK

HSSSSSSSSSSS

GASP

CLICK

WHAT IN THE WORLD?
GALAXY BATTLE

HUH?

EARTH BOY
TREKKER
1:22

EARTH BOY
TREKKER
2:31

EARTH BOY
TREKKER

EARTH BOY
TREKKER

EARTH BOY
TREKKER

"TODAY WE'RE GOING TO CONTINUE OUR LESSON ON THE HISTORY OF OUR TOWN."

NOW, I KNOW WE'VE ALL HEARD PLENTY OF **GHOST STORIES** ABOUT ANDER'S LANDING.
WHILE I DON'T BELIEVE IN GHOSTS, OUR FOUNDING MOTHERS AND FATHERS DID COME HERE UNDER A **SHROUD OF DARKNESS.**
NO DISCUSSION OF OUR HISTORY WOULD BE COMPLETE WITHOUT MENTIONING **THE SALEM WITCH TRIALS.**
SALEM WITCH TRIALS

NOW, WHO CAN TELL ME WHEN THE WITCH TRIALS OF SALEM OCCURRED?

1692, **CLOUD OF SUSPICION, FOUNDERS** OF ANDER'S LANDING ARRIVED
CRINKLE

THAP!
HNNH?
DUDE!
WAKE UP!
YOU'RE GONNA GET IN TROUBLE!

GREY?
I'M SORRY.
ARE YOU **BORED** BY TODAY'S LESSON?

NO, MRS. BEAMAN.
I'M SORRY.

VERY WELL.
LET'S STAY SEATED WITH OUR EYES TOWARD THE FRONT OF THE CLASS, SHALL WE?

NOW, IF YOU WILL ALL TURN IN YOUR BOOKS TO PAGE SEVENTY-FOUR, I'D LIKE YOU ALL TO

"SORRY, MAN."

I WAS JUST TRYING TO **WARN** YOU.
IT'S ALL RIGHT.
IT'S NOT YOUR FAULT.
I'M JUST NOT SLEEPING ALL THAT WELL.

LOOK WHAT I FOUND IN MY ROOM LAST NIGHT.

THAT'S **DISGUSTING!**
WHAT IS IT?
I THINK IT'S SUPPOSED TO BE **ME.**
LET ME SEE THAT THING.

WELL, IT **DOES** KINDA LOOK LIKE YOU.

SMACK!

HEY!
WHAT DO YOU THINK YOU'RE DOING?

I WAS JUST CHECKING TO SEE IF IT WAS SOME SORT OF **VOODOO DOLL** OR SOMETHING.
BY **PUNCHING** IT?
WHAT IF IT **WAS** A VOODOO DOLL?

I MIGHT NOT HAVE THOUGHT THAT ONE THROUGH.
GOOD THING FOR YOU, IT'S NOT.
IT'S JUST A **REGULAR** SUPER CREEPY DOLL.

SO...
...YOUR MONSTER LEFT THAT FOR YOU?
SEEMS LIKE IT.

YOU DON'T THINK IT'S GONNA **COME TO LIFE** AT NIGHT, DO YOU?
LIKE, MAYBE IT **WATCHES** YOU WHILE YOU SLEEP.
MAYBE IT STALKS DOWN TO THE KITCHEN AND GRABS A BUTCHER--
YOU'RE **NOT** HELPING.

WHAT ARE YOU GONNA DO?
I MEAN, IT KIND OF LOOKS LIKE YOU'VE GOT YOURSELF A **SECRET ADMIRER.**
YOU'RE FUNNY.

WHATEVER THIS THING IS, IT'S **FOLLOWING** ME.
IT'S **SNEAKING** INTO MY HOUSE AT NIGHT.
IT MIGHT EVEN BE **WATCHING** ME RIGHT NOW.

MY PARENTS AREN'T GONNA BELIEVE ME.
THEY ALREADY THINK I'M ACTING **CRAZY.**
BUT I'VE GOTTA FIND A WAY TO KEEP THIS MONSTER OUT OF MY LIFE.

MAYBE IT'LL GROW BORED WITH YOU.
SOONER OR LATER, IT'LL FIND **SOMEONE ELSE** TO BOTHER.
MAYBE.
I SURE HOPE SO.

THE NEXT NIGHT

AND THE NEXT
RAVE

AND THE NEXT

AND THE NEXT

"THIS IS GETTING OUT OF HAND, GREY.
"EVEN IF THIS ISN'T A MONSTER...
"EVEN IF IT'S JUST SOME KID PLAYING A PRANK ON YOU..."

...THAT'S FULL-ON YEEEECH.

MAYBE IT'S TIME FOR YOU TO START LOCKING YOUR WINDOW AT NIGHT.
YOU THINK I DIDN'T TRY THAT?

I CHECK ALL THE LOCKS BEFORE I GO TO BED.
I NAILED THE WINDOWS DOWN.
I EVEN SPRINKLED SOME OF MOM'S GARLIC SALT ALONG THE WINDOW LEDGE.

GARLIC SALT?

IN CASE IT'S A **VAMPIRE.**

I DON'T THINK VAMPIRES LEAVE **GIFTS.**
WHATEVER IT IS, I JUST WANT IT TO STOP.

I BET NONE OF THIS WOULD BE HAPPENING IF YOU HADN'T PICKED UP THAT UNLUCKY PENNY.
ARE YOU STILL WORRIED ABOUT THAT?
YOU'VE GOTTA DROP IT.

WHAT AM I GONNA DO?

CAN YOU JUST GIVE THE GIFTS BACK...
...MAYBE WITH A NICE CARD THAT SAYS, "THANKS FOR THE THOUGHT, BUT PLEASE STOP GIVING ME PIECES OF **DEAD BODIES**"?

Y'KNOW.
THAT'S NOT A BAD IDEA.

WHAT'S NOT?

I'LL GIVE IT ALL BACK.
"THANKS, BUT NO THANKS."
Y'KNOW?

YOU THINK YOUR FOLKS WILL LET YOU SPEND THE NIGHT TONIGHT?
SPEND THE NIGHT?
UH, NO OFFENSE, GREY...
...BUT YOU'VE GOT SOME SORT OF **CREEPY-CRAWLY** SNEAKING INTO YOUR HOUSE.
I DON'T THINK I'LL **EVER** SPEND THE NIGHT AGAIN.

WHATEVER IT IS, I DON'T THINK IT'S **DANGEROUS.**
IT'S NOT TRYING TO HURT ME.
YOU'LL BE **PERFECTLY SAFE.**
WHO KNOWS? IT MIGHT NOT EVEN SHOW UP.

UH--

HSSSSSSSS

YEEAAAAGGH!!
SKREEEEEEK!

YOU SCARED IT OFF!
I SCARED IT?!
WE CAN'T LET IT GET AWAY!
WHAT?!

COME ON!
IT'S HEADED FOR THE CEMETERY!
WHAT ARE YOU DOING?
YOU'RE NOT **FOLLOWING** THAT THING!
MARS
D-DON'T BE DUMB.

DIDN'T YOU SEE?
IT WAS MORE SCARED OF YOU THAN YOU WERE OF IT!
THAT'S WHAT PARENTS TELL KIDS ABOUT SPIDERS AND SNAKES AND STUFF.
AND IT'S **NEVER** TRUE, GREY!
NEVER!

WAIT!
HOLD ON A SECOND!
WAIT!

BOYS?
HEY, MOM!
JUST GOTTA CHECK ON SOMETHING!
WE'LL BE RIGHT BACK!

MAYBE WE SHOULD TELL YOUR FOLKS!
NO WAY!
THEY'D ONLY STOP US!
MAYBE WE SHOULD TELL YOUR FOLKS!

"THIS IS A BAD IDEA!
"MAYBE THE WORST YOU'VE EVER HAD!"

TELL ME AGAIN WHY WE'RE SNEAKING AROUND A GRAVEYARD AT NIGHT?
I KNOW WHAT I'M DOING.
REALLY?

ALL RIGHT. I DON'T KNOW WHAT I'M DOING.
BUT WE'LL BE ALL RIGHT.
WE TELL THE...UH...MONSTER THAT I DON'T WANT ANY MORE GIFTS.
WE CUT AND RUN.
CLEAN AND SIMPLE.

WATCH YOUR STEP, OKAY?
YOU DON'T WANT TO FALL INTO AN OPEN GRAVE OR ANYTHING.

I REALLY DON'T LIKE YOU RIGHT NOW.

UH--HELLO?
M-M-MONSTER? ARE YOU OUT THERE?
WE...UH... AREN'T GONNA HURT YOU.
WE JUST WANT TO **TALK.**

MARSHALL-- **LOOK OUT!**

A TUNNEL!
IT'S SORT OF LIKE THE ONE I FOUND THE OTHER DAY.
I THINK IT'S HOW THE MONSTER GETS AROUND.

I DON'T SEE A COFFIN OR ANYTHING.
THAT'S A **GOOD** THING, RIGHT?
WAIT A MINUTE...

SKREEEEEEEEEEE

SKREE-SKREEE-SKRE
SKREE!
SKREE-SKREEK!
RUH-RUH-RUH--
THEY'RE ON ME!
SKREEEK

YAAAAA!
SKREEEK!

RATS!
THOUSANDS OF THEM!
SKREEEK
SKREEEEE

HSSSSS
RIP
YAAAAA!

SKREEEEEE

GREY?
GREY!
WHERE ARE YOU?

UHHH--

Hsssss

YOU--
YOU **SAVED** ME!

THE CEMETERY'S NOT SAFE.
NOT AT NIGHT.
SURFACE-DWELLERS SHOULD STAY AWAY.
THIS IS A **KINGDOM OF THE DEAD.**

YOU...CAN **TALK?**

OF COURSE I CAN TALK.
HEY, I DIDN'T MEAN ANY HARM.
IT'S JUST THAT... Y'KNOW...
...SO FAR, I'VE ONLY HEARD YOU KIND OF **HISS.**

HSSSS

YEAH... LIKE THAT.

ARE...ARE YOU...
...A ZOMBIE?
OR MAYBE A VAMPIRE?
A GUARDIAN SPIRIT?

GHOULS.
WE'RE CALLED GHOULS.

WAIT!
WHERE ARE YOU GOING?

SKRK?

HNNNN

UNNF!
WUMP

GREY?
ARE YOU ALL RIGHT?
DID YOU GET **EATEN?**
I'M OVER HERE!

DID YOU SEE HER?
THE...CREATURE!
THE **GHOUL!**
SHE WAS RIGHT HERE!

SHE WAS RIGHT HERE.
WHERE--
YOU WANNA ASK "WHERE"?
MAYBE YOU SHOULD ASK YOURSELF WHERE ALL THOSE **RATS** WENT.
I THINK MAYBE--

--THEY ALL JUST RAN STRAIGHT INTO THE **NEIGHBORHOOD!**
MOEN
1897
1990
RIP
LIM
1920
2002

LIES
ARKER
91

Hsssssss

MARS
ACCORDING TO LEGENDS, A GHOUL IS A NOCTURNAL CREATURE THAT DWELLS IN, AROUND, AND **UNDERNEATH** CEMETERIES.

MARS
THE **OLDER** THE CEMETERY, THE **BETTER.**
THEY LIVE IN WARRENS UNDERGROUND, CRAWLING IN TUNNELS THAT CONNECT THE GRAVES.

MARS
GHOULS WERE ONCE **NORMAL PEOPLE.**
BUT THEY'VE **CHANGED.**

MARS
THEIR **DIET** HAS CAUSED THEM TO **MUTATE.**

MARS
THEY **EAT** THE **DEAD.**

IS THAT SUPPOSED TO **COMFORT** ME?
KEKKER
IN THE GRAVEYARD...
...SHE **HELPED** ME.
I DON'T THINK WE'RE IN **DANGER.**

YOU DON'T KNOW THAT, GREY.
I'M SORRY, BUT YOU DON'T KNOW **ANYTHING** ABOUT THIS THING!
I SAW IT, AND IT DID **NOT** LOOK **FRIENDLY.**

I THINK MAYBE WE JUST NEED TO LEARN A LITTLE MORE ABOUT--
"WE"?
WHO ARE YOU TALKING ABOUT?
EARTH BOY
NOT **ME,** I HOPE.

MY **MONSTER-HUNTING** DAYS ARE OVER.
I'M NOT LETTING YOU DRAG ME ALONG ON ANY MORE **CRAZY ADVENTURES.**
YOU WANNA LURK AROUND GRAVE-YARDS IN THE DEAD OF NIGHT, YOU'RE GONNA HAVE TO DO IT WITHOUT ME.
YOU DON'T MEAN THAT.
YOU'RE JUST A LITTLE SCARED IS ALL.

GREY--WE ALMOST GOT EATEN BY **RATS!**
RATS, GREY. BIG ONES.
AND THERE'S A MONSTER SNEAKING INTO YOUR HOUSE AT NIGHT.
YOU **BET** I'M SCARED.

AND YOU SHOULD BE, TOO!
SLAM

YAAAWN

HEY, KIDDO.
YOU DON'T LOOK LIKE YOU GOT MUCH SLEEP.
WHERE'S MARSHALL?
ANDER'S LANDING GAZETTE

AW.
I GUESS HE JUST GOT A LITTLE **HOMESICK** IS ALL.
HE TOOK OFF EARLY THIS MORNING.

EARLY?
THAT'S NOT LIKE MARSHALL.
YOU TWO DIDN'T HAVE A **FIGHT** OR SOMETHING, DID YOU?

NAH.
NOTHING LIKE THAT.
HE JUST FELT LIKE GOING HOME.

YOUR DAD AND I WERE THINKING ABOUT GOING OUT AND DOING A BIT OF ANTIQUE SHOPPING.
HAVE ANY INTEREST IN GOING WITH US?
IF IT'S OKAY WITH YOU, I THOUGHT MAYBE I'D JUST HAVE A LAZY DAY.

SUIT YOURSELF.
I DON'T KNOW, THOUGH.
IT MIGHT BE FUN.

COME ON, HONEY.
I'M SURE GREY HAS BETTER THINGS TO DO.
BESIDES, THE TWO OF US ARE PROBABLY TWO TOO MANY ANTIQUES AROUND THE HOUSE FOR HIS TASTES.
DA

THE OLD MAN'S GOT A POINT.

YOU WATCH IT, MISTER.

ARE YOU SURE YOU'LL BE ALL RIGHT?
YEAH, MOM.
I'LL BE FINE.
YOU GUYS HAVE FUN.

WE MIGHT BE GONE FOR A FEW HOURS.
WE'RE PROBABLY GOING TO GET A LATE LUNCH WHILE WE'RE OUT.
WANT US TO BRING SOMETHING BACK FOR YOU?
SURE.
THAT SOUNDS GREAT.

LOCK
K-CLICK

...THE LEGEND OF THE GHOUL CAN BE TRACED TO PRE-ISLAMIC RELIGION AND FOLKLORE.
THESE CREATURES ARE SAID TO BE ASSOCIATED WITH GRAVEYARDS AND OBSESSED WITH THE CONSUMPTION OF DEAD HUMAN FLESH.

SOME BELIEVE THE GHOUL TO BE A KIND OF **JINN** OR **GENIE...**
...WHILE OTHER LEGENDS HOLD THAT THE CREATURE IS A **SHAPESHIFTER, TRICKSTER,** OR EVEN **UNDEAD BEING.**

MODERN MYTHS SEEM TO COMBINE THE STORIES OF **GHOULS** WITH THE STORIES OF **GOBLINS** OF FOLKLORE...
...CASTING THEM AS CREATURES THAT KIDNAP INFANTS FROM THEIR CRIBS TO BOLSTER THEIR NUMBERS.

IN MOST STORIES, THE GHOUL IS DEPICTED AS MENACING AND DANGEROUS...
...A MONSTER KNOWN FOR DRINKING BLOOD, STEALING COINS AND BAUBLES, AND--OF COURSE--EATING THE DECEASED.

GHOUL LEGENDS HAVE SEEPED INTO POP CULTURE...
...WITH THE CREATURES APPEARING IN BOOKS, TELEVISION SHOWS, AND VIDEO GAMES.
ZZZZZ

SOME SCHOLARS OF SUPER-NATURAL LORE BELIEVE THAT STORIES OF MYSTERIOUS **MASS DISAPPEARANCES...**
...SUCH AS IN ROANOKE, VIRGINIA; SPIDER CREEK, MISSOURI; AND ANDER'S LANDING, MASSACHUSETTS...

...ARE CONNECTED IN SOME WAY TO GHOUL LEGENDS...
...WITH GHOULS DESCRIBED AS THOSE WHO FLED INTO THE BOWELS OF CEMETERIES TO ESCAPE **PERSECUTION.**
VIEWTOOB
GHOULS: A HISTORY
YOU MAY

OTHER MORE SENSATIONAL THEORIES SUGGEST THAT THESE SUBTERRANEAN CREATURES HAVE MADE STRANGE **PACTS** WITH THE SPIRITS THAT OCCUPY THEIR REALM...
PACTS SEALED WITH SINISTER **OFFERINGS AND SACRIFICES...**
TORY

IS IT POSSIBLE THAT GHOULS LIVE AMONG US...
...DWELLING IN THOSE SOMBER, FINAL RESTING PLACES THAT AWAIT US ALL?

BUMP!
TH-UMP!
THERE ARE FEW RARE REAL-LIFE ENCOUNTERS WITH GHOULS. IN FACT, IT WOULD APPEAR THAT THOSE WHO HAVE ENCOUNTERED GHOULS...
...ARE **SPIRITED AWAY** BEFORE THEY CAN MAKE CREDIBLE EYEWITNESS REPORTS.
HNNH?

THUMP THUMP TH-THUMP THUMP THUMP

H-HELLO?
MOM?
DAD?
IS THAT YOU?

GHOULS ARE NOCTURNAL.
THEY ONLY COME OUT AT NIGHT.

GALAXY BATTLE

COME ON, GREY.
YOU'RE DELIRIOUS.
YOU'RE LETTING YOUR IMAGINATION GET THE BEST OF YOU.

Hssssssssss

IS...
...IS SOMEONE HERE?
IF YOU ARE... I SHOULD WARN YOU...
...I'VE GOT--
--A LAMP.

Fsssssh

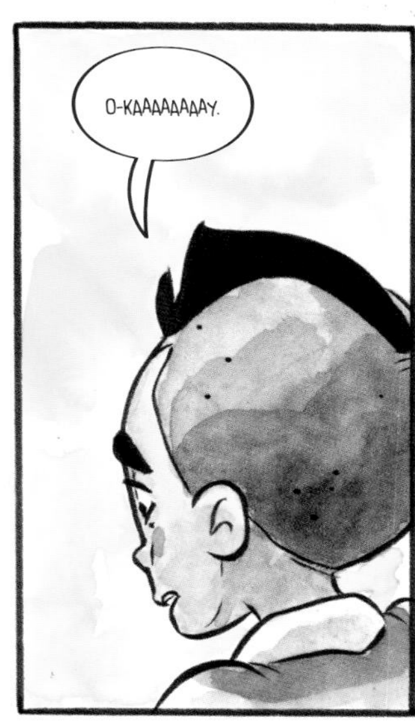
O-KAAAAAAAAY.

MARS
HSSSSSSSSSSSSSS

YOU'RE NOT HERE TO KILL ME, ARE YOU?
Y'KNOW...
...BECAUSE I DIDN'T WANT THE DOLL.

ARE YOU GONNA EAT ME?
FEH!

YOU'RE TOO FRESH.
ALIVE.
GROSS!

GUESS I DON'T NEED THIS, HUH?

SO... MY NAME'S **GREY.**
I KNOW.

DO YOU HAVE A NAME?

YES.
I CAN TALK **AND** I HAVE A NAME.
SURPRISE, SURPRISE.

HEY.
SORRY.
I'M NOT TRYING TO BE A JERK OR ANYTHING.
I JUST--

LAVINIA.
THAT'S MY NAME.
LAVINIA.

ALL RIGHT.
UH. COOL.
NICE TO MEET YOU, LAVINIA.

?

WHEN YOU MEET SOMEONE NEW...
...YOU SHAKE HANDS...
AT LEAST, THAT'S WHAT WE DO...
HUMANS, I MEAN...

Hssss

YOUR HANDS ARE ICE COLD.

YOURS...
...ARE SWEATY.

YEAH. SORRY ABOUT THAT.
I'M A LITTLE **NERVOUS.**
IT'S NOT EVERY DAY THAT I HAVE A CONVERSATION WITH A--

A ***GHOUL.***

YEAH.
RIGHT.
I'VE BEEN READING UP ON GHOULS.

AND WHAT YOU READ MADE YOU NERVOUS?
MAYBE A LITTLE.

Hss?

WHAT DID YOU LEARN?

WELL...GHOULS ARE NOCTURNAL.
OR YOU'RE SUPPOSED TO BE.
BUT IT'S--Y'KNOW--DAYTIME RIGHT NOW.
MOST OF US JUST DON'T LIKE THE LIGHT BECAUSE IT HURTS OUR EYES.

GHOULS LIVE IN CEMETERIES.
OKAY.
THAT'S TRUE.

AND GHOULS EAT DEAD BODIES.
IS THAT WHY YOU THINK I'M A **MONSTER?**

HEY! I DON'T--
I **HEARD** YOU.
YOU CALLED ME A MONSTER IN THE CEMETERY.
WELL, I GUESS I DIDN'T REALLY UNDERSTAND.

I MEAN-- I DON'T THINK YOU'RE A MONSTER.
YOU DON'T?

NO WAY.
YOU SAVED ME.

IS THAT THE **ONLY** REASON?
WHAT IF I HAD LET THE RATS PICK YOUR BONES CLEAN?

WELL, YEAH.
THAT WOULD HAVE BEEN A **TOTAL** MONSTER MOVE.
HEH.

THIS IS A **WHISPER DOLL.**
THE TEETH ARE FROM THE SKULL OF A **TATTLETALE.**
THEY SAY IT TELLS **SECRETS** WHEN THE MOON IS FULL.

UHM.
COOL?
YOU DIDN'T LIKE MY PRESENTS.
IT'S NOT THAT.
IT WAS JUST...
...I DUNNO...

...A LITTLE **WEIRD.**

WEIRD.

DON'T TAKE IT THE WRONG WAY.
I MEAN--
I WAS A LITTLE FREAKED OUT.
THAT'S JUST HOW PEOPLE REACT TO **THINGS THAT GO BUMP IN THE NIGHT.**
BIG FOOT

AND YOU **LITERALLY** WENT BUMP IN THE NIGHT.
YOU KNOW... WITH ALL THE SNEAKING IN AND OUT OF THE HOUSE.

SPEAKING OF WHICH, HOW DID YOU GET IN HERE?
I LOCKED ALL THE DOORS...
...ALL THE WINDOWS.

I'LL SHOW YOU.
THIS IS ***FUN.***
YOU'LL ***LOVE*** *IT.*

IT'S ***SPECIAL.***

THE FINGERBONES OF A **BURGLAR.**
THE HAIR OF AN **ESCAPE ARTIST.**
IT'S **SPECIAL.**

IT CAN UNLOCK ANY DOOR.

I MADE IT MYSELF.

HEH.
A **SKELETON KEY.**
RIGHT?
I DON'T GET IT.

IF YOU DON'T MIND ME ASKING...
...WHY DID YOU START LEAVING ALL THIS STUFF?
WHY DID YOU **TAKE** MY MODEL...AND THEN **REBUILD** IT?

I **LIKED** YOUR MODEL.
IT WAS **CUTE.**
LIKE A **BABY** MADE IT.

OUCH.

BUT IT WASN'T **ACCURATE.**
SO I MADE YOU A NEW ONE.
I EVEN INCLUDED TRINKETS YOU MIGHT FIND IN SPECIFIC GRAVES.
MARS
YOU **LIKED** IT, YES?

Y-YEAH.
IT WAS GREAT.
REALLY...

PERFECTO.

I SHOULD GET HOME...
...BEFORE I'M **MISSED.**
"WE."

HMM?
IN THE CEMETERY.
YOU SAID--

GHOULS.
WE'RE CALLED **GHOULS.**

YOU SAID "WE."
AND YOU SAID YOU'D BE MISSED.
SO...ARE THERE MORE OF YOU?
OH, YES.
MANY, **MANY** MORE.

PRAY YOU NEVER MEET THEM.

BATTLE

GALAXY
BATTLE

"HOLD ON
A SECOND."

"HER NAME IS **LAVINIA?**"
COMIX CORNER
YOU'RE ON A **FIRST-NAME BASIS** WITH HER?
THAT DOESN'T STRIKE YOU AS... **PECULIAR?**
YEAH, YEAH.
I **KNOW** IT'S STRANGE.
BUT IF YOU MET HER--
THAT KID
BANDETTE
DEFENDER OF THE NIGH

I DON'T **WANT** TO MEET HER, GREY.
EARTH BOY #2

I HAVE **NO INTEREST** IN MEETING A **MONSTER.**
HARROW COUNTY

COME ON, MARSHALL.
KEEP YOUR VOICE DOWN.
BLACK MAGE

AND SHE DOESN'T LIKE THAT.
SHE DOESN'T LIKE BEING CALLED A MONSTER.
THAT'S NOT--

WHATEVER!
YOUR NEW FRIEND EATS **DEAD BODIES,** GREY.
DEAD.
BODIES.
THAT KID

AND I DON'T WANT TO BE **ONE** OF THE DEAD BODIES SHE EATS.

SHE'S NOT LIKE THAT.
YEAH?
THAT'S **GREAT,** GREY.
I'M JUST GONNA HAVE TO TAKE YOUR WORD FOR IT.

ALL I'M SAYING IS...
...I DUNNO...
...MAYBE WE SHOULD **TELL** SOMEONE.

WHO ARE WE GONNA TELL?
THE POLICE? THE MILITARY?
WHAT ARE WE GONNA TELL THEM? THAT THE GRAVEYARD'S CRAWLING WITH GHOULS?
MAYBE WE SHOULD START WITH OUR PARENTS.
IT WOULD GO A LONG WAY TOWARD EXPLAINING WHY YOU'VE BEEN SO SPOOOOOOOKY-ACTING LATELY.

IF WE SAY SOMETHING, WE MIGHT CAUSE A **PANIC.**
MAYBE THAT'S A **GOOD** THING.
WHAT IF THE GHOULS OR WHATEVER THEY'RE CALLED TURN AGAINST US?
WHAT IF THEY SEND THEIR ATTACK-RATS AFTER THE WHOLE TOWN?

JUST...DON'T SAY ANYTHING YET, ALL RIGHT?
I DON'T THINK IT'S A GOOD IDEA AT ALL.
LET ME FIGURE THINGS OUT, OKAY?
I'M NOT MAKING ANY PROMISES, GREY.
IF I THINK YOU'RE GETTING INTO TROUBLE, I KINDA HAVE TO TELL **SOMEONE.**

HSSSSSSSSS

"YOU KNOW MY FRIEND MARSHALL?
"HE WAS WITH ME ON THE NIGHT I CAME TO THE CEMETERY."
"I REMEMBER.
"HE SCREAMED **VERY** LOUDLY."

"THAT'S HIM.
"I WAS TALKING TO HIM ABOUT YOU."
"YOU SHOULDN'T DO THAT, GREY.
"THE FEWER PEOPLE WHO KNOW ABOUT ME--THE BETTER."

"IT'S NOT LIKE I WAS REVEALING ANY BIG SECRETS.
"I MEAN, HE'S ALREADY **SEEN** YOU.
"BUT I THINK HE'S A LITTLE **FREAKED OUT.**"
"'FREAKED OUT?'"
ANDER'S LANDING
WITCH HOUSE

"HE JUST FOUND THE IDEA OF GHOULS LIVING IN THE CEMETERY...**UNSETTLING.**

"HE'S A LITTLE SCARED.
"THAT'S ALL.
"BUT MAYBE YOU DON'T UNDERSTAND THAT."
"WHY WOULDN'T I UNDERSTAND **FEAR?**"

BECAUSE I'M A MONSTER?
OF COURSE NOT.
THAT'S NOT WHAT I MEAN.

NO ONE IS **BORN** A GHOUL, GREY.
WE WERE ALL **HUMAN** ONCE.
AND ALL HUMANS ARE BORN WITH FEAR IN THEIR HEARTS.

MANY OF MY KIND REMEMBER THE WAYS HUMANS ACT...
HOW THEY **HUNT** THE THINGS THEY FEAR...
HOW THEY **DESTROY** WHAT THEY DO NOT UNDERSTAND...
AND THAT'S WHY YOU MUST BE CAREFUL WHO YOU TELL ABOUT US.
THE GHOULS ARE VERY **PROTECTIVE** OF THEIR SECRETS.
I COULD GET IN BIG TROUBLE FOR TALKING TO YOU.

WHY TAKE THE CHANCE?
LIKE I SAID, NO ONE IS BORN A GHOUL.
I WAS **CURIOUS** ABOUT HUMANS.
ABOUT **YOU.**

NOW, DO YOU WANT ME TO TELL YOU ABOUT ANDER'S LANDING OR WHAT?
S-SURE.
HOLD ON, THOUGH.
I BROUGHT SOMETHING.

WHAT DO YOU THINK?
YOU DON'T WANT TO MAKE ANYONE **SUSPICIOUS,** RIGHT?
WEAR THIS, AND THEY WON'T EVEN LOOK TWICE.
FIGHTING
RAVENS

IT **STINKS.**
FIGHTING

I THINK MAYBE THAT'S **LAUNDRY DETERGENT** YOU SMELL.
OR MAYBE **FABRIC SOFTENER.**

SOFT.
YES.

YOU LOOK AWESOME!
NOW NO ONE WILL KNOW THERE'S A GHOUL AMONG THEM!
IT'S A GREAT **DISGUISE!**

PERFECTO, REALLY.
⁂GRUMBLE⁂

THIS WASN'T ALWAYS A HOBBY SHOP.
ONCE, IT WAS A **LIBRARY**--THE **SECOND** LIBRARY IN ANDER'S LANDING.
IT WAS WHERE ALL THE **BAD** BOOKS-- THE BOOKS NO SANE PERSON SHOULD EVER READ-- WERE STORED.
THREE SISTERS HOBBIES
ONE NIGHT, A FIRE CONSUMED ALL THOSE TERRIBLE BOOKS.
THE PLACE STILL SMELLS LIKE SMOKE.

THIS IS **PAPER ALLEY.**
AROUND FIFTY YEARS AGO, A MAN'S DAUGHTER WENT MISSING.
HE STARTED HANGING UP THESE SIGNS TO SEE IF ANYONE HAD SEEN HER.
MISSING
HAVE YOU SEEN ME?
ONCE UPON A TIME, HE TACKED THEM UP ALL OVER TOWN, BUT THROUGHOUT THE YEARS, THE SIGNS STARTED APPEARING IN ONLY ONE PLACE--**HERE.**
THE MAN DIED NEARLY THIRTY YEARS AGO, BUT THE SIGNS KEEP SHOWING UP EVERY NIGHT.

THERE WAS A FISHERMAN OUT ON THESE VERY DOCKS ONE NIGHT.
HE SAID HE SAW A SCHOOL OF GIANT FISH-- WITH GLOWING SPOTS ON THEIR BACKS--OUT IN THE WATER.
HE SAW THEM EVERY NIGHT, BUT THEY KEPT GETTING FARTHER AND FARTHER AWAY.
HE STARTED ADDING PLANKS TO THE PIER, NIGHT AFTER NIGHT, SO HE COULD WATCH THE GIANT, GLOWING FISH.
THEN ONE DAY, HE JUST **VANISHED.**
SOME PEOPLE SAY THE FISH **LURED** HIM OUT TO HIS DOOM.

YOU KNOW WHY YOU NEVER SEE RATS ON BLEECH STREET?
WELL, AROUND FORTY YEARS AGO, A TRAVELING CARNIVAL CAME THROUGH TOWN.
THEY HAD ONE OF THEM HUGE SNAKES-- THE KIND THAT SWALLOWS BIG OL' HOGS WHOLE-- BUT IT ESCAPED!
SOME SAY IT STILL LIVES DOWN BELOW...AND IT'S GROWN HUGE OVER THE YEARS.
THAT'S WHY YOU NEVER SEE RATS HERE... OR CATS...OR DOGS.

A BEEKEEPER NAMED AGGY GREEN USED TO LIVE HERE.
SHE RAISED BEES, Y'SEE, AND SHE SOLD THE VERY BEST HONEY.
THERE WAS AN INSATIABLE DEMAND FOR THE HONEY, AND AGGY WOULD SUPPLY IT BY THE BARRELFUL.
NO ONE KNEW HOW SHE MADE SO MUCH HONEY.
BUT THEY SAY YOU USED TO BE ABLE TO HEAR A POWERFUL, DEEP BUZZING--LOUDER THAN ANY BEE ANYONE HAD EVER HEARD--IF YOU VENTURED ONTO OLD AGGY'S FARM.

WHAT ABOUT THE GHOULS?
WHERE DID THEY COME FROM?
HOW DID THEY GET HERE?

THE PEOPLE WHO WOULD BECOME THE GHOULS CAME HERE CENTURIES AGO.

"THEY FLED PERSECUTION AND DEATH.
"THEY THOUGHT THEY HAD FOUND A PLACE THEY COULD CALL HOME.
"BUT THEY WERE FOLLOWED...FOLLOWED BY THOSE WHO HATED THEM...HOUNDED BY THOSE WHO FEARED THEM.
"THEY WERE TRIED-- HERE IN THEIR NEW HOME--AS WITCHES AND WARLOCKS.
"AND THEY SUFFERED.

"THEY KNEW THEY WOULD NEVER BE FREE, NOT IN THE WORLD OF MAN...
"...AND SO THEY FOUND A PLACE TO HIDE WHERE THEIR SUPERSTITIOUS ENEMIES WOULD NOT FOLLOW.
"THEY WERE SCARED--TERRIFIED--BUT THEY HAD NO CHOICE.
"OVER TIME, THE FOUL HUMORS OF THE GRAVEYARD CHANGED THEM.
"IT TURNED THEM INTO HORRORS THAT NO MAN DARED CROSS."

WE BECAME--

--THIS.

THAT STINKS.
YOUR ANCESTORS WERE **FALSELY ACCUSED** OF BEING WITCHES--
NO.
NOT FALSELY.
AT LEAST, NOT FOR ALL OF US.

SOME OF THEM **WERE** WITCHES.
MOST OF THEM WEREN'T EVIL, LIKE YOU THINK.
BUT **SOME** WERE.

THERE WAS ONE WOMAN--**SALLY-BEA HURST.**
I KNOW THAT NAME.
MARSHALL DID A HISTORY PROJECT ABOUT HER.

SHE WAS A WITCH...AND SHE WAS CRUEL AND VICIOUS.
A **REAL** MONSTER.
AND THIS--

--IS HER GRAVE.

SHE BETRAYED HER COVEN...ALL THE OTHER WITCHES.
SHE STOOD ACCUSED.
SO SHE HELPED THOSE WHO WERE HUNTING HER FRIENDS IN ORDER TO SAVE HER OWN SKIN.

SHE'S PART OF THE REASON THE WITCHES PERFORMED THE DARK RITUALS.
SHE'S THE REASON THEY TOOK THEIR FIRST BITE OF DEAD FLESH.
SHE'S THE REASON THEY BECAME GHOULS TO ESCAPE THOSE WHO WOULD KILL THEM.

EVENTUALLY, SHE WAS FOUND OUT, THOUGH.
RIGHT?
I MEAN--

"IT'S HISTORICAL FACT THAT SHE WAS LIKE...A BAD PERSON."
Y-BEA HURST
FOR
TCHERY

OH, YES.
HER WICKEDNESS COULDN'T STAY HIDDEN FOREVER.
THEY KILLED HER AND BURIED HER WHERE FEW WOULD EVER--

SKRRRRRKKK!

YAAAAAAA!
WHAT IS **THAT?!**
WHAT IS IT?!
GET AWAY!
YOU SHOULDN'T BE HERE!
GET BACK! **BACK!**
GET AWAY--
--OR I'LL EAT YOUR **FACE!**

AGGGK!
SHE SEES YOU, LITTLE GHOUL!
SHE--
PUNT!
EEEEEP!

SKREEEEEEEE!

RUN!
RUN, GREY!
COME ON!
DON'T COME BACK!
SHE SEES YOU!
SALLY-BEA SEES YOU!

YAAAAAAGH!!

IT'S ALL RIGHT.
IT'S OKAY.
I DON'T THINK HE FOLLOWED US.
WHAT **WAS** THAT THING?
WHY'D IT HAVE A **HUMAN FACE?**
WHAT'S WITH GRAVEYARDS AND RATS?
I THINK THAT WAS **MILES JENKINS.**

YOU KNOW ITS **NAME?**
HE WAS SALLY-BEA HURST'S SERVANT. HER **FAMILIAR.**
HE WAS ONCE A MAN, BUT HE WAS CHANGED BY HER MAGIC.
NO ONE HAS SEEN HIM IN **DECADES!**

IS HE FOLLOWING US?
WHAT DID HE MEAN WHEN HE SAID SALLY-BEA COULD SEE US?
IS SHE STILL **ALIVE?**
IS SHE A **GHOUL,** TOO?

NO.
SHE'S SOMETHING MUCH **WORSE.**

I GUESS YOU DON'T WANT TO CONTINUE THE TOUR, HUH?

NO WAY, NO HOW.
I THINK I BETTER BE GETTING HOME ANYHOW.
MY FOLKS AREN'T GONNA LIKE IT IF I'M OUT TOO LATE ON A SCHOOL NIGHT.
IF I COME BACK WITH MY FACE CHEWED OFF BY A RAT-MONSTER, I'LL NEVER HEAR THE END OF IT!

HEH.
YOU'RE WHISTLING PAST THE GRAVEYARD.

WHAT'S THAT MEAN?
IT'S SOMETHING HUMANS DO.
WHEN YOU'RE SCARED OR WORRIED OR SAD.
YOU MAKE JOKES.

WHEN YOU WALK PAST A GRAVEYARD FULL OF GHOSTS...
...YOU WHISTLE.
IT TAKES YOUR MIND OFF THE BAD THINGS THAT ARE WAITING FOR YOU IN THE SHADOWS.

"HEY, THANKS FOR SHOWING ME AROUND AND ALL.
"IT WAS... KINDA COOL.
"CREEPY BUT COOL."
I CAN'T WAIT TO TELL MARSHALL ABOUT SALLY-BEA'S GRAVE.
HE'S GONNA **FLIP.**
WHEN CAN WE HANG OUT AGAIN?
I BET THERE ARE OTHER COOL SIGHTS TO SEE, AREN'T THERE?
MAYBE LATER IN THE WEEK?
...
MAYBE.

"MARSHALL?"

DON'T FORGET TO TAKE THE TRASH OUT, DEAR!
I WON'T, MOM!
I'M DOING IT RIGHT NOW!

Hsssssssss

"...MAYBE WE SHOULD TELL SOMEONE..."
"...START WITH OUR PARENTS..."
"...IF I THINK YOU'RE GETTING INTO TROUBLE..."

CRASH
RATTLE

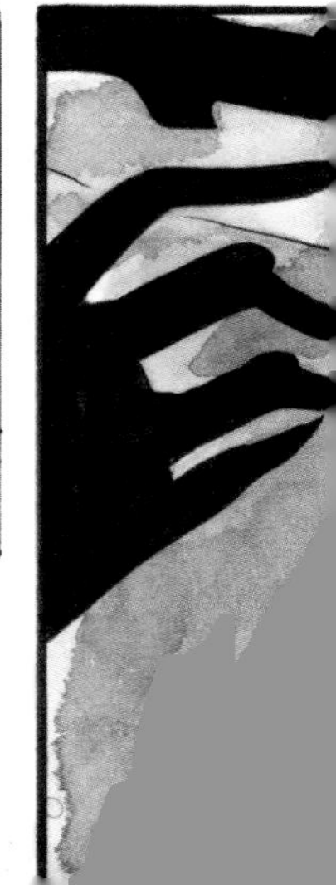

LAVINIA?

I THINK M-MAYBE THERE'S BEEN A **MISUNDER-STANDING.**
"...TELL SOMEONE..."
"...SPOOOOOOOKY ..."
"...THE GRAVEYARD IS CRAWLING WITH GHOULS..."

HEY!
HEY! WAIT!
DON'T!
NOOOOOOO-

"MARSHALL?"

NO MARSHALL TODAY?
THAT'S REALLY TOO BAD.
HE'S GOING TO HAVE TO MAKE UP TODAY'S QUIZ.

I DON'T BELIEVE HIS PARENTS CALLED IN.

GREY, YOU AND MARSHALL ARE FRIENDS.
DO YOU KNOW ANYTHING ABOUT WHY HE ISN'T HERE?
NO, MA'AM.
I GUESS MAYBE HE'S JUST SICK.
9:30-10:30
ENGLISH

OR **SOMETHING.**

POLICE

WEIRD.

KNOCK
KNOCK

SOMETHING'S NOT RIGHT.
SOMEBODY'S **ALWAYS** HOME THIS TIME OF DAY.

CREAAK

IS ANYBODY HOME?
HELLO?
IT'S GREY.
KNOCK
KNOCK
KNOCK

ARMITAGE
EAST
GATE

L-LAVINIA?
HELLO?
CAN YOU HEAR ME?

LAVINIA, IF YOU CAN HEAR ME...
...I **REALLY** THINK WE NEED TO TALK.

I THINK SOMETHING MIGHT HAVE HAPPENED TO MARSHALL--TO MY FRIEND.
SOMETHING **BAD.**

I THINK I NEED YOUR HELP.

SKRRF

LAVINIA--
GREY?
WHAT ARE YOU DOING OUT THERE IN THE RAIN?
GET INSIDE--

--QUICK--
--BEFORE YOU CATCH YOUR **DEATH!**

TH-THANKS.
I...
I THINK.

IS THERE A **DEAD BODY** IN THERE?

NOT ANYMORE.

OH.
YEAH.
RIGHT.

SKRRRRRRR

WAIT!
I WON'T BE ABLE TO--

--SEE.

DON'T BE SCARED.
JUST HOLD ON A SECOND.
I ALMOST FORGOT THAT YOU CAN'T SEE IN THE DARK.
IS **THAT** BETTER?

THANKS.

WHY ARE YOU TRAIPSING AROUND THE GRAVEYARD?

MARSHALL DIDN'T COME TO SCHOOL TODAY...
...AND WHEN I WENT TO HIS HOUSE...
...I FOUND WHAT LOOKED LIKE A GHOUL TUNNEL...
...ONLY IT WAS COLLAPSED BY THE RAIN.
OH.

"OH?"
WHAT'S THAT MEAN?
LAVINIA-- DO YOU KNOW SOMETHING ABOUT WHAT HAPPENED TO MARSHALL?

IT'S MY FAULT.
THE COUNCIL DOESN'T LIKE THAT I MADE CONTACT WITH HUMANS.
THEY DON'T LIKE THAT YOU KNOW ABOUT US.

THEY DID SOMETHING TO MARSHALL?
THEY'RE COMING AFTER ME?

NOT YOU.
I CONVINCED THEM TO LEAVE YOU ALONE.
I TRIED TO TELL THEM THAT YOU AND MARSHALL MEANT US NO HARM, BUT--
--MY TRANSGRESSION COULD NOT GO UNPUNISHED.

YOU KNEW THEY WERE COMING FOR MARSHALL AND YOU DIDN'T TELL ME?
I TRIED TO CONVINCE THEM TO LEAVE YOU BOTH ALONE.
AND THEY WARNED ME TO STAY AWAY.
IF THEY KNEW I WAS HERE NOW--

WHERE IS HE?

IS HE--

HE'S ALIVE.
HE'S BEEN TAKEN DOWN BELOW--INTO NECROPOLIS.

IF I HAD WARNED YOU, THEY WOULD HAVE TAKEN YOU, TOO.
I SHOULDN'T EVEN BE HERE RIGHT NOW.
TALKING TO HUMANS--
--IT IS FORBIDDEN.

WHY DID YOU DO IT?
THIS CAN'T JUST BE BECAUSE OF SOME MODEL CEMETERY.
WHY DID YOU PUT US AT RISK?
IT WASN'T ALL THAT LONG AGO THAT I WAS HUMAN.
BUT I DON'T REMEMBER.

I JUST WANTED TO SEE... WHAT IT MIGHT HAVE BEEN LIKE IF I WASN'T A GHOUL.

HEY--I'M SORRY.
I GUESS I FORGOT THAT YOU COME FROM A DIFFERENT WORLD THAN I DO.

YOU **FORGOT** I WAS A **GHOUL?**

THAT'S RIGHT.
BUT HUMANS DON'T LET THEIR FRIENDS GET KIDNAPPED AND DRAGGED OFF TO SOME UNDERGROUND KINGDOM.
ARE YOU GONNA HELP ME FIND HIM OR WHAT?

WHAT ARE YOU LOOKING FOR?

A TUNNEL OR SOMETHING.
THERE MUST BE ONE SOME--
KRRRRSH! THUMP!

OVER HERE.
THIS WAY.
THIS IS THE WAY DOWN.

WHOA.
THAT COVERING MUST WEIGH A TON.
HOW **STRONG** ARE YOU ANYHOW?

HSSS

I SHOULD WARN YOU.
IF YOU DESCEND THESE STEPS, YOU'LL SEE THINGS HUMANS WERE NOT MEANT TO WITNESS.
IF I DON'T, WHAT HAPPENS TO MARSHALL?

THAT'S WHAT I WAS **AFRAID** YOU'D SAY.

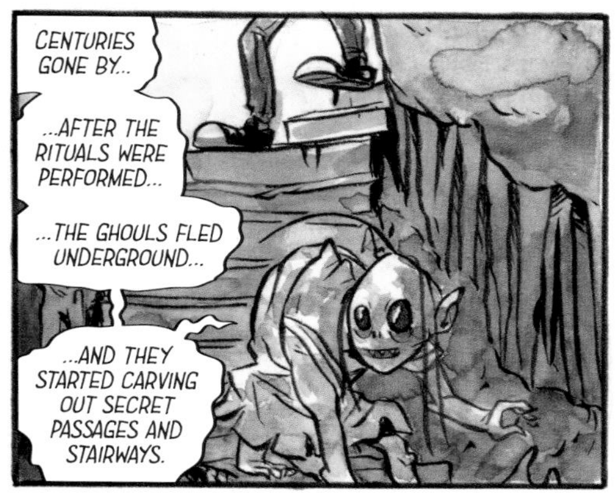
CENTURIES GONE BY...
...AFTER THE RITUALS WERE PERFORMED...
...THE GHOULS FLED UNDERGROUND...
...AND THEY STARTED CARVING OUT SECRET PASSAGES AND STAIRWAYS.

I'M SORRY IT HAS COME TO THIS.
I'M SORRY ABOUT WHAT HAPPENED TO MARSHALL.
I'M SORRY I BROUGHT YOU HERE.

IT'S ALL RIGHT.
YOU'RE HELPING ME NOW.
THAT'S WHAT'S IMPORTANT.

I LIKE YOU, GREY.
I DON'T THINK YOU'LL EVER SEE THE SURFACE WORLD AGAIN.
BUT I LIKE YOU.

THIS PLACE...
...THESE TUNNELS...
...ARE HUGE...

UGH!
THAT **SMELL!**
IT'S **HORRIBLE!**

THIS ONE TIME, A RAT GOT INTO OUR ATTIC AND COULDN'T GET OUT.
IT DIED UP THERE AND STARTED TO ROT BEFORE MY DAD FOUND IT AND GOT RID OF IT.
THIS SMELLS LIKE THAT--ONLY A **THOUSAND TIMES WORSE!**

IT'S THE MAIN PATH TO NECROPOLIS...
...THE MOST DIRECT ROUTE...

I GUESS I'LL JUST HOLD MY BREATH--

WAAGH!
YOU MUST WATCH YOUR STEP!

WE DON'T WANT HUMANS FINDING US, REMEMBER?

TAK
TAK
SHUNK

WE SET **BOOBY TRAPS.**
I...
...SEE THAT.

"THEY WERE BUILT DURING THE DAYS OF THE WITCH TRIALS.
"THE GHOULS DIDN'T WANT ANYONE PURSUING THEM INTO THE DEPTHS.
"NOW, THEY JUST KEEP PRYING EYES AWAY."

GHOULS STILL USE THIS PATH.
IT'S SAFE AS LONG AS YOU KNOW WHERE TO WALK.
BUT I'M THINKING SURFACE DWELLERS ARE A LOT CLUMSIER THAN I EXPECTED.
WOW.
THANKS.

SO WHAT DO WE DO?
THERE'S ONLY ONE OTHER PATH.

THE **GRAVEROBBER'S THOROUGHFARE.**

GRAVE...
...ROBBERS?

IT'S A **SECRET PATH.**
ONCE UPON A TIME, GRAVEROBBERS WOULD TRAVEL THE PATH TO COME BARTER WITH US.
THEY'D BRING US TREASURES FROM THE LIVING WORLD, AND WE'D GIVE THEM TREASURES FROM THE WORLD OF THE DEAD.
IT'S NOT USED ALL THAT MUCH ANYMORE.

IT WILL TAKE LONGER...
...BUT IT'S SAFER...
...FOR THE MOST PART.

I DON'T LIKE THE SOUND OF THAT.

GAH!
IT'S **C-C-COLD!**

WELL, WHAT DO YOU KNOW?
I DIDN'T THINK TO FIND **YOU** HERE.
FIND--

--WHO?

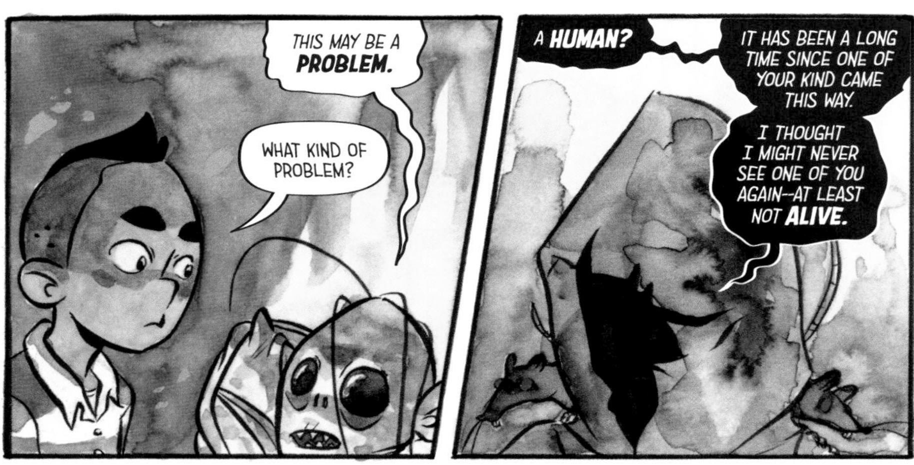
THIS MAY BE A **PROBLEM.**
WHAT KIND OF PROBLEM?
A **HUMAN?**
IT HAS BEEN A LONG TIME SINCE ONE OF YOUR KIND CAME THIS WAY.
I THOUGHT I MIGHT NEVER SEE ONE OF YOU AGAIN--AT LEAST NOT **ALIVE.**

TOLL.

I DON'T...
...I DIDN'T EXPECT A TOLL...
...I DON'T THINK I HAVE...

HMM.
MAYBE WE CAN WORK SOMETHING OUT.
MAYBE YOU CAN OWE ME ONE.

OWE YOU?
YOU MEAN LIKE A FAVOR OR SOMETHING?
I GUESS I COULD--
NO, GREY.

YOU DON'T WANT TO DO THAT.
IF THAT GUY COMES ASKING FOR A FAVOR... TRUST ME...YOU WON'T LIKE IT.
WHAT CHOICE DO I HAVE?
I DON'T HAVE ANY MONEY OR--

WAIT A MINUTE!
WHAT IS IT?

MY UNLUCKY PENNY!
PERFECTO!
YOU THINK THAT WOULD WORK?

GIVE IT TO ME.
LET ME SEE IT.
FROM THE HUMAN WORLD...
...YESSSSS...
...AND UNLUCKY, YOU SAY?
YOU MAY PASS.
TH-THANKS.

WHO WAS THAT GUY?
HE'S SORT OF A GATEKEEPER, I GUESS.
I WOULD HAVE THOUGHT HE MIGHT HAVE GIVEN UP HIS POST AFTER SO LONG.
I MEAN, IT'S NOT LIKE THERE ARE ANY GRAVEROBBERS USING THE PATH ANYMORE.

HE THINKS I'M A **GRAVEROBBER?**
WELL, YOU'VE COME FROM ABOVE TO TRADE WITH THE GHOULS...
...ONLY INSTEAD OF TRINKETS AND TEETH WITH GOLD FILLINGS, YOU WANT YOUR FRIEND BACK.

HOW LONG DO GHOULS LIVE?
I MEAN, IF THE GATEKEEPER'S JUST BEEN STANDING THERE FOR YEARS AND YEARS--
FOREVER, MAYBE.

FOREVER? YOU CAN'T REALLY MEAN THAT.
DON'T YOU GET **SICK?**
CAN'T YOU GET **HURT?**

WE HEAL FROM CUTS AND SCRAPES AND BROKEN BONES PRETTY FAST.
WE DON'T REALLY GET SICK.
AND WE GET OLD, BUT THAT DOESN'T SLOW US DOWN ALL THAT MUCH.

BUT WE CAN DIE...
...FROM MORTAL WOUNDS...FROM MAGIC...
MAGIC?

AFTER ALL YOU'VE SEEN, YOU DON'T BELIEVE IN MAGIC?

WATCH YOUR STEP, GREY.
FEW HUMANS HAVE EVER BEEN HERE BEFORE.
FEWER STILL HAVE LEFT.

WHY DON'T THEY--
SOME OF THE "GRAVEROBBERS" WHO VISITED NECROPOLIS WANTED TO **BECOME** GHOULS.
EVERLASTING LIFE...NO SICKNESS... YOU KNOW.

OTHERS...
...WELL...
...SOME GHOULS CAN BE PRETTY **GRUMPY** WHEN IT COMES TO HUMANS...

MURDEROUSLY GRUMPY?

THERE'S STILL TIME TO TURN BACK.

KEEP YOUR LANTERN LIGHT LOW.

HERE!
YOU NEED A **DISGUISE!**

YOU KNOW...LIKE WHEN YOU GAVE ME THE SHIRT.
YOU LOOK... **GREAT.**

AHH--

SHUSH!
YOU ACT LIKE YOU'VE NEVER SEEN A **DEATH'S SHROUD SPIDER** BEFORE!
THEY'RE ONLY DEADLY IF THEY BITE YOU!
TRY TO BE INCONSPICUOUS.

I KNOW WHERE YOUR FRIEND WILL BE HELD.
IF WE'RE LUCKY, THE **TRANSFORMATION PROCESS** HAS NOT YET BEGUN.
TRANSFORMATION?

MOST LIKELY, THAT'S WHAT THE ELDERS WILL DO.
THEY'LL MAKE MARSHALL UNDERGO THE RITUAL.
THEY'LL TURN HIM INTO ONE OF US.

THERE.
I BET THAT'S WHERE WE'LL FIND HIM.

BUT...
...THEY'RE GOING TO TURN HIM INTO A GHOUL?
THEY MIGHT.
IT'S ONE OF THE WAYS THEY KEEP OUR EXISTENCE SECRET.
IT'S BETTER THAN SOME OF THE ALTERNATIVES, BELIEVE ME.

DOES IT SOUND SO AWFUL...BEING LIKE ME?

IT'S NOT THAT.
THEY JUST CAN'T...
...THEY CAN'T CHANGE SOMEONE AGAINST THEIR WILL.

IT...HAPPENS.

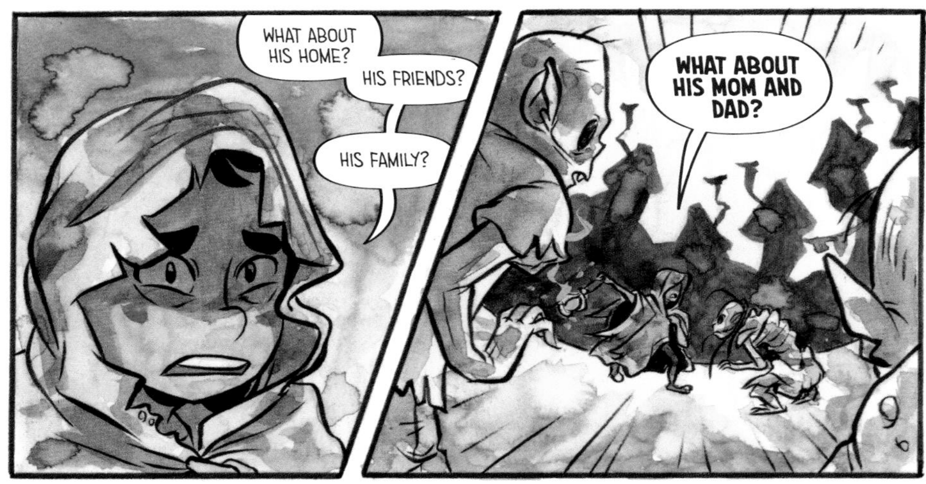
WHAT ABOUT HIS HOME?
HIS FRIENDS?
HIS FAMILY?
WHAT ABOUT HIS MOM AND DAD?

AT LEAST HE'LL REMEMBER THEM.

YOU'RE DRAWING ATTENTION TO YOURSELF.

WE CAN STOP THE RITUAL.
IT TAKES TIME.
WE CAN SAVE HIM.

HEY, LAVINIA.

WHO'S YOUR FRIEND?

OH.
HEY, BOYS.
THIS? THIS IS GREY.
HE'S NEW IN TOWN, FROM ANOTHER WARREN.

THIS IS MAGGOT...
...PICK...
...AND CYRUS.
THEY'RE MY **FRIENDS.**
SORT OF.

OH, H-HI.
IT'S NICE TO MEET--

AHEM

HIIISSSSSSSS

HEH.
Hsssss ss
SKREEEE

HEY!
I MEAN--
HEY!
WHAT DO YOU THINK YOU'RE DOING?
WELL, WELL, WELL.
LOOK WHAT WE HAVE HERE.
A **SURFACE DWELLER.**

LET HIM GO!
YOU KNOW WE CAN'T DO THAT, LAVINIA.
YOU SHOULDN'T HAVE BROUGHT HIM HERE.
YOU KNOW WHAT MUST BE DONE WITH ANY HUMAN CAUGHT IN GHOUL TERRITORY.
COME ON, GUYS.
CAN'T YOU JUST--
SORRY, LAVINIA.

"RULES ARE RULES."

LAVINIA!
YOU BROUGHT A SURFACE DWELLER TO NECROPOLIS?
WHY WOULD YOU **DO** SUCH A THING?
SUCH A **TRANSGRESSION** CANNOT BE **TOLERATED!**

SORRY.
BUT COULD I HAVE A LITTLE LIGHT?
I CAN'T SEE A THING.

THANKS.
THAT'S MUCH--

--BETTER.

YOU MADE A MISTAKE COMING HERE.
A **GRAVE** MISTAKE.
THE GHOULS PROTECT THEIR SECRETS...
...AND WE HAVE WAYS OF DEALING WITH TRESPASSERS.

LEAVE HIM ALONE, **SKULLBACK!**
IF YOU WANT TO PUNISH SOMEONE-- PUNISH **ME!**
I WENT TO THE SURFACE!
I BECAME FRIENDS WITH GREY!
EVEN AFTER I BEGGED FOR MERCY ON GREY'S BEHALF...
...EVEN AFTER YOU TOLD ME NOT TO VISIT HIM AGAIN...
...I BROUGHT HIM HERE.

AH, LAVINIA.
WHAT ARE WE TO DO WITH YOU?
YOU'VE ALWAYS BEEN TOO **HARDHEADED** AND **FREE-WILLED** FOR YOUR OWN GOOD.

SIR, I KNOW YOU HAVE RULES.
AND I KNOW YOU DON'T TRUST HUMANS.
BUT-- I PROMISE YOU--

A **PROMISE?**
THAT'S A VERY **HUMAN** THING TO OFFER.
GHOULS DO NOT DEAL IN PROMISES...NOT WITH THE LIVING.
SUCH PROMISES ARE ALMOST ALWAYS **EMPTY.**

WE'RE FRIENDS--GREY AND I--A SURFACE DWELLER AND A GHOUL.
HE MEANS US NO HARM.
IF YOU JUST RELEASED THE OTHER BOY--MARSHALL--I KNOW THEY WOULDN'T REVEAL OUR SECRETS.
IF THEY DO, YOU CAN PUNISH **ME** FOR IT.

FEH!
YOU ASK FOR SOMETHING I CANNOT GIVE.
THE BOY'S FRIEND IS **GONE.**
GONE?

WE HAVE MORE THAN ONE WAY OF DEALING WITH OUR ENEMIES.
SOMETIMES, THE **OLD METHODS** WORK BEST...
...ESPECIALLY FOR A SURFACE DWELLER WHO **MEWLED** AND **CRIED** AS MUCH AS THAT ONE.
WE OFFERED HIM UP.
WE GAVE HIM TO THE **LONELY SPIRITS** THAT HAUNT THE **FORBIDDEN PLACES.**
WE **SACRIFICED** HIM.

WHAT?
ALL THAT REMAINS...
...IS TO DECIDE WHAT TO DO...
...WITH YOU.

HAVEN'T WE DONE **ENOUGH?**
YOU TOOK HIS FRIEND FROM HIM!
I'LL RETURN HIM TO THE SURFACE WORLD.

THAT WAS BEFORE YOU BROUGHT HIM **HERE,** LAVINIA.
HE HAS SEEN TOO MUCH.
HE MUST STAY HERE--
--FOREVER.

TAKE HIM.
GREY!
NO!
LET ME GO!
LET GO!
LAVINIA--
HELP!

LEAVE IT ALONE, GIRL.
THERE'S NOTHING YOU CAN DO TO CHANGE SKULLBACK'S DECISION.
F-FINNICK?

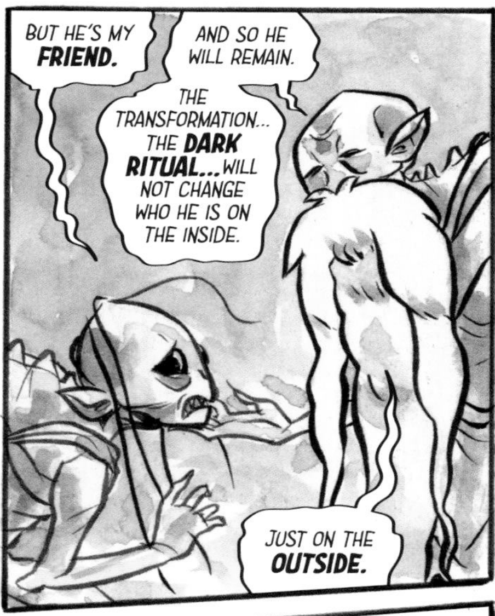
BUT HE'S MY FRIEND.
AND SO HE WILL REMAIN.
THE TRANSFORMATION... THE DARK RITUAL... WILL NOT CHANGE WHO HE IS ON THE INSIDE.
JUST ON THE OUTSIDE.

HE DOESN'T WANT TO BE A GHOUL!
HE WANTS TO BE HUMAN!
I BET YOU REMEMBER WHAT THAT FEELS LIKE, FINNICK!

YOU OF ALL GHOULS!
LAVINIA, YOU MUST UNDERSTAND.

"THERE IS
NOTHING
WE CAN DO."

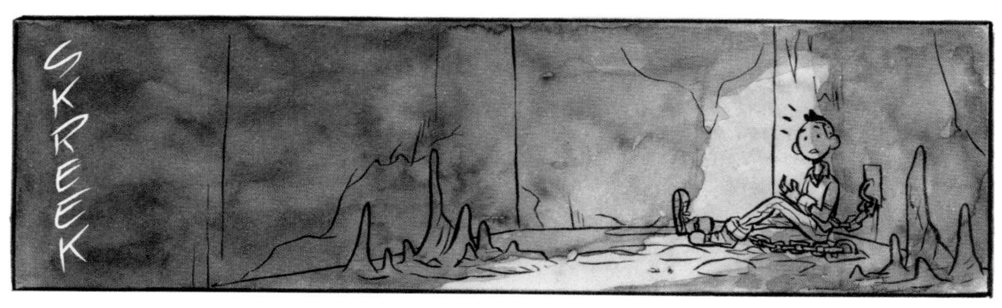
SKREEK

LAVINIA?

ARE YOU... **RESCUING** ME?

WE NEED TO GET YOU OUT OF HERE.
THEY'LL **STARVE** YOU FOR A FEW DAYS...THEN DRAG IN A CORPSE...ONE THAT'S BEEN SPECIALLY SEASONED WITH ALL SORTS OF WEIRD ALCHEMICAL SOLUTIONS AND HERBS...
BUT YOU DON'T WANT THAT.

YOU DON'T WANT TO BE LIKE **ME.**
DON'T WORRY.
I WOULDN'T HAVE LET THAT HAPPEN.
I MIGHT NOT HAVE HAD A CHOICE, BUT **YOU** DO.

"I DON'T REMEMBER BEING TURNED.
"I WAS JUST A **BABY.**
"BUT SOMETIMES GHOULS...ESPECIALLY THOSE WHO WERE OLDER WHEN THEY WERE CHANGED...
"...REMEMBER THEIR **MORTAL LIFE.**

"THEY REMEMBER THEIR **FAMILY.**
"THEY REMEMBER THEIR **CHILDREN'S FACES.**

"THEY WANT WHAT THEY HAVE **LOST.**
"THEY WANT WHAT THEY'VE **MISSED.**

"AND THEY'LL **STEAL** TO GET IT BACK."

SO THEY JUST...
...KIDNAP...
...BABIES?
THEY MUST GET SPECIAL PERMISSION FROM THE ELDERS.
IT'S NOT OFTEN GRANTED.
BUT **SOMETIMES.**
WHAT ABOUT YOUR PARENTS?
ARE THEY STILL...UP THERE?
I NEVER REALLY KNEW THEM.
I WENT LOOKING FOR THEM, BUT THEY MOVED AWAY A LONG TIME AGO.
CLANK
THEY WERE GONNA WAIT UNTIL I WAS HUNGRY ENOUGH TO **EAT** A DEAD BODY?
LAVINIA, THAT'S JUST--
SHHH!

Hssssssss

IF THEY CATCH US...
...THEY'LL PROBABLY END UP OFFERING US **BOTH** TO THE **RESTLESS ONES.**

IF WE'RE LUCKY, WE CAN GET YOU TO THE SURFACE BEFORE ANYONE REALIZES YOU'RE GONE.
WHAT GOOD WILL THAT DO?
WON'T THEY JUST COME AFTER ME--THE WAY THEY CAME AFTER MARSHALL?

IT'S MY FAULT YOU GOT MIXED UP IN ALL THIS.
I'LL TAKE THE BLAME.
I'LL OFFER MYSELF UP IN HOPES THAT THEY'LL GRANT YOU **LENIENCY.**
NO WAY!
YOU'RE NOT DOING **THAT!**
THE GHOULS DON'T SEEM LIKE THE **LENIENT** TYPES ANYHOW.
WE'LL FIGURE SOMETHING ELSE OUT--

"--BUT FIRST WE NEED TO FIND **MARSHALL.**"

THIS IS A BAD IDEA, GREY.
THIS PLACE--IT'S **FORBIDDEN.**
SO WAS NECROPOLIS, BUT WE WENT THERE.

THIS IS WHERE **BAD THINGS** GO WHEN THEY **DIE.**

THAT OLD GHOUL--
OL' SKULLBACK.
--HE BROUGHT MARSHALL HERE?
HE BROUGHT HIM HERE TO SACRIFICE HIM?

GHOULS ARE NOT THE ONLY CREATURES TO BE FOUND BELOW.
THERE ARE **GHOSTS,** TOO.
GHOSTS AND GHOULS--THEY **HATE** EACH OTHER.
BUT THERE ARE **PEACE TREATIES.**
MARSHALL WAS OFFERED UP AS PART OF THE OLD PACTS.
HE WAS GIVEN TO A GHOST.
A G-GHOST?
WHAT DOES A GHOST WANT WITH A--

TH-THAT SOUND!
IT'S HORRIBLE!

IT'S A **HOWLING GARDEN.**
DON'T WORRY. WE'LL BE SAFE.
IF WE MOVE FAST.

WHOEVER'S IN THE CASKETS...
...THEY'RE **SCREAMING.**

YEAH.
GHOSTS CAN BE SUCH BABIES.

WHAT'S WITH GHOULS AND GHOSTS?
WHY DON'T YOU LIKE EACH OTHER?

RESTLESS SPIRITS AND GHOULS HAVE A **COMPLICATED** RELATIONSHIP.
NOT EVERYBODY WHO DIES BECOMES A GHOST.
MOST PEOPLE DON'T UNLESS THEY'VE GOT **UNFINISHED BUSINESS...**
...OR THEY'RE **REALLY** MEAN...

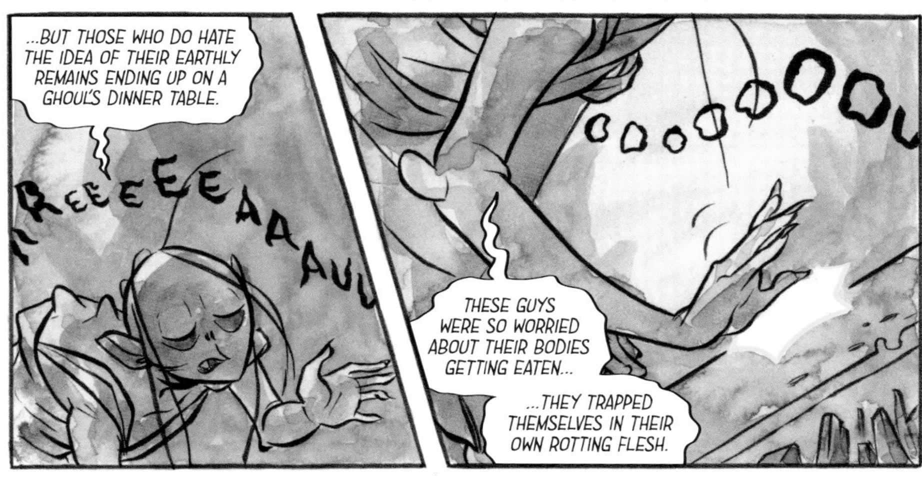
...BUT THOSE WHO DO HATE THE IDEA OF THEIR EARTHLY REMAINS ENDING UP ON A GHOUL'S DINNER TABLE.
REEEEEAAAUU
THESE GUYS WERE SO WORRIED ABOUT THEIR BODIES GETTING EATEN...
...THEY TRAPPED THEMSELVES IN THEIR OWN ROTTING FLESH.

IT'S DRIVEN THEM **MAD.**
AUU UUGGGHHH

WE STICK AROUND TOO LONG, THEY MIGHT DRIVE US MAD, TOO!

ALL THESE BONES...
...DID GHOULS EAT THESE?
I'M AFRAID NOT.
THEY WERE **ALIVE** WHEN THEY WERE BROUGHT DOWN HERE.

MALEVOLENT SPIRITS--EVIL GHOSTS--ARE **ALWAYS** HUNGRY.
THEY'RE NOT UNLIKE GHOULS IN THAT RESPECT.
ONLY NO AMOUNT OF FOOD COULD EVER SATISFY THEM.
THEY'RE **GHOSTS,** AFTER ALL. ANYTHING THEY EAT JUST FALLS RIGHT OUT THEIR STOMACHS.

SO THEY DRAIN THE **LIFE-FORCE** FROM THEIR VICTIMS.

TODAY JUST KEEPS GETTING--
HSSSSSS

CAREFUL.

ULP!

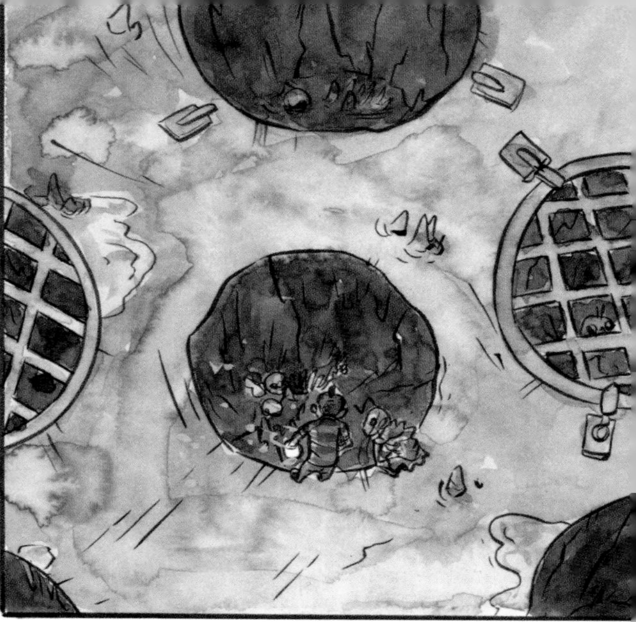

IF GHOSTS D-D-DRAIN THE LIFE FROM THEIR VICTIMS...
...I GUESS THIS IS LIKE THEIR **PANTRY.**

IT'S **COLD** HERE.
DO YOU FEEL IT?
SOMETHING **POWERFUL...** SOMETHING **EVIL...** LURKS NEARBY.

C-C-COLD?
I B-B-BARELY NOTICED.

H-HELLO?
WHO'S OUT THERE?
IS SOMEONE OUT THERE?

THAT VOICE!
IT SOUNDS LIKE--

WHO--
WHO'S THERE?
H-HELLO?

WE **FOUND** HIM!

GREY?
GREY--IS THAT YOU?
HOW DID YOU--
UH-OH.
I DON'T LIKE THE LOOKS OF THIS.

THAT'S A **WITCH'S LOCK.**
MY KEY WILL OPEN IT BUT...
...WE NEED TO **HURRY.**

GET THE GATE OPEN.

MARSHALL!
STAY CALM!
WE'RE GONNA GET YOU OUT OF THERE!

Y-YOU DIDN'T HAVE TO COME FOR ME, GREY.
DON'T BE DUMB.
OF COURSE I DID.
I KIND OF GOT YOU INTO THIS MESS.
TRUE.

I GOT IT!
CLIK!

WHAT ARE YOU DOING?
WHAT'S IT **LOOK** LIKE?
UH...I DUNNO... THAT'S WHY I'M ASKING!

JUST GET THE GATE OPENED.
NNNNN!

SKREEEEEE
OH, THAT'S--
--DISGUSTING!

DON'T WORRY ABOUT THAT!
JUST-- COME ON!
CLIMB OUT!
EW!
EW!
EW!

YOU'RE OKAY NOW.
YOU'RE OUT.
HUFF
HUFF

MARSHALL--THIS IS THE NEW FRIEND I TOLD YOU ABOUT.
HER NAME'S **LAVINIA.**

WE NEED TO MOVE.
LET'S GET OUT OF HERE BEFORE--
UH--GUYS?
I THINK WE'RE **TOO LATE!**

WHAT IS THIS?
WHO DARES STEAL THAT WHICH WAS OFFERED TO SALLY-BEA?
YOU LITTLE SCOUNDRELS!
YOU LITTLE THIEVES!
DID YOU THINK YOU COULD ROB SALLY-BEA AND NOT PAY THE PRICE?
OH--SUCH A TERRIBLE PRICE!

IT'S HER!
IT'S SALLY-BEA HURST!
OH...NO...

THE RAT...THE FAMILIAR.
GHOSTS HAVE NO VOICE OF THEIR OWN EXCEPT TO SCREAM AND HOWL.
MILES ACTS AS SALLY-BEA'S VOICE.

SALLY-BEA WAS GOING TO TAKE HER TIME WITH YOU...
...DRAIN THE LIFE ENERGIES FROM YOU SLOWLY...
...BUT THAT'S NOT POSSIBLE NOW...
...SO WE'LL HAVE TO KILL YOU QUICKLY!
EVERYBODY--

--RUN!

YEEEEEAAAAAAARRRGG
WE CAN'T OUTRUN HER!
SHE'S A GHOST!
SHE CAN FLY! SHE CAN FLY THROUGH WALLS!
CLANK CL-
CLANK
UNNF!

CL- CLANK
THE LANTERN!
WE'LL NEED IT IN THE CAVES!
NNNNN--

SKREEEEE
WHAT ARE YOU LOOKING AT?
GET BACK, YOU LITTLE WORM!
DON'T YOU LOOK IN THERE!

OUCH!
MARSHALL!
SHE'LL CLAW YOUR LIFE-FORCE FROM YOUR BODY!
SHE'LL TEAR IT FROM YOU PIECE BY PIECE!
NOT AS NOURISHING, BUT SO MUCH MORE FUN!

GET AWAY FROM ME, YOU LITTLE CREEP!
TRACK

GREY!
OVER HERE!
THIS WAY!

SALLY-BEA SEES YOU!
YOU'LL NOT ELUDE HER!
SHE'LL FEAST ON YOUR SOULS!
GO-GO-GO!
I'LL BE RIGHT--

SNAP
SNP
SNAP

UNF!
I'VE GOT YOU!

AND SALLY-BEA'S GOT YOU!
HSSSSSSSSSSSS

A LITTLE GHOUL!
YOU BETRAYED THE COVENANTS!
NOW MY MISTRESS WILL SEE WHAT A GHOUL'S SOUL TASTES LIKE!
MARSHALL!
WE GOTTA--

RUN!
GET OUT OF HERE!
GET BACK TO THE SURFACE WHILE YOU CAN!

N-NO!
WE'RE NOT LEAVING YOU!

ReeEEAAAAARRRGG
AND SALLY-BEA WILL FEED ON YOU ALL THE SOONER!

NNNNNNNN

R-RUN, GREY.
PLEASE.
COME ON, GREY!
WE HAVE TO!

YES!
RUN!
RUN FOR ALL THE GOOD IT WILL DO YOU!

SALLY-BEA SEES YOU!

LAVINIA!
GREY--THE GHOST GOT HER!
SALLY-BEA-- SHE TOOK LAVINIA!
W-WHAT DO WE DO?
DO YOU KNOW THE WAY OUT OF HERE?

WE CAN'T LEAVE HER.
WE HAVE TO **GO BACK.**

IF SHE CATCHES US, SHE'LL KILL US! SHE'LL SWALLOW OUR SOULS OR WHATEVER!
THAT'S WHY WE CAN'T LEAVE LAVINIA BEHIND!
SHE GOT CAUGHT BECAUSE SHE WAS TRYING TO SAVE OUR LIVES!
WE'VE GOTTA HELP HER!
MAYBE I CAN HELP?

YOU?
YOU'RE **M-MAGGOT,** RIGHT?
DUDE!
MAYBE DON'T **INSULT** THE CREATURE?
I'M NOT.
THAT'S HIS **NAME.**

WHAT ARE YOU DOING HERE?
DID Y-YOU FOLLOW US?

THAT'S RIGHT.
AS SOON AS I FIGURED LAVINIA WAS SNEAKING OUT TO HELP YOU, I STARTED TRACKING HER.
TRACKING YOU **BOTH,** REALLY.
SURFACE DWELLERS SMELL **TERRIBLE** WHEN THEY'RE **FRESH.**

LAVINIA MIGHT BE **ANNOYING,** BUT SHE'S THE CLOSEST THING I HAVE TO A SISTER.
I THOUGHT I COULD TALK HER OUT OF HELPING YOU.
I DIDN'T WANT TO SEE HER GET HURT FOR A HUMAN.
WHY DIDN'T YOU HELP US?
BEFORE--WITH THE GHOST?
YOU COULD HAVE DONE SOMETHING--**ANYTHING!**

I HEARD THE SCREAMING.
I KNEW THERE WAS TROUBLE.
I...I JUST...

GHOULS KNOW WHAT IT IS TO BE **AFRAID.**

BUT YOU'RE WILLING TO GO BACK TO SAVE HER.
MAYBE YOU'RE NOT SO BAD--FOR A MISERABLE SURFACE DWELLER.
MAYBE WE CAN RESCUE HER.

SOUNDS GOOD TO ME.
WHAT ARE YOU DOING?
WHY ARE YOU HOLDING YOUR SWEATY SURFACE DWELLER HAND OUT LIKE THAT?
WHATEVER YOU'RE DOING, JUST **STOP IT.**
YOU'RE **EMBARRASSING** YOURSELF.

OOOOOKAY.

I SAW SOME-THING...BACK IN THE CAVE.
I THINK I MIGHT HAVE A **PLAN.**

"BUT WE'RE GONNA NEED A **DISTRACTION.**"

THIS IDEA OF YOURS...
...IT'S GONNA GET US ALL **KILLED.**

MAYBE SO.
BUT I SPOTTED THIS COFFIN EARLIER AND I'VE BEEN THINKING ABOUT IT EVER SINCE.
WHY WOULD A GHOST KEEP SOMETHING LIKE THIS LOCKED UP IN THE DARK?
PROBABLY PROTECTING SOME **TREASURE.**

EXACTLY!

HEY! COME ON OUT!
SALLY-BEA HURST!
I'VE GOT **UNFINISHED BUSINESS** WITH YOU!

YOU KNOW, I DID MY SCHOOL PROJECT ON YOU.
I DREW A REALLY BAD PORTRAIT OF YOU.
REAL **UGLY.**

NOW YOU'VE GOT MY...
...UH...
...MY **FRIEND!**
AND I WANT HER BACK!
COME ON OUT, YOU **CRUSTY OLD HAG!**

UNFINISHED BUSINESS, YOU SAY?

TELL ME...
...WHAT BUSINESS COULD SALLY-BEA POSSIBLY HAVE WITH YOU?

THAP

LADY--YOU BETTER LET LAVINIA GO RIGHT NOW...
...OR WE'RE GONNA HAVE A **BIG PROBLEM!**
YOU'RE GOING TO **REGRET** COMING BACK HERE, BOY!

REEEAAAAAAUUUHG.
TWUMP
UNNFFH!

AAAAHHH!

YOU'VE SACRIFICED YOURSELF FOR A GHOUL!
THEY HATE AND FEAR YOU!

TO THEM, YOU ARE NOTHING BUT A RIPENING FRUIT!
YOU'RE USELESS TO THEM UNTIL YOU'RE DEAD!
ONLY THEN WILL THEY FEAST ON YOUR DECAYING FLESH!
ACTUALLY, SALLY--
--THEY EAT YOUR FLESH, TOO!

THAT IS...THEY MIGHT...
...IF THEY KNEW WHERE YOUR BODY WAS HIDDEN.

WHAT IS THIS?
CL-
CLANK

G-GREY?

I FOUND THEM, SALLY.

"I FOUND WHERE YOU HID YOUR EARTHLY REMAINS."

ARE YOU TRYING TO THREATEN SALLY-BEA, BOY?
BECAUSE IF YOU ARE, YOU HAVE MADE A TERRIBLE MISTAKE.
THE GHOULS HAVE STRUCK A BARGAIN WITH MY MISTRESS.
EVERY SO OFTEN, THEY BRING OFFERINGS.
AND IN RETURN SALLY-BEA DOES NOT RAIN AWFULNESS DOWN UPON THEM.

ONLY THE MOST FOOLISH OF THEIR NUMBER WOULD DARE COME HERE.
AND, EVEN IF THEY DID, WHAT COULD THEY DO?
SALLY-BEA IS BEYOND THEM.
SHE HAS TRANSCENDED THE MORTAL FORM.

YEAH. I FIGURED YOU'D SAY SOMETHING LIKE THAT.
BUT I GOT TO THINKING.
WHY WOULD YOU GO TO SO MUCH TROUBLE TO PROTECT YOUR ROTTING CORPSE?
I'M GUESSING BECAUSE YOU DON'T WANT TO SEE SOME VITAL PART GET EATEN.

HEY, HEY.
LOOK WHAT I GOT HERE!

MAGGOT?

MMMMMM.
IT'S NOT AS JUICY AS I NORMALLY LIKE, BUT I'VE BEEN WORKING UP A HECK OF AN APPETITE.
SNF SNF

SALLY-BEA'S HEART!

THAT'S RIGHT.
YOUR HEART.
AND UNLESS YOU LET MY FRIENDS GO--
YOU CAN'T FORCE SALLY-BEA'S HAND!
SHE DOES AS SHE WISHES!

FINE! FINE!
TAKE THEM AND BEGONE FROM THIS PLACE!
JUST GO AND VEX SALLY-BEA NO LONGER!

HEAR THAT?
WE'RE **VEXING!**
SOME OF US MORE THAN OTHERS.

PLEASURE DOING BUSINESS WITH YOU!

CURSE YOU!

CUUURSE YOOOUU AAALLL!!

YOU CAME BACK FOR ME!
OF COURSE WE DID.

Y'KNOW, WE ALL CAME BACK FOR YOU.
GIVE IT UP, MAN.
NO WAY ARE YOU GONNA GET BETWEEN GREY AND HIS GHOUL-FRIEND.
THAT'S NOT FUNNY.

WE SHOULD GET LOST BEFORE SALLY COMES LOOKING FOR TROUBLE.

I DON'T KNOW THAT I'D WORRY ABOUT THAT.

IS THAT...
...WHAT I THINK IT IS?
IN THE FLESH--

"--SALLY-BEA HURST'S WITHERED OLD **BRAIN!**"
IT WAS MAGGOT WHO TOOK IT.
HE THOUGHT MAYBE...
...IT MIGHT GIVE YOU SOME LONG-LASTING **PROTECTION** AGAINST ANYTHING SALLY MIGHT TRY.
I TOOK IT, YEAH.
BUT IT WAS GREY WHO FOUND WHERE THE WITCH'S GHOST HID HER BODY.
IT WAS HIS IDEA TO USE IT AGAINST HER.
Hssssssss
AND HE DID THIS TO SAVE LAVINIA.
HE RESCUED HER.
THE GHOULS ARE IN HIS **DEBT.**
I AM IN HIS DEBT.

THEIR ANTICS WILL HAVE ANGERED THE WITCH.
IT WILL TAKE YEARS TO ESTABLISH ANY SORT OF PEACE WITH HER AGAIN.

JUST SO YOU KNOW...
...IF YOU TURN US INTO GHOULS...
...WE'RE STILL PROBABLY GONNA CAUSE PROBLEMS.
IT'S TRUE.
CAUSING PROBLEMS IS GREY'S SPECIALTY.

VERY WELL.
FEH!
I'LL MAKE AN **EXCEPTION** FOR THESE CHILDREN.

THEY ARE FREE TO GO.
THE CITIZENS OF NECROPOLIS WILL WORRY THEM NO LONGER.
AND WE EXPECT THE **SAME** FROM THEM.

DON'T YOU WORRY, MR. SKULLBACK, SIR.
WE AREN'T GONNA TELL ANYONE ABOUT THE THINGS WE'VE SEEN.
I MEAN, NO ONE WOULD BELIEVE US ANYHOW.
YES, YES.
WE EXPECT YOUR **SILENCE.**
BUT THERE'S SOMETHING MORE.
YOU ARE FORBIDDEN TO HAVE CONTACT WITH LAVINIA AFTER THIS NIGHT.
AND **SHE** IS FORBIDDEN FROM SEEKING YOU OUT.
THIS RULING IS **IRREFUTABLE...**

"...AND **DISOBEDIENCE** WILL HAVE SEVERE **CONSEQUENCES!**"

WELL...
I GUESS THIS IS **GOODBYE** THEN.

THANK YOU FOR EVERYTHING, GREY.
GHOULS LIVE A LONG, LONG TIME.
BUT IN ALL MY YEARS, I'LL NEVER FORGET YOU.

I'M REALLY GLAD I MET YOU, LAVINIA.
I'M GLAD YOU STOLE MY HOMEWORK AND ALMOST GOT ME TURNED INTO A GHOUL.
I'M...GONNA **MISS** YOU.

HEY, MARSHALL.
HEY, GREY.
HOW'RE YOU DOING?

I'M ALL RIGHT.

STILL NO WORD FROM **YOU-KNOW-WHO?**
NAH.
IT'S BEEN A WEEK NOW AND NOTHING.
I THINK LAVINIA'S GONNA FOLLOW ALONG WITH OL' SKULL-BACK'S RULING... FOR HER SAFETY...

...AND OURS.

HEY!
LOOK!

A PENNY!
HOLD ON, GREY.
IS IT HEADS-DOWN OR--
IN GOD WE TRUST
LIBERTY
1919
DON'T SWEAT IT.
IT'S HEADS-UP THIS TIME.

1919.

HEH.

PERFECTO!
THE END